Edna Earl

The Quintessence of

BEAUTY AND ROMANCE

Compiled by
MARJORIE BARROWS

SPENCER PRESS, INC., CHICAGO

ACKNOWLEDGMENTS

The editor and publishers wish to thank the following publishers, authors and agents for permission to reprint poems and stories in this book:

NOEL AMES for "Afflatus" and "Garden."

APPLETON-CENTURY-CROFTS, INC., for part of Chapter 16 and Chapters 17, 18, and 19 ("In the Garden of Golden Bells") from *Messer Marco Polo* by Donn Byrne, copyright 1921, Century Co.

BRANDT & BRANDT for "A Friend of Napoleon" by Richard Connell, copyright 1923 by Richard Connell; "Night Bus" by Samuel Hopkins Adams, copyright 1933, Hearst Magazines; "Music I Heard" by iii

CONTENTS

PART I · IN OUR DAY   PAGE

A FRIEND OF NAPOLEON   *Richard Connell*   1

SCHERZANDO   *Jake Falstaff*   18

BIRTHRIGHT   *John Drinkwater*   19

THE BRUSHWOOD BOY   *Rudyard Kipling*   20

BREDON HILL   *A. E. Housman*   49

WITH RUE MY HEART IS LADEN   *A. E. Housman*   50

WHITE IN THE MOON   *A. E. Housman*   50

MY HEART IS LIKE A SINGING BIRD   *Dorothy Thomas*   51

AFFLATUS   *Anthony Lane*   68

A BIRTHDAY   *Christina Rossetti*   69

FLOWERING NIGHT   *Scharmel Iris*   69

NIGHT BUS   *Samuel Hopkins Adams*   70

MAY NIGHT   *Adelaide Love*   123

POEM IN PROSE   *Archibald MacLeish*   123

SIMPLE LIFE   *Rose Franken*   125

I THOUGHT I HEARD THEM SINGING *Dorothy Canfield*   143

THE LOOK   *Sara Teasdale*   151

CATALOGUE OF LOVELY THINGS   *Richard Le Gallienne*   152

A RETRIEVED REFORMATION   *O. Henry*   153

GARDEN   *Anthony Lane*   160

SONG   *Sara Teasdale*   160

LOVE COMES TO MISS KISSINGER   *Winfred Van Atta*   161

WHEN I WAS ONE-AND-TWENTY   *A. E. Housman*   176

RECUERDO   *Edna St. Vincent Millay* 177

TO SPRINGVALE FOR CHRISTMAS   *Zona Gale*   178

v

TO F. W.	*Edith Franklin Wyatt*	185
THE LESSON	*Pearl Buck*	186
THE GREAT LOVER	*Rupert Brooke*	202
From PORTRAIT OF JENNIE	*Robert Nathan*	204
DUST	*Rupert Brooke*	209
MUSIC I HEARD	*Conrad Aiken*	210
THE OLD LADY SHOWS HER MEDALS	*James M. Barrie*	211
From THE PROPHET	*Kahlil Gibran*	236
APPRAISAL	*Sara Teasdale*	238
"I LOVE YOU"	*Sara Teasdale*	239
FOR A YOUNG FRIEND	*Adelaide Love*	240
FOR THE BELOVED	*Adelaide Love*	240
GOOD-BYE, MR. CHIPS!	*James Hilton*	241
BARTER	*Sara Teasdale*	280
FAR IN A WESTERN BROOKLAND	*A. E. Housman*	281
APRIL	*Scharmel Iris*	281
THE POOL	*Dana Burnet*	282
THE HILL	*Rupert Brooke*	295
PART II · IN OTHER DAYS		
PATTERNS	*Amy Lowell*	296
GARDEN FANCIES	*Robert Browning*	299
O MY LUVE'S LIKE A RED, RED ROSE	*Robert Burns*	300
ARISTOCRACY	*Emily Dickinson*	300
EXCEPT FOR YOU	*Adelaide Love*	301
AN EPITAPH	*Walter de la Mare*	301
THE NIGHTINGALE AND THE ROSE	*Oscar Wilde*	302
TO ―――	*Percy Bysshe Shelley*	307
MEETING AT NIGHT	*Robert Browning*	308

vi

PARTING AT MORNING	*Robert Browning*	308
THE YEAR'S AT THE SPRING	*Robert Browning*	308
ROMANCE	*Robert Louis Stevenson*	309
MY OWN TRUE LOVE	*Marian Lagrange Wyatt*	309
OFT HAVE I SEEN	*Henry Wadsworth Longfellow*	310
LOVE'S PHILOSOPHY	*Percy Bysshe Shelley*	310
THE SIRE DE MALÉTROIT'S DOOR	*Robert Louis Stevenson*	311
I SHALL NOT LIVE IN VAIN	*Emily Dickinson*	329
From RESOLUTION AND INDEPENDENCE	*William Wordsworth*	329
IN THE GARDEN OF GOLDEN BELLS	*Donn Byrne*	330
ROSE AYLMER	*Walter Savage Landor*	335
WHEN LILACS LAST IN THE DOORYARD BLOOM'D	*Walt Whitman*	336
INDIAN LOVE SONG	*Elizabeth-Ellen Long*	342
THE MEETING	*George Meredith*	343
MOONLIGHT	*Guy de Maupassant—adapted by Rollo St. John Fogarty*	352
HOW DO I LOVE THEE?	*Elizabeth Barrett Browning*	357
BELOVÈD, MY BELOVÈD	*Elizabeth Barrett Browning*	357
ROMEO AND JULIET (BALCONY SCENE)	*William Shakespeare*	358
From O MISTRESS MINE	*William Shakespeare*	363
HARK, HARK! THE LARK	*William Shakespeare*	364
MY GARDEN	*Thomas Edward Brown*	364
THE NIGHT HAS A THOUSAND EYES	*F. W. Bourdillon*	364
THE STARS	*Alphonse Daudet—adapted by Rollo St. John Fogarty*	365
VALLEY SONG	*Carl Sandburg*	371

vii

A Friend of Napoleon

Richard Connell

> *This ingenious tale of a watchman in a Paris wax-works became the film* SEVEN FACES, *in which audiences wildly acclaimed the sympathetic and competent characterization of Papa Chibou portrayed by Paul Muni.*

ALL PARIS held no happier man than Papa Chibou. He loved his work—that was why. Other men might say—did say, in fact—that for no amount of money would they take his job; no, not for ten thousand francs for a single night. It would turn their hair white and give them permanent goose flesh, they averred. On such men Papa Chibou smiled with pity. What stomach had such zestless ones for adventure? What did they know of romance? Every night of his life Papa Chibou walked with adventure and held the hand of romance.

Every night he conversed intimately with Napoleon; with Marat and his fellow revolutionists; with Carpentier and Caesar; with Victor Hugo and Lloyd George; with Foch and with Bigarre, the Apache murderer whose unfortunate penchant for making ladies into curry led him to the guillotine; with Louis XVI and with Madame Lablanche, who poisoned eleven husbands and was working to make it an even dozen when the police deterred her; with Marie Antoinette and with sundry early Christian martyrs who lived in sweet resignation in electric-lighted catacombs under the sidewalk of the Boulevard des Capucines in the very heart of Paris. They were all his friends and he had a word and a joke for each of them, as on his nightly rounds he washed their faces and dusted out their ears, for Papa Chibou was night watchman at the Musée Pratoucy—"The World in Wax. Admission, one franc. Children and soldiers, half price. Nervous ladies enter the Chamber of Horrors at their own risk. One is prayed not to touch the wax figures or to permit dogs to circulate in the establishment."

1

He had been at the Musée Pratoucy so long that he looked like a wax figure himself. Visitors not infrequently mistook him for one and poked him with inquisitive fingers or canes. He did not undeceive them; he did not budge. Spartanlike he stood stiff under the pokes; he was rather proud of being taken for a citizen of the world of wax, which was, indeed, a much more real world to him than the world of flesh and blood. He had cheeks like the small red wax pippins used in table decorations, round eyes, slightly poppy, and smooth white hair, like a wig. He was a diminutive man and, with his horseshoe moustache of surprising luxuriance, looked like a gnome going to a fancy-dress ball as a small walrus. Children who saw him flitting about the dim passages that led to the catacombs were sure he was a brownie.

His title "Papa" was a purely honorary one, given him because he had worked some twenty-five years at the museum. He was unwed, and slept at the museum in a niche of a room just off the Roman arena where papier-mâché lion and tigers breakfasted on assorted martyrs. At night, as he dusted off the lions and tigers, he rebuked them sternly for their lack of delicacy.

"Ah," he would say, cuffing the ear of the largest lion, which was earnestly trying to devour a grandfather and an infant simultaneously, "sort of a pig that you are! I am ashamed of you, eater of babies. You will go to hell for this, Monsieur Lion, you may depend upon it. Monsieur Satan will poach you like an egg, I promise you. Ah, you bad one, you species of a camel, you Apache, you profiteer—"

Then Papa Chibou would bend over and very tenderly address the elderly martyr who was lying beneath the lion's paws and exhibiting signs of distress and say, "Patience, my brave one. It does not take long to be eaten, and then, consider: The good Lord will take you up to heaven, and there, if you wish, you yourself can eat a lion every day. You are a man of holiness, Phillibert. You will be Saint Phillibert, beyond doubt, and then won't you laugh at lions!"

Phillibert was the name Papa Chibou had given to the venerable martyr; he had bestowed names on all of them. Having consoled Phillibert, he would softly dust the fat wax infant whom the lion was in the act of bolting.

"Courage, my poor little Jacob," Papa Chibou would say. "It is not every baby that can be eaten by a lion; and in such a good cause too. Don't cry, little Jacob. And remember: When you get inside Monsieur Lion, kick and kick and kick! That will give him a great sickness

2

of the stomach. Won't that be fun, little Jacob?"

So he went about his work, chatting with them all, for he was fond of them all, even of Bigarre the Apache and the other grisly inmates of the Chamber of Horrors. He did chide the criminals for their regrettable proclivities in the past and warn them that he would tolerate no such conduct in his museum. It was not his museum of course. Its owner was Monsieur Pratoucy, a long-necked, melancholy marabou of a man who sat at the ticket window and took in the francs. But, though the legal title to the place might be vested in Monsieur Pratoucy, at night Papa Chibou was the undisputed monarch of his little wax kingdom. When the last patron had left and the doors were closed Papa Chibou began to pay calls on his subjects; across the silent halls he called greetings to them:

"Ah, Bigarre, you old rascal, how goes the world? And you, Madame Marie Antoinette; did you enjoy a good day? Good evening, Monsieur Caesar; aren't you chilly in that costume of yours? Ah, Monsieur Charlemagne, I trust your health continues to be of the best."

His closest friend of them all was Napoleon. The others he liked; to Napoleon he was devoted. It was a friendship cemented by years, for Napoleon had been in the museum as long as Papa Chibou. Other figures might come and go at the behest of a fickle public, but Napoleon held his place, albeit he had been relegated to a dim corner.

He was not much of a Napoleon. He was smaller even than the original Napoleon, and one of his ears had come in contact with a steam radiator and as a result it was gnarled into a lump the size of a hickory nut; it was a perfect example of that phenomenon of the prize ring, the cauliflower ear. He was supposed to be at St. Helena and he stood on a papier-mâché rock, gazing out wistfully over a nonexistent sea. One hand was thrust into the bosom of his long-tailed coat, the other hung at his side. Skin-tight breeches, once white but white no longer, fitted snugly over his plump bump of waxen abdomen. A Napoleonic hat, frayed by years of conscientious brushing by Papa Chibou, was perched above a pensive waven brow.

Papa Chibou had been attracted to Napoleon from the first. There was something so forlorn about him. Papa Chibou had been forlorn, too, in his first days at the museum. He had come from Bouloire, in the south of France, to seek his fortune as a grower of asparagus in Paris. He was a simple man of scant schooling and he had fancied that there were asparagus beds along the Paris boulevards. There were none. So

3

necessity and chance brought him to the Museum Pratoucy to earn his bread and wine, and romance and his friendship for Napoleon kept him there.

The first day Papa Chibou worked at the museum Monsieur Pratoucy took him round to tell him about the figures.

"This," said the proprietor, "is Toulon, the strangler. This is Mademoiselle Merle, who shot the Russian duke. This is Charlotte Corday, who stabbed Marat in the bathtub; that gory gentleman is Marat." Then they had come to Napoleon. Monsieur Pratoucy was passing him by.

"And who is this sad-looking gentleman?" asked Papa Chibou.

"Name of a name! Do you not know?"

"But no, monsieur."

"But that is Napoleon himself."

That night, his first in the museum, Papa Chibou went round and said to Napoleon, "Monsieur, I do not know with what crimes you are charged, but I, for one, refuse to think you are guilty of them."

So began their friendship. Thereafter he dusted Napoleon with especial care and made him his confidant. One night in his twenty-fifth year at the museum Papa Chibou said to Napoleon, "You observed those two lovers who were in here tonight, did you not, my good Napoleon? They thought it was too dark in this corner for us to see, didn't they? But we saw him take her hand and whisper to her. Did she blush? You were near enough to see. She is pretty, isn't she, with her bright dark eyes? She is not a French girl; she is an American; one can tell that by the way she doesn't roll her r's. The young man, he is French; and a fine young fellow he is, or I'm no judge. He is so slender and erect, and he has courage, for he wears the war cross; you noticed that, didn't you? He is very much in love, that is sure. This is not the first time I have seen them. They have met here before, and they are wise, for is this not a spot most romantic for the meetings of lovers?"

Papa Chibou flicked a speck of dust from Napoleon's good ear.

"Ah," he exclaimed, "it must be a thing most delicious to be young and in love! Were you ever in love, Napoleon? No? Ah, what a pity! I know, for I, too, have had no luck in love. Ladies prefer the big, strong men, don't they? Well, we must help these two young people, Napoleon. We must see that they have the joy we missed. So do not let them know you are watching them if they come here tomorrow night. I will pretend I do not see."

4

Each night after the museum had closed, Papa Chibou gossiped with Napoleon about the progress of the love affair between the American girl with the bright dark eyes and the slender, erect young Frenchman.

"All is not going well," Papa Chibou reported one night, shaking his head. "There are obstacles to their happiness. He has little money, for he is just beginning his career. I heard him tell her so tonight. And she has an aunt who has other plans for her. What a pity if fate should part them! But you know how unfair fate can be, don't you, Napoleon? If only we had some money we might be able to help him, but I, myself, have no money, and I suppose you, too, were poor, since you look so sad. But attend; tomorrow is a day most important for them. He has asked her if she will marry him, and she has said that she will tell him tomorrow night at nine in this very place. I heard them arrange it all. If she does not come it will mean no. I think we shall see two very happy ones here tomorrow night, eh, Napoleon?"

The next night, when the last patron had gone and Papa Chibou had locked the outer door, he came to Napoleon, and tears were in his eyes.

"You saw, my friend?" broke out Papa Chibou. "You observed? You saw his face and how pale it grew? You saw his eyes and how they held a thousand agonies? He waited until I had to tell him three times that the museum was closing. I felt like an executioner, I assure you; and he looked up at me as only a man condemned can look. He went out with heavy feet; he was no longer erect. For she did not come, Napoleon; that girl with the bright dark eyes did not come. Our little comedy of love has become a tragedy, monsieur. She has refused him, that poor, that unhappy young man."

On the following night at closing time Papa Chibou came hurrying to Napoleon; he was a-quiver with excitement.

"She was here!" he cried. "Did you see her? She was here and she kept watching and watching; but, of course, he did not come. I could tell from his stricken face last night that he had no hope. At last I dared to speak to her. I said to her, 'Madamoiselle, a thousand pardons for the very great liberty I am taking, but it is my duty to tell you—he was here last night and he waited till closing time. He was all of a paleness, mademoiselle, and he chewed his fingers in his despair. He loves you, mademoiselle; a cow could see that. He is devoted to you; and he is a fine young fellow, you can take an old man's word for it. Do not break his heart, mademoiselle.' She grasped my sleeve. 'You know him, then?' she asked. 'You know where I can find him?' 'Alas, no,' I said. 'I have only seen him here with you.' 'Poor boy!' she kept saying. 'Poor boy! Oh, what shall I do? I am in dire trouble. I love him, monsieur.' 'But you did not come,' I said. 'I could not,' she replied, and she was weeping. 'I live with an aunt; a rich tiger she is, monsieur, and she wants me to marry a count, a fat leering fellow who smells of attar of roses and garlic. My aunt locked me in my room. And now I have lost the one I love, for he will think I have refused him, and he is so proud he will never ask me again.' 'But surely you could let him know?' I suggested. 'But I do not know where he lives,' she said. 'And in a few days my aunt is taking me off to Rome, where the count is, and oh, dear, oh, dear, oh, dear——' And she wept on my shoulder. On *my* shoulder! Napoleon, that poor little American girl with the bright dark eyes did that."

Papa Chibou began to brush the Napoleonic hat.

"I tried to comfort her," he said. "I told her that the young man would surely find her, that he would come back and haunt the spot where they had been happy, but I was telling her what I did not believe. 'He may come tonight,' I said, 'or tomorrow.' She waited until it was time to close the museum. You saw her face as she left; did it not touch you in the heart?"

Papa Chibou was downcast when he approached Napoleon the next night.

"She waited again till closing time," he said, "but he did not come. It made me suffer to see her as the hours went by and her hope ebbed away. At last she had to leave, and at the door she said to me, 'If you see him here again, please give him this.' She handed me this card, Napoleon. See, it says, 'I am at the Villa Rosina, Rome. I love you, Nina.' Ah, the poor, poor young man. We must keep a sharp watch for him, you and I."

Papa Chibou and Napoleon did watch at the Musée Pratoucy night after night. One, two, three, four, five nights they watched for him. A week, a month, more months passed, and he did not come. There came instead one day news of so terrible a nature that it left Papa Chibou ill and trembling. The Musée Pratoucy was going to have to close its doors.

"It is no use," said Monsieur Pratoucy, when he dealt this blow to Papa Chibou. "I cannot go on. Already I owe much, and my creditors are clamouring. People will no longer pay a franc to see a few old dummies when they can see an army of red Indians, Arabs, brigands and

6

dukes in the moving pictures. Monday the Musée Pratoucy closes its doors for ever."

"But, Monsieur Pratoucy," exclaimed Papa Chibou, aghast, "what about the people here? What will become of Marie Antoinette, and the martyrs, and Napoleon?"

"Oh," said the proprietor, "I'll be able to realize a little on them, perhaps. On Tuesday they will be sold at auction. Someone may buy them to melt up."

"To melt up, monsieur?" Papa Chibou faltered.

"But certainly. What else are they good for?"

"But surely monsieur will want to keep them; a few anyhow?"

"Keep them? Aunt of the devil, but that is a droll idea! Why should anyone want to keep shabby old wax dummies?"

"I thought," murmured Papa Chibou, "that you might keep just one —Napoleon, for example—as a remembrance——"

"Uncle of Satan, but you have odd notions! To keep a souvenir of one's bankruptcy!"

Papa Chibou went away to his little hole in the wall. He sat on his cot and fingered his moustache for an hour; the news had left him dizzy, had made a cold vacuum under his belt buckle. From under his cot, at last, he took a wooden box, unlocked three separate locks, and extracted a sock. From the sock he took his fortune, his hoard of big copper ten-centime pieces, tips he had saved for years. He counted them over five times most carefully; but no matter how he counted them he could not make the total come to more than two hundred and twenty-one francs.

That night he did not tell Napoleon the news. He did not tell any of them. Indeed he acted even more cheerful than usual as he went from one figure to another. He complimented Madame Lablanche, the lady of the poisoned spouses, on how well she was looking. He even had a kindly word to say to the lion that was eating the two martyrs.

"After all, Monsieur Lion," he said, "I supposed it is as proper for you to eat martyrs as it is for me to eat bananas. Probably bananas do not enjoy being eaten any more than martyrs do. In the past I have said harsh things to you, Monsieur Lion; I am sorry I said them, now. After all, it is hardly your fault that you eat people. You were born with an appetite for martyrs, just as I was born poor." And he gently tweaked the lion's papier-mâché ear.

When he came to Napoleon, Papa Chibou brushed him with unusual care and thoroughness. With a moistened cloth he polished the imperial nose, and he took pains to be gentle with the cauliflower ear. He told Napoleon the latest joke he had heard at the cabmen's café where he ate his breakfast of onion soup, and, as the joke was mildly improper, nudged Napoleon in the ribs, and winked at him.

"We are men of the world, eh, old friend?" said Papa Chibou. "We are philosophers, is that not so?" Then he added, "We take what life sends us, and sometimes it sends hardnesses."

He wanted to talk more with Napoleon, but somehow he couldn't; abruptly, in the midst of a joke, Papa Chibou broke off and hurried down into the depths of the Chamber of Horrors and stood there for a very long time staring at an unfortunate native of Siam being trodden on by an elephant.

It was not until the morning of the auction sale that Papa Chibou told Napoleon. Then, while the crowd was gathering, he slipped up to Napoleon in his corner and laid his hand on Napoleon's arm.

"One of the hardnesses of life has come to us, old friend," he said. "They are going to try to take you away. But, courage! Papa Chibou does not desert his friends. Listen!" And Papa Chibou patted his pocket, which gave forth a jingling sound.

The bidding began. Close to the auctioneer's desk stood a man, a wizened, rodent-eyed man with a diamond ring and dirty fingers. Papa Chibou's heart went down like an express elevator when he saw him, for he knew that the rodent-eyed man was Mogen, the junk king of Paris. The auctioneer in a voice slightly encumbered by adenoids, began to sell the various items in a hurried, perfunctory manner.

"Item 3 is Julius Caesar, toga and sandals thrown in. How much am I offered? One hundred and fifty francs? Dirt cheap for a Roman emperor, that is. Who'll make it two hundred? Thank you, Monsieur Mogen. The noblest Roman of them all is going at two hundred francs. Are you all through at two hundred? Going, going, gone! Julius Caesar is sold to Monsieur Mogen."

Papa Chibou patted Caesar's back sympathetically.

"You are worth more, my good Julius," he said in a whisper. "Goodbye."

He was encouraged. If a comparatively new Caesar brought only two hundred, surely an old Napoleon would bring no more.

The sale progressed rapidly. Monsieur Mogen bought the entire Chamber of Horrors. He bought Marie Antoinette, and the martyrs

8

and lions. Papa Chibou, standing near Napoleon, withstood the strain of waiting by chewing his moustache.

The sale was very nearly over and Monsieur Mogen had bought every item, when, with a yawn, the auctioneer droned: "Now, ladies and gentlemen, we come to Item 573, a collection of odds and ends, mostly damaged goods, to be sold in one lot. The lot includes one stuffed owl that seems to have moulted a bit; one Spanish shawl, torn; the head of an Apache who has been guillotined, body missing; a small wax camel, no humps; and an old wax figure of Napoleon, with one ear damaged. What am I offered for the lot?"

Papa Chibou's heart stood still. He laid a reassuring hand on Napoleon's shoulder.

"The fool," he whispered in Napoleon's good ear, "to put you in the same class as a camel, no humps, and an owl. But never mind. It is lucky for us, perhaps."

"How much for this assortment?" asked the auctioneer.

"One hundred francs," said Mogen, the junk king.

"One hundred and fifty," said Papa Chibou, trying to be calm. He had never spent so vast a sum all at once in his life.

Mogen fingered the material in Napoleon's coat.

"Two hundred," said the junk king.

"Are you all through at two hundred?" queried the auctioneer.

"Two hundred and twenty-one," called Papa Chibou. His voice was a husky squeak.

Mogen from his rodent eyes glared at Papa Chibou with annoyance and contempt. He raised his dirtiest finger—the one with the diamond ring on it—toward the auctioneer.

"Monsieur Mogen bids two hundred and twenty-five," droned the auctioneer. "Do I hear two hundred and fifty?"

Papa Chibou hated the world. The auctioneer cast a look in his direction.

"Two hundred and twenty-five is bid," he repeated. "Are you all through at two hundred and twenty-five? Going, going—sold to Monsieur Mogen for two hundred and twenty-five francs."

Stunned, Papa Chibou heard Mogen say casually, "I'll send round my carts for this stuff in the morning."

This stuff!

Dully and with an aching breast Papa Chibou went to his room down by the Roman arena. He packed his few clothes into a box. Last of all he slowly took from his cap the brass badge he had worn for so many years; it bore the words "Chief Watchman." He had been proud of that title, even if it was slightly inaccurate; he had been not only the chief but the only watchman. Now he was nothing. It was hours before he summoned up the energy to take his box round to the room he had rented high up under the roof of a tenement in a near-by alley. He knew he should start to look for another job at once, but he could not force himself to do so that day. Instead, he stole back to the deserted museum and sat down on a bench by the side of Napoleon. Silently he sat there all night; but he did not sleep; he was thinking, and the thought that kept pecking at his brain was to him a shocking one. At last, as day began to edge its pale way through the dusty windows of the museum, Papa Chibou stood up with the air of a man who has been through a mental struggle and has made up his mind.

"Napoleon," he said, "we have been friends for a quarter of a century and now we are to be separated because a stranger had four francs more than I had. That may be lawful, my old friend, but it is not justice. You and I, we are not going to be parted."

Paris was not yet awake when Papa Chibou stole with infinite caution into the narrow street beside the museum. Along this street toward the tenement where he had taken a room crept Papa Chibou. Sometimes he had to pause for breath, for in his arms he was carrying Napoleon.

Two policemen came to arrest Papa Chibou that very afternoon. Mogen had missed Napoleon, and he was a shrewd man. There was not the slightest doubt of Papa Chibou's guilt. There stood Napoleon in the corner of his room, gazing pensively out over the housetops. The police bundled the overwhelmed and confused Papa Chibou into the police patrol, and with him, as damning evidence, Napoleon.

In his cell in the city prison Papa Chibou sat with his spirit caved in. To him jails and judges and justice were terrible and mysterious affairs. He wondered if he would be guillotined; perhaps not, since his long life had been one of blameless conduct; but the least he could expect, he reasoned, was a long sentence to hard labour on Devil's Island, and guillotining had certain advantages over that. Perhaps it would be better to be guillotined, he told himself, now that Napoleon was sure to be melted up.

The keeper who brought him his meal of stew was a pessimist of jocular tendencies.

"A pretty pickle," said the keeper; "and at your age too. You must be a very wicked old man to go about stealing dummies. What will be safe now? One may expect to find the Eiffel Tower missing any morning. Dummy stealing! What a career! We have had a man in here who stole a trolley car, and one who made off with the anchor of a steamship, and even one who pilfered a hippopotamus from a zoo, but never one who stole a dummy—and an old one-eared dummy, at that! It is an affair extraordinary!"

"And what did they do to the gentleman who stole the hippopotamus?" inquired Papa Chibou tremulously.

The keeper scratched his head to indicate thought.

"I think," he said, "that they boiled him alive. Either that or they transported him for life to Morocco; I don't recall exactly."

Papa Chibou's brow grew damp.

"It was a trial most comical, I can assure you," went on the keeper. "The judges were Messieurs Bertouf, Goblin, and Perouse—very amusing fellows, all three of them. They had fun with the prisoner; how I laughed. Judge Bertouf said, in sentencing him, 'We must be severe with you, pilferer of hippopotamuses. We must make of you an example. This business of hippopotamus pilfering is getting all too common in Paris.' They are witty fellows, those judges."

Papa Chibou grew a shade paler.

"The Terrible Trio?" he asked.

"The Terrible Trio," replied the keeper cheerfully.

"Will they be my judges?" asked Papa Chibou.

"Most assuredly," promised the keeper, and strolled away humming happily and rattling his big keys.

Papa Chibou knew then that there was no hope for him. Even into the Musée Pratoucy the reputation of those three judges had penetrated, and it was a sinister reputation indeed. They were three ancient, grim men, who had fairly earned their title, The Terrible Trio, by the severity of their sentences; evildoers blanched at their names, and this was a matter of pride to them.

Shortly the keeper came back; he was grinning.

"You have the devil's own luck, old-timer," he said to Papa Chibou. "First you have to be tried by The Terrible Trio, and then you get assigned to you as a lawyer none other than Monsieur Georges Dufayel."

"And this Monsieur Dufayel, is he then not a good lawyer?" questioned Papa Chibou miserably.

11

The keeper snickered.

"He has not won a case for months," he answered, as if it were the most amusing thing imaginable. "It is really better than a circus to hear him muddling up his clients' affairs in court. His mind is not on the case at all. Heaven knows where it is. When he rises to plead before the judges he has no fire, no passion. He mumbles and stutters. It is a saying about the courts that one is as good as convicted who has the ill luck to draw Monsieur Georges Dufayel as his advocate. Still, if one is too poor to pay for a lawyer, one must take what he can get. That's philosophy, eh, old-timer?"

Papa Chibou groaned.

"Oh, wait till tomorrow," said the keeper gayly. "Then you'll have a real reason to groan."

"But surely I can see this Monsieur Dufayel."

"Oh, what's the use? You stole the dummy, didn't you? It will be there in court to appear against you. How entertaining! Witness for the prosecution: Monsieur Napoleon. You are plainly as guilty as Cain, old-timer, and the judges will boil your cabbage for you very quickly and neatly, I can promise you that. Well, see you tomorrow. Sleep well."

Papa Chibou did not sleep well. He did not sleep at all, in fact, and when they marched him into the inclosure where sat the other non-descript offenders against the law he was shaken and utterly wretched. He was overawed by the great court room and the thick atmosphere of seriousness that hung over it.

He did pluck up enough courage to ask a guard, "Where is my lawyer, Monsieur Dufayel?"

"Oh, he's late, as usual," replied the guard. And then, for he was a waggish fellow, he added, "If you're lucky he won't come at all."

Papa Chibou sank down on the prisoner's bench and raised his eyes to the tribunal opposite. His very marrow was chilled by the sight of The Terrible Trio. The chief judge, Bertouf, was a vast puff of a man, who swelled out of his judicial chair like a poisonous fungus. His black robe was familiar with spilled brandy, and his dirty judicial bib was askew. His face was bibulous and brutal, and he had the wattles of a turkey gobbler. Judge Goblin, on his right, looked to have mummified; he was at least a hundred years old and had wrinkled parchment skin and red-rimmed eyes that glittered like the eyes of a cobra. Judge Perouse was one vast jungle of tangled grizzled whisker, from the midst

12

of which projected a cockatoo's beak of a nose; he looked at Papa Chibou and licked his lips with a long pink tongue. Papa Chibou all but fainted; he felt no bigger than a pea, and less important; as for his judges, they seemed enormous monsters.

The first case was called, a young swaggering fellow who had stolen an orange from a pushcart.

"Ah, Monsieur Thief," rumbled Judge Bertouf with a scowl, "you are jaunty now. Will you be so jaunty a year from today when you are released from prison? I rather think not. Next case."

Papa Chibou's heart pumped with difficulty. A year for an orange— and he had stolen a man! His eyes roved round the room and he saw two guards carrying in something which they stood before the judges. It was Napoleon.

A guard tapped Papa Chibou on the shoulder. "You're next," he said.

"But my lawyer, Monsieur Dufayel—" began Papa Chibou.

"You're in hard luck," said the guard, "for here he comes."

Papa Chibou in a daze found himself in the prisoner's dock. He saw coming toward him a pale young man. Papa Chibou recognized him at once. It was the slender erect young man of the museum. He was not very erect now; he was listless. He did not recognize Papa Chibou; he barely glanced at him.

"You stole something," said the young lawyer, and his voice was toneless. "The stolen goods were found in your room. I think we might better plead guilty and get it over with."

"Yes, monsieur," said Papa Chibou, for he had let go all his hold on hope. "But attend a moment. I have something—a message for you."

Papa Chibou fumbled through his pockets and at last found the card of the American girl with the bright dark eyes. He handed it to Georges Dufayel.

"She left it with me to give to you," said Papa Chibou. "I was chief watchman at the Musée Pratoucy, you know. She came there night after night, to wait for you."

The young man gripped the sides of the card with both hands; his face, his eyes, everything about him seemed suddenly charged with new life.

"Ten thousand million devils," he cried. "And I doubted her! I owe you much, monsieur. I owe you everything." He wrung Papa Chibou's hand.

Judge Bertouf gave an impatient judicial grunt.

13

"We are ready to hear your case, Advocate Dufayel," said the judge, "if you have one."

The court attendants sniggered.

"A little moment, monsieur the judge," said the lawyer. He turned to Papa Chibou. "Quick," he shot out, "tell me about the crime you are charged with. What did you steal?"

"Him," replied Papa Chibou, pointing.

"That dummy of Napoleon?"

Papa Chibou nodded.

"But why?"

Papa Chibou shrugged his shoulders.

"Monsieur could not understand."

"But you must tell me!" said the lawyer urgently. "I must make a plea for you. These savages will be severe enough, in any event; but I may be able to do something. Quick; why did you steal this Napoleon?"

"I was his friend," said Papa Chibou. "The museum failed. They were going to sell Napoleon for junk, Monsieur Dufayel. He was my friend. I could not desert him."

The eyes of the young advocate had caught fire; they were lit with a flash. He brought his fist down on the table.

"Enough!" he cried.

Then he rose in his place and addressed the court. His voice was low, vibrant and passionate; the judges, in spite of themselves, leaned forward to listen to him.

"May it please the honourable judges of this court of France," he began, "my client is guilty. Yes, I repeat in a voice of thunder, for all France to hear, for the enemies of France to hear, for the whole wide world to hear, he is guilty. He did steal this figure of Napoleon, the lawful property of another. I do not deny it. This old man, Jerome Chibou, is guilty, and I am proud of his guilt."

Judge Bertouf grunted.

"If your client is guilty, Advocate Dufayel," he said, "that settles it. Despite your pride in his guilt, which is a peculiar notion, I confess, I am going to sentence him to—"

"But wait, your honor!" Dufayel's voice was compelling. "You must, you shall hear me! Before you pass sentence on this old man, let me ask you a question."

"Well?"

"Are you a Frenchman, Judge Bertouf?"

"But certainly."

"And you love France?"

"Monsieur has not the effrontery to suggest otherwise?"

"No. I was sure of it. That is why you will listen to me."

"I listen."

"I repeat then: Jerome Chibou is guilty. In the law's eye he is a criminal. But in the eyes of France and those who love her his guilt is more honourable than innocence itself."

The three judges looked at one another blankly; Papa Chibou regarded his lawyer with wide eyes; Georges Dufayel spoke on.

"These are times of turmoil and change in our country, messieurs the judges. Proud traditions which were once the birthright of every Frenchman have been allowed to decay. Enemies beset us within and without. Youth grows careless of that honour which is the soul of a nation. Youth forgets the priceless heritages of the ages, the great names that once brought glory to France in the past, when Frenchmen were Frenchmen. There are some in France who may have forgotten the respect due a nation's great"—here Advocate Dufayel looked very hard at the judges—"but there are a few patriots left who have not forgotten. And there sits one of them.

"This poor old man has deep within him a glowing devotion to France. You may say that he is a simple, unlettered peasant. You may say that he is a thief. But I say, and true Frenchmen will say with me, that he is a patriot, messieurs the judges. He loves Napoleon. He loves him for what he did for France. He loves him because in Napoleon burned that spirit which has made France great. There was a time, messieurs the judges, when your fathers and mine dared share that love for a great leader. Need I remind you of the career of Napoleon? I know I need not. Need I tell you of his victories? I know I need not."

Nevertheless, Advocate Dufayel did tell them of the career of Napoleon. With a wealth of detail and many gestures he traced the rise of Napoleon; he lingered over his battles; for an hour and ten minutes he spoke eloquently of Napoleon and his part in the history of France.

"You may have forgotten," he concluded, "and others may have forgotten, but this old man sitting here a prisoner—he did not forget. When mercenary scoundrels wanted to throw on the junk heap this effigy of one of France's greatest sons, who was it that saved him? Was it you, messieurs the judges? Was it I? Alas, no. It was a poor old man

15

who loved Napoleon more than he loved himself. Consider, messieurs the judges; they were going to throw on the junk heap Napoleon—France's Napoleon—our Napoleon. Who would save him? Then up rose this man, Jerome Chibou, whom you would brand as a thief, and he cried aloud for France and for the whole world to hear, 'Stop! Desecraters of Napoleon, stop! There still lives one Frenchman who loves the memories of his native land; there is still one patriot left. I, I, Jerome Chibou, will save Napoleon!' And he did save him, messieurs the judges."

Advocate Dufayel mopped his brow, and leveling an accusing finger at The Terrible Trio he said, "You may send Jerome Chibou to jail. But when you do, remember this: You are sending to jail the spirit of France. You may find Jerome Chibou guilty. But when you do, remember this: You are condemning a man for love of country, for love of France. Wherever true hearts beat in French bosoms, messieurs the judges, there will the crime of Jerome Chibou be understood, and there will the name of Jerome Chibou be honoured. Put him in prison, messieurs the judges. Load his poor feeble old body with chains. And a nation will tear down the prison walls, break his chains, and pay homage to the man who loved Napoleon and France so much that he was willing to sacrifice himself on the altar of patriotism."

Advocate Dufayel sat down; Papa Chibou raised his eyes to the judges' bench. Judge Perouse was ostentatiously blowing his beak of a nose. Judge Goblin, who wore a Sedan ribbon in his buttonhole, was sniffling into his inkwell. And Chief Judge Bertouf was openly blubbering.

"Jerome Chibou, stand up." It was Chief Judge Bertouf who spoke, and his voice was thick with emotion.

Papa Chibou, quaking, stood up. A hand like a hand of pink bananas was thrust down at him.

"Jerome Chibou," said Chief Judge Bertouf, "I find you guilty. Your crime is patriotism in the first degree. I sentence you to freedom. Let me have the honour of shaking the hand of a true Frenchman."

"And I," said Judge Goblin, thrusting out a hand as dry as autumn leaves.

"And I also," said Judge Perouse, reaching out a hairy hand.

"And, furthermore," said Chief Judge Bertouf, "you shall continue to protect the Napoleon you saved. I subscribe a hundred francs to buy him for you."

16

"And I," said Judge Goblin.

"And I also," said Judge Perouse.

As they left the court room, Advocate Dufayel, Papa Chibou and Napoleon, Papa Chibou turned to his lawyer.

"I can never repay monsieur," he began.

"Nonsense!" said the lawyer.

"And would Monsieur Dufayel mind telling me again the last name of Napoleon?"

"Why, Bonaparte, of course. Surely you knew——"

"Alas, no, Monsieur Dufayel. I am a man the most ignorant. I did not know that my friend had done such great things."

"You didn't? Then what in the name of heaven did you think Napoleon was?"

"A sort of murderer," said Papa Chibou humbly.

Out beyond the walls of Paris in a garden stands the villa of Georges Dufayel, who has become, everyone says, the most eloquent and successful lawyer in the Paris courts. He lives there with his wife, who has bright dark eyes. To get to his house one must pass a tiny gatehouse, where lives a small old man with a prodigious walrus moustache. Visitors who peer into the gatehouse as they pass sometimes get a shock, for standing in one corner of its only room they see another small man, in uniform and a big hat. He never moves, but stands there by the window all day, one hand in the bosom of his coat, the other at his side, while his eyes look out over the garden. He is waiting for Papa Chibou to come after his work among the asparagus beds to tell him the jokes and the news of the day.

Scherzando

Jake Falstaff

I have been so busy, beloved,
Rummaging the world for small, important things
That, now that you have come,
I am all vague and breathless,
Like a woman who knew that company was coming
And spent all morning tidying her house
And changing things around.

So sit down, lovely and expected stranger,
Sit in the brown chair; let me look at you;
Give me a little time to remember who I am,
And what I am called, and what I meant to say.

This is my lesser house.
I live here when I have my hat off.
These are my chairs—that over there's the table.
The windows could stand washing, couldn't they?
Do you like the pictures?
Sometime I will hire
An old man with a wrinkled woman-face
To put new paper on the walls.

I have kept a room for you, beloved stranger,
I have given thought to everything it holds.
But now that you are here
I see you'll live in every room but that.

Tell me about your family. Are your aunts
Sturdy like bumblebees, or lean and capable, like hoes?
Did your mother ever wake up in the morning
With flamingoes in her arms?

Now let us go and see my other house,
This is the earth. Out yonder is the sun.
Above's the sky. Beyond the smoky edge
Are mountains and an ocean. There are clouds.

18

And—look—there are my birds.
You will see all plainer after you have lain
For half a night in darkness, with the night
Cooling your eyes.

Oh, grave one, I have been so much afraid
That this would end—this world—before you came
And I could take you all around to see
Its great green splendors and its wild red glories,
Its little beauties and its small surprises
Hidden under leaves and blades of grass!

Oh, beloved, here I will lie and here you will stand,
With the wind in your hair and your skirt, and the sun in your face,
Watching a day sail past like a full-sailed galleon!
There, with the rock for a shed,
I will sit, and you, with your head in my lap,
There you will lie, smiling softly,
When the great storms come in spring and the thunderheads
Darken the world and, waving a wand of lightning,
Bring down a marvel of blossoms!

Birthright

John Drinkwater

Lord Rameses of Egypt sighed
   Because a summer evening passed;
And little Ariadne cried
   That summer fancy fell at last
To dust; and young Verona died
   When beauty's hour was overcast.

Theirs was the bitterness we know
   Because the clouds of hawthorne keep
So short a state, and kisses go
   To tombs unfathomably deep,
While Rameses and Romeo
   And little Ariadne sleep.

The Brushwood Boy

Rudyard Kipling

> *"We are such stuff as dreams are made on."*
> *A famous love story uses this theme.*

A CHILD of three sat up in his crib and screamed at the top of his voice, his fists clinched and his eyes full of terror. At first no one heard, for his nursery was in the west wing, and the nurse was talking to a gardener among the laurels. Then the housekeeper passed that way, and hurried to soothe him. He was her special pet, and she disapproved of the nurse.

"What was it, then? What was it, then? There's nothing to frighten him, Georgie dear."

"It was—it was a policeman! He was on the Down—I saw him! He came in. Jane *said* he would."

"Policemen don't come into houses, dearie. Turn over, and take my hand."

"I saw him—on the Down. He came here. Where is your hand, Harper?"

The housekeeper waited till the sobs changed to the regular breathing of sleep before she stole out.

"Jane, what nonsense have you been telling Master Georgie about policemen?"

"I haven't told him anything."

"You have. He's been dreaming about them."

"We met Tisdall on Dowhead when we were in the donkey-cart this morning. P'r'aps that's what put it into his head."

"Oh! Now you aren't going to frighten the child into fits with your silly tales, and the master know nothing about it. If ever I catch you again," etc.

* * * * * * * * * *

A child of six was telling himself stories as he lay in bed. It was a new power, and he kept it a secret. A month before it had occurred to him to carry on a nursery tale left unfinished by his mother, and he was delighted to find the tale as it came out of his own head just as surprising as though he were listening to it "all new from the beginning." There was a prince in that tale, and he killed dragons, but only for one night. Ever afterwards Georgie dubbed himself prince, pasha, giant-killer, and all the rest (you see, he could not tell any one, for fear of being laughed at), and his tales faded gradually into dreamland, where adventures were so many that he could not recall the half of them. They all began in the same way, or, as Georgie explained to the shadows of the night-light, there was "the same starting-off place"—a pile of brushwood stacked somewhere near a beach; and round this pile Georgie found himself running races with little boys and girls. These ended, ships ran high up the dry land and opened into cardboard boxes; or gilt-and-green iron railings that surrounded beautiful gardens turned all soft and could be walked through and overthrown so long as he remembered it was only a dream. He could never hold that knowledge more than a few seconds ere things became real, and instead of pushing down houses full of grown-up people (a just revenge), he sat miserably upon gigantic door-steps trying to sing the multiplication-table up to four times six.

The princess of his tales was a person of wonderful beauty (she came from the old illustrated edition of Grimm, now out of print), and as she always applauded Georgie's valour among the dragons and buffaloes, he gave her the two finest names he had ever heard in his life—Annie and Louise, pronounced "Annie*an*louise." When the dreams swamped the stories, she would change into one of the little girls round the brushwood-pile, still keeping her title and crown. She saw Georgie drown once in a dream-sea by the beach (it was the day after he had been taken to bathe in a real sea by his nurse); and he said as he sank: "Poor Annie*an*louise! She'll be sorry for me now!" But "Annie*an*louise," walking slowly on the beach, called, " 'Ha! ha!' said the duck, laughing," which to a waking mind might not seem to bear on the situation. It consoled Georgie at once, and must have been some kind of spell, for it raised the bottom of the deep, and he waded out with a twelve-inch flower-pot on each foot. As he was strictly forbidden to meddle with flower-pots in real life, he felt triumphantly wicked.

*   *   *   *   *   *   *   *   *   *

The movements of the grown-ups, whom Georgie tolerated, but did not pretend to understand, removed his world, when he was seven years old, to a place called "Oxford-on-a-visit." Here were huge buildings surrounded by vast prairies, with streets of infinite length, and, above all, something called the "buttery," which Georgie was dying to see, because he knew it must be greasy, and therefore delightful. He perceived how correct were his judgments when his nurse led him through a stone arch into the presence of an enormously fat man, who asked him if he would like some bread and cheese. Georgie used to eat all round the clock, so he took what "buttery" gave him, and would have taken some brown liquid called "auditale" but that his nurse led him away to an afternoon performance of a thing called "Pepper's Ghost." This was intensely thrilling. People's heads came off and flew all over the stage, and skeletons danced bone by bone, while Mr. Pepper himself, beyond question a man of the worst, waved his arms and flapped a long gown, and in a deep bass voice (Georgie had never heard a man sing before) told of his sorrows unspeakable. Some grown-up or other tried to explain that the illusion was made with mirrors, and that there was no need to be frightened. Georgie did not know what illusions were, but he did know that a mirror was the looking-glass with the ivory handle on his mother's dressing-table. Therefore the "grown-up" was "just saying things" after the distressing custom of "grown-ups," and Georgie cast about for amusement between scenes. Next to him sat a little girl dressed all in black, her hair combed off her forehead exactly like the girl in the book called "Alice in Wonderland," which had been given him on his last birthday. The little girl looked at Georgie, and Georgie looked at her. There seemed to be no need of any further introduction.

"I've got a cut on my thumb," said he. It was the first work of his first real knife, a savage triangular hack, and he esteemed it a most valuable possession.

"I'm tho thorry!" she lisped. "Let me look—pleathe."

"There's a di-ack-lum plaster on, but it's all raw under," Georgie answered, complying.

"Dothent it hurt?"—her gray eyes were full of pity and interest.

"Awf'ly. Perhaps it will give me lockjaw."

"It lookth very horrid. I'm *tho* thorry!" She put a forefinger to his hand, and held her head sidewise for a better view.

Here the nurse turned, and shook him severely. "You mustn't talk to strange little girls, Master Georgie."

22

"She isn't strange. She's very nice. I like her, an' I've showed her my new cut."

"The idea! You change places with me."

She moved him over, and shut out the little girl from his view, while the grown-up behind renewed the futile explanations.

"I am *not* afraid, truly," said the boy, wriggling in despair; "but why don't you go to sleep in the afternoons, same as Provost of Oriel?"

Georgie had been introduced to a grown-up of that name, who slept in his presence without apology. Georgie understood that he was the most important grown-up in Oxford; hence he strove to gild his rebuke with flatteries. This grown-up did not seem to like it, but he collapsed, and Georgie lay back in his seat, silent and enraptured. Mr. Pepper was singing again, and the deep, ringing voice, the red fire, and the misty, waving gown all seemed to be mixed up with the little girl who had been so kind about his cut. When the performance was ended she nodded to Georgie, and Georgie nodded in return. He spoke no more than was necessary till bedtime, but meditated on new colors and sounds and lights and music and things as far as he understood them; the deep-mouthed agony of Mr. Pepper mingling with the little girl's lisp. That night he made a new tale, from which he shamelessly removed the Rapunzel-Rapunzel-let-down-your-hair princess, gold crown, Grimm edition, and all, and put a new Annie*an*louise in her place. So it was perfectly right and natural that when he came to the brushwood-pile he should find her waiting for him, her hair combed off her forehead more like Alice in Wonderland than ever, and the races and adventures began.

* * * * * * * * * *

Ten years at an English public school do not encourage dreaming. Georgie won his growth and chest measurement, and a few other things which did not appear in the bills, under a system of cricket, foot-ball, and paper-chases, from four to five days a week, which provided for three lawful cuts of a ground-ash if any boy absented himself from these entertainments. He became a rumple-collared, dusty-hatted fag of the Lower Third, and a light half-back at Little Side football; was pushed and prodded through the slack back-waters of the Lower Fourth, where the raffle of a school generally accumulates; won his "second-fifteen" cap at football, enjoyed the dignity of a study with two companions in it, and began to look forward to office as a sub-prefect. At last he blossomed into full glory as head of the school,

23

ex-officio captain of the games; head of his house, where he and his lieutenants preserved discipline and decency among seventy boys from twelve to seventeen; general arbiter in the quarrels that spring up among the touchy Sixth—and intimate friend and ally of the Head himself. When he stepped forth in the black jersey, white knickers, and black stockings of the First Fifteen, the new match-ball under his arm, and his old and frayed cap at the back of his head, the small fry of the lower forms stood apart and worshipped, and the "new caps" of the team talked to him ostentatiously, that the world might see. And so, in summer, when he came back to the pavilion after a slow but eminently safe game, it mattered not whether he had made nothing or, as once happened, a hundred and three, the school shouted just the same, and women-folk who had come to look at the match looked at Cottar—Cottar, *major;* "that's Cottar!" Above all, he was responsible for that thing called the tone of the school, and few realise with what passionate devotion a certain type of boy throws himself into this work. Home was a far-away country, full of ponies and fishing and shooting, and men-visitors who interfered with one's plans; but school was the real world, where things of vital importance happened, and crises arose that must be dealt with promptly and quietly. Not for nothing was it written, "Let the Consuls look to it that the Republic takes no harm," and Georgie was glad to be back in authority when the holidays ended. Behind him, but not too near, was the wise and temperate Head, now suggesting the wisdom of the serpent, now counselling the mildness of the dove; leading him on to see, more by half-hints than by any direct word, how boys and men are all of a piece, and how he who can handle the one will assuredly in time control the other.

For the rest, the school was not encouraged to dwell on its emotions, but rather to keep in hard condition, to avoid false quantities, and to enter the army direct, without the help of the expensive London crammer, under whose roof young blood learns too much. Cottar, *major,* went the way of hundreds before him. The Head gave him six months' final polish, taught him what kind of answers best please a certain kind of examiners, and handed him over to the properly constituted authorities, who passed him into Sandhurst. Here he had sense enough to see that he was in the Lower Third once more, and behaved with respect toward his seniors, till they in turn respected him, and he was promoted to the rank of corporal, and sat in authority over mixed peoples with all the vices of men and boys combined. His reward was another string of athletic cups, a good-conduct sword, and, at last, Her Majesty's commission as a subaltern in a first-class line regiment. He did not know that he bore with him from school and college a character worth much fine gold, but was pleased to find his mess so kindly. He had plenty of money of his own; his training had set the public-school mask upon his face, and had taught him how many were the "things no fellow can do." By virtue of the same training he kept his pores open and his mouth shut.

The regular working of the Empire shifted his world to India, where he tasted utter loneliness in subaltern's quarters,—one room and one bullock-trunk,—and, with his mess, learned the new life from the beginning. But there were horses in the land—ponies at reasonable price, there was polo for such as could afford it; there were the disreputable remnants of a pack of hounds; and Cottar worried his way along without too much despair. It dawned on him that a regiment in India was nearer the chance of active service than he had conceived, and that a man might as well study his profession. A major of the new school backed this idea with enthusiasm, and he and Cottar accumulated a library of military works, and read and argued and disputed far into the nights. But the adjutant said the old thing: "Get to know your men, young un, and they'll follow you anywhere. That's all you want— know your men." Cottar thought he knew them fairly well at cricket and the regimental sports, but he never realised the true inwardness of them till he was sent off with a detachment of twenty to sit down in a mud fort near a rushing river which was spanned by a bridge of boats. When the floods came they went forth and hunted strayed pontoons along the banks. Otherwise there was nothing to do, and the men got drunk, gambled, and quarrelled. They were a sickly crew, for a junior subaltern is by custom saddled with the worst men. Cottar endured their rioting as long as he could, and then sent down-country for a dozen pairs of boxing-gloves.

"I wouldn't blame you for fightin'," said he, "if you only knew how to use your hands; but you don't. Take these things, and I'll show you." The men appreciated his efforts. Now, instead of blaspheming and swearing at a comrade, and threatening to shoot him, they could take him apart, and soothe themselves to exhaustion. As one explained whom Cottar found with a shut eye and a diamond-shaped mouth spitting blood through an embrasure: "We tried it with the gloves, sir, for twenty minutes, and *that* done us no good, sir. Then we took off the

25

gloves and tried it that way for another twenty minutes, same as you showed us, sir, an' that done us a world o' good. 'Twasn't fightin', sir; there was a bet on."

Cottar dared not laugh, but he invited his men to other sports, such as racing across country in shirt and trousers after a trail of torn paper, and to single-stick in the evenings, till the native population, who had a lust for sport in every form, wished to know whether the white men understood wrestling. They sent in an ambassador, who took the soldiers by the neck and threw them about the dust; and the entire command were all for this new game. They spent money on learning new falls and holds, which was better than buying other doubtful commodities; and the peasantry grinned five deep round the tournaments.

That detachment, who had gone up in bullock-carts, returned to headquarters at an average rate of thirty miles a day, fair heel-and-toe; no sick, no prisoners, and no court martials pending. They scattered themselves among their friends, singing the praises of their lieutenant and looking for causes of offense.

"How did you do it, young un?" the adjutant asked.

"Oh, I sweated the beef off 'em, and then I sweated some muscle on to 'em. It was rather a lark."

"If that's your way of lookin' at it, we can give you all the larks you want. Young Davies isn't feelin' quite fit, and he's next for detachment duty. Care to go for him?"

"'Sure he wouldn't mind? I don't want to shove myself forward, you know."

"You needn't bother on Davies's account. We'll give you the sweepin's of the corps, and you can see what you can make of 'em."

"All right," said Cottar. "It's better fun than loafin' about cantonments."

"Rummy thing," said the adjutant, after Cottar had returned to his wilderness with twenty other devils worse than the first. "If Cottar only knew it, half the women in the station would give their eyes—confound 'em!—to have the young un in tow."

"That accounts for Mrs. Elery sayin' I was workin' my nice new boy too hard," said a wing commander.

"Oh, yes; and 'Why doesn't he come to the bandstand in the evenings?' and 'Can't I get him to make up a four at tennis with the Hammon girls?' " the adjutant snorted. "Look at young Davies makin' an ass of himself over mutton-dressed-as-lamb old enough to be his mother!"

26

"No one can accuse young Cottar of runnin' after women, white *or* black," the major replied thoughtfully. "But, then, that's the kind that generally goes the worst mucker in the end."

"Not Cottar. I've only run across one of his muster before—a fellow called Ingles, in South Africa. He was just the same hard-trained, athletic-sports build of animal. Always kept himself in the pink of condition. Didn't do him much good, though. 'Shot at Wesselstroom the week before Majuba. Wonder how the young un will lick his detachment into shape."

Cottar turned up six weeks later, on foot, with his pupils. He never told his experiences, but the men spoke enthusiastically, and fragments of it leaked back to the colonel through sergeants, bâtmen, and the like.

There was great jealousy between the first and second detachments, but the men united in adoring Cottar, and their way of showing it was by sparing him all the trouble that men know how to make for an un-loved officer. He sought popularity as little as he had sought it at school, and therefore it came to him. He favoured no one—not even when the company sloven pulled the company cricket-match out of the fire with an unexpected forty-three at the last moment. There was very little getting round him, for he seemed to know by instinct exactly when and where to head off a malingerer; but he did not forget that the difference between a dazed and sulky junior of the upper school and a bewildered, browbeaten lump of a private fresh from the depot was very small indeed. The sergeants, seeing these things, told him secrets generally hid from young officers. His words were quoted as barrack authority on bets in canteen and at tea; and the veriest shrew of the corps, bursting with charges against other women who had used the cooking-ranges out of turn, forbore to speak when Cottar, as the regu-lations ordained, asked of a morning if there were "any complaints."

"I'm full o' complaints," said Mrs. Corporal Morrison, "an' I'd kill O'Halloran's fat sow of a wife any day, but ye know how it is. 'E puts 'is head just inside the door, an' looks down 'is blessed nose so bashful, an' 'e whispers, 'Any complaints?' Ye can't complain after that. *I* want to kiss him. Some day I think I will. Heigh-ho! she'll be a lucky woman that gets Young Innocence. See 'im now, girls. Do ye blame me?"

Cottar was cantering across to polo, and he looked a very satisfactory figure of a man as he gave easily to the first excited bucks of his pony, and slipped over a low mud wall to the practice-ground. There were more than Mrs. Corporal Morrison who felt as she did. But Cottar was busy for eleven hours of the day. He did not care to have his tennis spoiled by petticoats in the court; and after one long afternoon at a garden-party, he explained to his major that this sort of thing was "futile piffle," and the major laughed. Theirs was not a married mess, except for the colonel's wife, and Cottar stood in awe of the good lady. She said "my regiment," and the world knows what that means. None the less, when they wanted her to give away the prizes after a shooting-match, and she refused because one of the prize-winners was married to a girl who had made a jest of her behind her broad back, the mess ordered Cottar to "tackle her," in his best calling-kit. This he did, simply and laboriously, and she gave way altogether.

"She only wanted to know the facts of the case," he explained. "I just told her, and she saw at once."

"Ye-es," said the adjutant. "I expect that's what she did. Comin' to the Fusiliers' dance tonight, Galahad?"

"No, thanks. I've got a fight on with the major." The virtuous apprentice sat up till midnight in the major's quarters, with a stop-watch and a pair of compasses, shifting little painted lead blocks about a four-inch map.

Then he turned in and slept the sleep of innocence, which is full of healthy dreams. One peculiarity of his dreams he noticed at the beginning of his second hot weather. Two or three times a month they duplicated or ran in series. He would find himself sliding into dreamland by the same road—a road that ran along a beach near a pile of brushwood. To the right lay the sea, sometimes at full tide, sometimes withdrawn to the very horizon; but he knew it for the same sea. By that road he would travel over a swell of rising ground covered with short, withered grass, into valleys of wonder and unreason. Beyond the ridge, which was crowned with some sort of street-lamp, anything was possible; but up to the lamp it seemed to him that he knew the road as well as he knew the parade-ground. He learned to look forward to the place; for, once there, he was sure of a good night's rest, and Indian hot weather can be rather trying. First, shadowy under closing eyelids, would come the outline of the brushwood-pile; next the white sand of the beach-road, almost overhanging the black, changeful sea; then the turn inland and uphill to the single light. When he was unrestful for any reason, he would tell himself how he was sure to get there—sure to get there—if he shut his eyes and surrendered to the drift of things. But one night after a foolishly hard hour's polo (the thermometer was

28

94° in his quarters at ten o'clock), sleep stood away from him altogether, though he did his best to find the well-known road, the point
where true sleep began. At last he saw the brushwood-pile, and hurried
along to the ridge, for behind him he felt was the wide-awake, sultry
world. He reached the lamp in safety, tingling with drowsiness, when
a policeman—a common country policeman—sprang up before him and
touched him on the shoulder ere he could dive into the dim valley below. He was filled with terror,—the hopeless terror of dreams,—for the
policeman said, in the awful, distinct voice of dream-people, "I am
Policeman Day coming back from the City of Sleep. You come with
me." Georgie knew it was true—that just beyond him in the valley lay
the lights of the City of Sleep, where he would have been sheltered,
and that this Policeman-Thing had full power and authority to head
him back to miserable wakefulness. He found himself looking at the
moonlight on the wall, dripping with fright; and he never overcame
that horror, though he met the Policeman several times that hot
weather, and his coming was the forerunner of a bad night.

But other dreams—perfectly absurd ones—filled him with an incom-
municable delight. All those that he remembered began by the brushwood-pile. For instance, he found a small clockwork steamer (he had
noticed it many nights before) lying by the sea-road, and stepped into
it, whereupon it moved with surpassing swiftness over an absolutely
level sea. This was glorious, for he felt he was exploring great matters;
and it stopped by a lily carved in stone, which, most naturally, floated
on the water. Seeing the lily was labelled "Hong-Kong," Georgie said:
"Of course. This is precisely what I expected Hong-Kong would be
like. How magnificent!" Thousands of miles farther on it halted at
yet another stone lily, labelled "Java"; and this, again, delighted him
hugely, because he knew that now he was at the world's end. But the
little boat ran on and on till it lay in a deep fresh-water lock, the sides
of which were carven marble, green with moss. Lily-pads lay on the
water, and reeds arched above. Some one moved among the reeds—
some one whom Georgie knew he had travelled to this world's end to
reach. Therefore everything was entirely well with him. He was un-
speakably happy, and vaulted over the ship's side to find this person.
When his feet touched that still water, it changed, with the rustle of
unrolling maps, to nothing less than a sixth quarter of the globe, beyond the most remote imagining of man—a place where islands were
coloured yellow and blue, their lettering strung across their faces.

29

They gave on unknown seas, and Georgie's urgent desire was to return swiftly across this floating atlas to known bearings. He told himself repeatedly that it was no good to hurry; but still he hurried desperately, and the islands slipped and slid under his feet, the straits yawned and widened, till he found himself utterly lost in the world's fourth dimension, with no hope of return. Yet only a little distance away he could see the old world with the rivers and mountain-chains marked according to the Sandhurst rules of map-making. Then that person for whom he had come to the Lily Lock (that was its name) ran up across unexplored territories, and showed him a way. They fled hand in hand till they reached a road that spanned ravines, and ran along the edge of precipices, and was tunnelled through mountains. "This goes to our brushwood-pile," said his companion; and all his trouble was at an end. He took a pony, because he understood that this was the Thirty-Mile Ride and he must ride swiftly, and raced through the clattering tunnels and round the curves, always downhill, till he heard the sea to his left, and saw it raging under a full moon, against sandy cliffs. It was heavy going, but he recognised the nature of the country, the dark-purple downs inland, and the bents that whistled in the wind. The road was eaten away in places, and the sea lashed at him—black, foamless tongues of smooth and glossy rollers; but he was sure that there was less danger from the sea than from "Them," whoever "They" were, inland to his right. He knew, too, that he would be safe if he could reach the down with the lamp on it. This came as he expected: he saw the one light a mile ahead along the beach, dismounted, turned to the right, walked quietly over to the brushwood-pile, found the little steamer had returned to the beach whence he had unmoored it, and—must have fallen asleep, for he could remember no more. "I'm gettin' the hang of the geography of that place," he said to himself, as he shaved next morning. "I must have made some sort of circle. Let's see. The Thirty-Mile Ride (now how the deuce did I know it was called the Thirty-Mile Ride?) joins the sea-road beyond the first down where the lamp is. And that atlas-country lies at the back of the Thirty-Mile Ride, somewhere out to the right beyond the hills and tunnels. Rummy things, dreams. 'Wonder what makes mine fit into each other so?"

He continued on his solid way through the recurring duties of the seasons. The regiment was shifted to another station, and he enjoyed road-marching for two months, with a good deal of mixed shooting thrown in, and when they reached their new cantonments he became a member of the local Tent Club, and chased the mighty boar on horseback with a short stabbing-spear. There he met the *mahseer* of the Poonch, beside whom the tarpon is as a herring, and he who lands him can say that he is a fisherman. This was as new and as fascinating as the big-game shooting that fell to his portion, when he had himself photographed for the mother's benefit, sitting on the flank of his first tiger.

Then the adjutant was promoted, and Cottar rejoiced with him, for he admired the adjutant greatly, and marvelled who might be big enough to fill his place; so that he nearly collapsed when the mantle fell on his own shoulders, and the colonel said a few sweet things that made him blush. An adjutant's position does not differ materially from that of head of the school, and Cottar stood in the same relation to the colonel as he had to his old Head in England. Only, tempers wear out in hot weather, and things were said and done that tried him sorely, and he made glorious blunders, from which the regimental sergeant-major pulled him with a loyal soul and a shut mouth. Slovens and incompetents raged against him; the weak-minded strove to lure him from the ways of justice; the small-minded—yea, men whom Cottar believed would never do "things no fellow can do"—imputed motives mean and circuitous to actions that he had not spent a thought upon; and he tasted injustice, and it made him very sick. But his consolation came on parade, when he looked down the full companies, and reflected how few were in hospital or cells, and wondered when the time would come to try the machine of his love and labour.

But they needed and expected the whole of a man's working-day, and maybe three or four hours of the night. Curiously enough, he never dreamed about the regiment as he was popularly supposed to. The mind, set free from the day's doings, generally ceased working altogether, or, if it moved at all, carried him along the old beach-road to the downs, the lamp-post, and, once in a while, to terrible Policeman Day. The second time that he returned to the world's lost continent (this was a dream that repeated itself again and again, with variations, on the same ground) he knew that if he only sat still the person from the Lily Lock would help him, and he was not disappointed. Sometimes he was trapped in mines of vast depth hollowed out of the heart of the world, where men in torment chanted echoing songs; and he heard this person coming along through the galleries, and everything was made safe and delightful. They met again in low-roofed Indian

31

railway-carriages that halted in a garden surrounded by gilt-and-green railings, where a mob of stony white people, all unfriendly, sat at breakfast-tables covered with roses, and separated Georgie from his companion, while underground voices sang deep-voiced songs. Georgie was filled with enormous despair till they two met again. They foregathered in the middle of an endless, hot tropic night, and crept into a huge house that stood, he knew, somewhere north of the railway-station where the people ate among the roses. It was surrounded with gardens, all moist and dripping; and in one room, reached through leagues of whitewashed passages, a Sick Thing lay in bed. Now the least noise, Georgie knew, would unchain some waiting horror, and his companion knew it, too; but when their eyes met across the bed, Georgie was disgusted to see that she was a child—a little girl in strapped shoes, with her black hair combed back from her forehead.

"What disgraceful folly!" he thought. "Now she could do nothing whatever if Its head came off."

Then the Thing coughed, and the ceiling shattered down in plaster on the mosquito-netting, and "They" rushed in from all quarters. He dragged the child through the stifling garden, voices chanting behind them, and they rode the Thirty-Mile Ride under whip and spur along the sandy beach by the booming sea, till they came to the downs, the lamp-post, and the brushwood-pile, which was safety. Very often dreams would break up about them in this fashion, and they would be separated, to endure awful adventures alone. But the most amusing times were when he and she had a clear understanding that it was all make-believe, and walked through mile-wide roaring rivers without even taking off their shoes, or set light to populous cities to see how they would burn, and were rude as any children to the vague shadows met in their rambles. Later in the night they were sure to suffer for this, either at the hands of the Railway People eating among the roses, or in the tropic uplands at the far end of the Thirty-Mile Ride. Together, this did not much affright them; but often Georgie would hear her shrill cry of "Boy! Boy!" half a world away, and hurry to her rescue before "They" maltreated her.

He and she explored the dark-purple downs as far inland from the brushwood-pile as they dared, but that was always a dangerous matter. The interior was filled with "Them," and "They" went about singing in the hollows, and Georgie and she felt safer on or near the seaboard. So thoroughly had he come to know the place of his dreams that even waking he accepted it as a real country, and made a rough sketch of it. He kept his own counsel, of course; but the permanence of the land puzzled him. His ordinary dreams were as formless and as fleeting as any healthy dreams could be, but once at the brushwood-pile he moved within known limits and could see where he was going. There were months at a time when nothing notable crossed his sleep. Then the dreams would come in a batch of five or six, and next morning the map that he kept in his writing-case would be written up to date, for Georgie was a most methodical person. There was, indeed, a danger—his seniors said so—of his developing into a regular "Auntie Fuss" of an adjutant, and when an officer once takes to old-maidism there is more hope for the virgin of seventy than for him.

But fate sent the change that was needed, in the shape of a little winter campaign on the Border, which, after the manner of little campaigns, flashed out into a very ugly war; and Cottar's regiment was chosen among the first.

"Now," said a major, "this'll shake the cobwebs out of us all—especially you, Galahad; and we can see what your hen-with-one-chick attitude has done for the regiment."

Cottar nearly wept with joy as the campaign went forward. They were fit—physically fit beyond the other troops; they were good children in camp, wet or dry, fed or unfed; and they followed their officers with the quick suppleness and trained obedience of a first-class football fifteen. They were cut off from their apology for a base, and cheerfully cut their way back to it again; they crowned and cleaned out hills full of the enemy with the precision of well-broken dogs of chase; and in the hour of retreat, when, hampered with the sick and wounded of the column, they were persecuted down eleven miles of waterless valley, they, serving as rear-guard, covered themselves with a great glory in the eyes of fellow-professionals. Any regiment can advance, but few know how to retreat with a sting in the tail. Then they turned to make roads, most often under fire, and dismantled some inconvenient mud redoubts. They were the last corps to be withdrawn when the rubbish of the campaign was all swept up; and after a month in standing camp, which tries morals severely, they departed to their own place in column of fours, singing:

> " 'E's goin' to do without 'em—
> Don't want 'em any more;

33

'E's goin' to do without 'em,
   As 'e's often done before.
'E's goin' to be a martyr
On a 'ighly novel plan,
An' all the boys and girls will say,
   'Ow! what a nice young man—man—man!
   Ow! what a nice young man!' "

There came out a "Gazette" in which Cottar found that he had been behaving with "courage and coolness and discretion" in all his capacities; that he had assisted the wounded under fire, and blown in a gate, also under fire. Net result, his captaincy and a brevet majority, coupled with the Distinguished Service Order.

As to his wounded, he explained that they were both heavy men, whom he could lift more easily than any one else. "Otherwise, of course, I should have sent out one of my men; and, of course, about that gate business, we were safe the minute we were well under the walls." But this did not prevent his men from cheering him furiously whenever they saw him, or the mess from giving him a dinner on the eve of his departure to England. (A year's leave was among the things he had "snaffled out of the campaign," to use his own words.) The doctor, who had taken quite as much as was good for him, quoted poetry about "a good blade carving the casques of men," and so on, and everybody told Cottar that he was an excellent person; but when he rose to make his maiden speech they shouted so that he was understood to say, "It isn't any use tryin' to speak with you chaps rottin' me like this. Let's have some pool."

*   *   *   *   *   *   *   *   *   *

It is not unpleasant to spend eight-and-twenty days in an easy-going steamer on warm waters, in the company of a woman who lets you see that you are head and shoulders superior to the rest of the world, even though that woman may be, and most often is, ten counted years your senior. P. O. boats are not lighted with the disgustful particularity of Atlantic liners. There is more phosphorescence at the bows, and greater silence and darkness by the hand-steering gear aft.

Awful things might have happened to Georgie but for the little fact that he had never studied the first principles of the game he was expected to play. So when Mrs. Zuleika, at Aden, told him how motherly an interest she felt in his welfare, medals, brevet, and all, Georgie took her at the foot of the letter, and promptly talked of his own mother, three hundred miles nearer each day, of his home, and so forth, all the way up the Red Sea. It was much easier than he had supposed to converse with a woman for an hour at a time. Then Mrs. Zuleika, turning from parental affection, spoke of love in the abstract as a thing not unworthy of study, and in discreet twilights after dinner demanded confidences. Georgie would have been delighted to supply them, but he had none, and did not know it was his duty to manufacture them. Mrs. Zuleika expressed surprise and unbelief, and asked those questions which deep asks of deep. She learned all that was necessary to conviction, and, being very much a woman, resumed (Georgie never knew that she had abandoned) the motherly attitude.

"Do you know," she said, somewhere in the Mediterranean, "I think you're the very dearest boy I have ever met in my life, and I'd like you to remember me a little. You will when you are older, but I want you to remember me now. You'll make some girl very happy."

"Oh! Hope so," said Georgie, gravely; "but there's heaps of time for marryin' an' all that sort of thing, ain't there?"

"That depends. Here are your bean-bags for the Ladies' Competition. I think I'm growing too old to care for these *tamashas*."

They were getting up sports, and Georgie was on the committee. He never noticed how perfectly the bags were sewn, but another woman did, and smiled—once. He liked Mrs. Zuleika greatly. She was a bit old, of course, but uncommonly nice. There was no nonsense about her.

A few nights after they passed Gibraltar his dream returned to him. She who waited by the brushwood-pile was no longer a little girl, but a woman with black hair that grew into a "widow's peak," combed back from her forehead. He knew her for the child in black, the companion of the last six years, and, as it had been in the time of the meetings on the Lost Continent, he was filled with delight unspeakable. "They," for some dreamland reason, were friendly or had gone away that night, and the two flitted together over all their country, from the brushwood-pile up the Thirty-Mile Ride, till they saw the House of the Sick Thing, a pin-point in the distance to the left; stamped through the Railway Waiting-room where the roses lay on the spread breakfast-tables; and returned, by the ford and the city they had once burned for sport, to the great swells of the downs under the lamp-post. Wherever they moved a strong singing followed them underground, but this night there was no panic. All the land was empty except for themselves, and at the last (they were sitting by the lamp-post hand in hand) she turned and kissed him. He woke with a start, staring at the waving curtain of the cabin door; he could almost have sworn that the kiss was real.

Next morning the ship was rolling in a Biscay sea, and people were not happy; but as Georgie came to breakfast, shaven, tubbed, and smelling of soap, several turned to look at him because of the light in his eyes and the splendour of his countenance.

"Well, you look beastly fit," snapped a neighbour. "Any one left you a legacy in the middle of the Bay?"

Georgie reached for the curry, with a seraphic grin. "I suppose it's the gettin' so near home, and all that. I do feel rather festive this mornin'. 'Rolls a bit, doesn't she?"

Mrs. Zuleika stayed in her cabin till the end of the voyage, when she left without bidding him farewell, and wept passionately on the dockhead for pure joy of meeting her children, who, she had often said, were so like their father.

Georgie headed for his own country, wild with delight of his first long furlough after the lean seasons. Nothing was changed in that orderly life, from the coachman who met him at the station to the white peacock that stormed at the carriage from the stone wall above the shaven lawns. The house took toll of him with due regard to precedence—first the mother; then the father; then the housekeeper, who wept and praised God; then the butler, and so on down to the underkeeper, who had been dog-boy in Georgie's youth, and called him "Master Georgie," and was reproved by the groom who had taught Georgie to ride.

"Not a thing changed," he sighed contentedly, when the three of them sat down to dinner in the late sunlight, while the rabbits crept out upon the lawn below the cedars, and the big trout in the ponds by the home paddock rose for their evening meal.

"*Our* changes are all over, dear," cooed the mother; "and now I am getting used to your size and your tan (you're very brown, Georgie), I see you haven't changed in the least. You're exactly like the pater."

The father beamed on this man after his own heart,—"youngest major in the army, and should have had the V. C., sir,"—and the butler listened with his professional mask off when Master Georgie spoke of war as it is waged today, and his father cross-questioned.

36

They went out on the terrace to smoke among the roses, and the shadow of the old house lay long across the wonderful English foliage, which is the only living green in the world.

"Perfect! By Jove, it's perfect!" Georgie was looking at the round-bosomed woods beyond the home paddock, where the white pheasant boxes were ranged; and the golden air was full of a hundred sacred scents and sounds. Georgie felt his father's arm tighten in his.

"It's not half bad—but *hodie mihi, cras tibi*, isn't it? I suppose you'll be turning up some fine day with a girl under your arm, if you haven't one now, eh?"

"You can make your mind easy, sir. I haven't one."

"Not in all these years?" said the mother.

"I hadn't time, mummy. They keep a man pretty busy, these days, in the service, and most of our mess are unmarried, too."

"But you must have met hundreds in society—at balls, and so on?"

"I'm like the Tenth, mummy: I don't dance."

"Don't dance! What have you been doing with yourself, then—backing other men's bills?" said the father.

"Oh, yes; I've done a little of that too; but you see, as things are now, a man has all his work cut out for him to keep abreast of his profession, and my days were always too full to let me lark about half the night."

"Hmm!"—suspiciously.

"It's never too late to learn. We ought to give some kind of house-warming for the people about, now you've come back. Unless you want to go straight up to town, dear?"

"No. I don't want anything better than this. Let's sit still and enjoy ourselves. I suppose there will be something for me to ride if I look for it?"

"Seeing I've been kept down to the old brown pair for the last six weeks because all the others were being got ready for Master Georgie, I should say there might be," the father chuckled. "They're reminding me in a hundred ways that I must take the second place now."

"Brutes!"

"The pater doesn't mean it, dear; but every one has been trying to make your home-coming a success; and you *do* like it, don't you?"

"Perfect! Perfect! There's no place like England—when you've done your work."

"That's the proper way to look at it, my son."

37

And so up and down the flagged walk till their shadows grew long in the moonlight, and the mother went indoors and played such songs as a small boy once clamoured for, and the squat silver candlesticks were brought in, and Georgie climbed to the two rooms in the west wing that had been his nursery and his playroom in the beginning. Then who should come to tuck him up for the night but the mother? And she sat down on the bed, and they talked for a long hour, as mother and son should, if there is to be any future for the Empire. With a simple woman's deep guile she asked questions and suggested answers that should have waked some sign in the face on the pillow, and there was neither quiver of eyelid nor quickening of breath, neither evasion nor delay in reply. So she blessed him and kissed him on the mouth, which is not always a mother's property, and said something to her husband later, at which he laughed a profane and a somewhat incredulous laugh.

All the establishment waited on Georgie next morning, from the tallest six-year-old, "with a mouth like a kid glove, Master Georgie," to the under-keeper strolling carelessly along the horizon, Georgie's pet rod in his hand, and "There's a four-pounder risin' below the lasher. You don't 'ave 'em in Injia, Mast—Major Georgie." It was all beautiful beyond telling, even though the mother insisted on taking him out in the landau (the leather had the hot Sunday smell of his youth) and showing him off to her friends at all the houses for six miles round; and the pater bore him up to town and a lunch at the club, where he introduced him, quite carelessly, to not less than thirty ancient warriors whose sons were not the youngest majors in the army and had not the D. S. O. After that it was Georgie's turn; and remembering his friends, he filled up the house with that kind of officer who live in cheap lodgings at Southsea or Montpelier Square, Brompton—good men all, but not well off. The mother perceived that they needed girls to play with; and as there was no scarcity of girls, the house hummed like a dovecote in spring. They tore up the place for amateur theatricals; they disappeared in the gardens when they ought to have been rehearsing; they swept off every available horse and vehicle, especially the governess-cart and the fat pony; they fell into the trout-ponds; they picnicked and they tennised; and they sat on gates in the twilight, two by two, and Georgie found that he was not in the least necessary to their entertainment.

"My word!" said he, when he saw the last of their dear backs. "They

38

told me they've enjoyed 'emselves, but they haven't done half the things they said they would."

"I know they've enjoyed themselves—immensely," said the mother. "You're a public benefactor, dear."

"Now we can be quiet again, can't we?"

"Oh, quite. I've a very dear friend of mine that I want you to know. She couldn't come with the house so full, because she's an invalid, and she was away when you first came home. She's a Mrs. Lacy and—"

"Lacy! I don't remember the name about here."

"No; they came after you went to India—from Oxford. Her husband died there, and she lost some money, I believe. They bought The Firs on the Bassett Road. She's a very sweet woman, and we're very fond of them both."

"She's a widow, didn't you say?"

"She has a daughter. Surely I said so, dear?"

"Does she fall into trout-ponds, and gas and giggle, and 'Oh, Major Cottah!' and all that sort of thing?"

"No, indeed. She's a very quiet girl, and very musical. She always came over here with her music-books—composing, you know; and she generally works all day, so you won't—"

"'Talking about Miriam?" said the pater, coming up. The mother edged toward him within elbow-reach. There was no finesse about Georgie's father. "Oh, Miriam's a dear girl. Plays beautifully. Rides beautifully, too. She's a regular pet of the household. Used to call me—" The elbow went home, and ignorant but obedient always, the pater shut himself off.

"What used she to call you, sir?"

"All sorts of pet names. I'm very fond of Miriam. She's one of the Herefordshire Lacys. When her aunt dies—" Again the elbow.

"Oh, you won't see anything of her, Georgie. She's busy with her music or her mother all day. Besides, you're going up to town to-morrow, aren't you? I thought you said something about an Institute meeting?" The mother spoke.

"Go up to town *now!* What nonsense!" Once more the pater was shut off.

"I had some idea of it, but I'm not quite sure," said the son of the house. Why did the mother try to get him away because a musical girl and her invalid parent were expected? He did not approve of unknown females calling his father pet names. He would observe these pushing persons who had been only seven years in the county.

All of which the delighted mother read in his countenance, herself keeping an air of sweet disinterestedness.

"They'll be here this evening for dinner. I'm sending the carriage over for them, and they won't stay more than a week."

"Perhaps I shall go up to town. I don't quite know yet." Georgie moved away irresolutely. There was a lecture at the United Services Institute on the supply of ammunition in the field, and the one man whose theories most irritated Major Cottar would deliver it. A heated discussion was sure to follow, and perhaps he might find himself moved to speak. He took his rod that afternoon and went down to thrash it out among the trout.

"Good sport, dear!" said the mother, from the terrace.

" 'Fraid it won't be, mummy. All those men from town, and the girls particularly, have put every trout off his feed for weeks. There isn't one of 'em that cares for fishin'—really. Fancy stampin' and shoutin' on the bank, and tellin' every fish for half a mile exactly what you're goin' to do, and then chuckin' a brute of a fly at him! By Jove, it would scare *me* if I was a trout!"

But things were not as bad as he had expected. The black gnat was on the water, and the water was strictly preserved. A three-quarter-pounder at the second cast set him for the campaign, and he worked down-stream, crouching behind the reed and meadow-sweet; creeping between a hornbeam hedge and a foot-wide strip of bank, where he could see the trout, but where they could not distinguish him from the background; lying almost on his stomach to switch the blue-upright sidewise through the checkered shadows of a gravelly ripple under overarching trees. But he had known every inch of the water since he was four feet high. The aged and astute between sunk roots, with the large and fat that lay in the frothy scum below some strong rush of water, sucking as lazily as carp, came to trouble in their turn, at the hand that imitated so delicately the flicker and wimple of an egg-dropping fly. Consequently, Georgie found himself five miles from home when he ought to have been dressing for dinner. The house-keeper had taken good care that her boy should not go empty, and before he changed to the white moth he sat down to excellent claret with sandwiches of potted egg and things that adoring women make and men never notice. Then back, to surprise the otter grubbing for

40

fresh-water mussels, the rabbits on the edge of the beechwoods forag-
ing in the clover, and the policeman-like white owl stooping to the
little field-mice, till the moon was strong, and he took his rod apart,
and went home through well-remembered gaps in the hedges. He
fetched a compass round the house, for, though he might have broken
every law of the establishment every hour, the law of his boyhood was
unbreakable: after fishing you went in by the south garden back-door,
cleaned up in the outer scullery, and did not present yourself to your
elders and your betters till you had washed and changed.

"Half-past ten, by Jove! Well, we'll make the sport an excuse. They
wouldn't want to see me the first evening, at any rate. Gone to bed,
probably." He skirted by the open French windows of the drawing-
room. "No, they haven't. They look very comfy in there."

He could see his father in his own particular chair, the mother in
hers, and the back of a girl at the piano by the big potpourri-jar. The
gardens looked half divine in the moonlight, and he turned down
through the roses to finish his pipe.

A prelude ended, and there floated out a voice of the kind that in
his childhood he used to call "creamy"—a full, true contralto; and this
is the song that he heard, every syllable of it:

> Over the edge of the purple down,
>   Where the single lamplight gleams,
> Know ye the road to the Merciful Town
>   That is hard by the Sea of Dreams—
> Where the poor may lay their wrongs away,
>   And the sick may forget to weep?
> But we—pity us! Oh, pity us!
>   We wakeful; ah, pity us!—
> We must go back with Policeman Day—
>   Back from the City of Sleep!
>
> Weary they turn from the scroll and crown
>   Fetter and prayer and plough—
> They that go up to the Merciful Town,
>   For her gates are closing now.
> It is their right in the Baths of Night
>   Body and soul to steep:
> But we—pity us! ah, pity us!
>   We wakeful; oh, pity us!—

41

We must go back with Policeman Day—
  Back from the City of Sleep!

Over the edge of the purple down,
  Ere the tender dreams begin,
Look—we may look—at the Merciful Town,
  But we may not enter in!
Outcasts all, from her guarded wall
  Back to our watch we creep:
We—pity us! ah, pity us!
  We wakeful; oh, pity us!—
We that go back with Policeman Day—
  Back from the City of Sleep!

At the last echo he was aware that his mouth was dry and unknown pulses were beating in the roof of it. The housekeeper, who would have it that he must have fallen in and caught a chill, was waiting to catch him on the stairs, and, since he neither saw nor answered her, carried a wild tale abroad that brought his mother knocking at the door.

"Anything happened, dear? Harper said she thought you weren't—"

"No; it's nothing. I'm all right, mummy. *Please* don't bother."

He did not recognise his own voice, but that was a small matter beside what he was considering. Obviously, most obviously, the whole coincidence was crazy lunacy. He proved it to the satisfaction of Major George Cottar, who was going up to town tomorrow to hear a lecture on the supply of ammunition in the field; and having so proved it, the soul and brain and heart and body of Georgie cried joyously: "That's the Lily Lock girl—the Lost Continent girl—the Thirty-Mile Ride girl—the Brushwood girl! *I* know her!"

He waked, stiff and cramped in his chair, to reconsider the situation by sunlight, when it did not appear normal. But a man must eat, and he went to breakfast, his heart between his teeth, holding himself severely in hand.

"Late, as usual," said the mother. " 'My boy, Miss Lacy."

A tall girl in black raised her eyes to his, and Georgie's life training deserted him—just as soon as he realised that she did not know. He stared coolly and critically. There was the abundant black hair, growing in a widow's peak, turned back from the forehead, with that peculiar ripple over the right ear; there were the gray eyes set a little close together; the short upper lip, resolute chin, and the known poise of the head. There was also the small well-cut mouth that had kissed him.

"Georgie—*dear!*" said the mother, amazedly, for Miriam was flushing under the stare.

"I—I beg your pardon!" he gulped. "I don't know whether the mother has told you, but I'm rather an idiot at times, specially before I've had my breakfast. It's—it's a family failing."

He turned to explore among the hot-water dishes on the sideboard, rejoicing that she did not know—she did not know.

His conversation for the rest of the meal was mildly insane, though the mother thought she had never seen her boy look half so handsome. How could any girl, least of all one of Miriam's discernment, forbear to fall down and worship? But deeply Miriam was displeased. She had never been stared at in that fashion before, and promptly retired into her shell when Georgie announced that he had changed his mind about going to town, and would stay to play with Miss Lacy if she had nothing better to do.

"Oh, but don't let me throw you out. I'm at work. I've things to do all the morning."

"What possessed Georgie to behave so oddly?" the mother sighed to herself. "Miriam's a bundle of feelings—like her mother."

"You compose—don't you? Must be a fine thing to be able to do that. ["Pig—oh, pig!" thought Miriam.] I think I heard you singin' when I came in last night after fishin'. All about a Sea of Dreams, wasn't it? [Miriam shuddered to the core of the soul that afflicted her.] Awfully pretty song. How d'you think of such things?"

"You only composed the music, dear, didn't you?"

"The words too. I'm sure of it," said Georgie, with a sparkling eye. No; she did not know.

"Yeth; I wrote the words too." Miriam spoke slowly, for she knew she lisped when she was nervous.

"Now how *could* you tell, Georgie?" said the mother, as delighted as though the youngest major in the army were ten years old, showing off before company.

"I was sure of it, somehow. Oh, there are heaps of things about me, mummy, that you don't understand. Looks as if it were goin' to be a hot day—for England. Would you care for a ride this afternoon, Miss Lacy? We can start out after tea, if you'd like it."

Miriam could not in decency refuse, but any woman might see she was not filled with delight.

"That will be very nice, if you take the Bassett Road. It will save me sending Martin down to the village," said the mother, filling in gaps.

Like all good managers, the mother had her one weakness—a mania for little strategies that should economise horses and vehicles. Her men-folk complained that she turned them into common carriers, and there was a legend in the family that she had once said to the pater on the morning of a meet: "If you *should* kill near Bassett, dear, and if it isn't too late, would you mind just popping over and matching me this?"

"I knew that was coming. You'd never miss a chance, mother. If it's a fish or a trunk I won't." Georgie laughed.

"It's only a duck. They can do it up very neatly at Mallett's," said the mother, simply. "You won't mind, will you? We'll have a scratch dinner at nine, because it's so hot."

The long summer day dragged itself out for centuries; but at last there was tea on the lawn, and Miriam appeared.

She was in the saddle before he could offer to help, with the clean spring of the child who mounted the pony for the Thirty-Mile Ride. The day held mercilessly, though Georgie got down thrice to look for imaginary stones in Rufus's foot. One cannot say even simple things in broad light, and this that Georgie meditated was not simple. So he spoke seldom, and Miriam was divided between relief and scorn. It annoyed her that the great hulking thing should know she had written the words of the song overnight; for though a maiden may sing her most secret fancies aloud, she does not care to have them trampled over by the male Philistine. They rode into the little red-brick street of Bassett, and Georgie made untold fuss over the disposition of that duck. It must go in just such a package, and be fastened to the saddle in just such a manner, though eight o'clock had struck and they were miles from dinner.

"We must be quick!" said Miriam, bored and angry.

"There's no great hurry; but we can cut over Dowhead Down, and let 'em out on the grass. That will save us half an hour."

The horses capered on the short, sweet-smelling turf, and the delaying shadows gathered in the valley as they cantered over the great dun down that overhangs Bassett and the Western coaching-road. Insensibly the pace quickened without thought of mole-hills; Rufus, gentleman that he was, waiting on Miriam's Dandy till they should have cleared the rise. Then down the two-mile slope they raced together, the wind whistling in their ears, to the steady throb of eight hoofs and the light click-click of the shifting bits.

"Oh, that was glorious!" Miriam cried, reining in. "Dandy and I are old friends, but I don't think we've ever gone better together."

"No; but you've gone quicker, once or twice."

"Really? When?"

Georgie moistened his lips. "Don't you remember the Thirty-Mile Ride—with me—when 'They' were after us—on the beach-road, with the sea to the left—going toward the lamp-post on the downs?"

The girl gasped. "What—what do you mean?" she said hysterically.

"The Thirty-Mile Ride, and—and all the rest of it."

"You mean—? I didn't sing anything about the Thirty-Mile Ride. I know I didn't. I have never told a living soul."

"You told about Policeman Day, and the lamp at the top of the downs, and the City of Sleep. It all joins on, you know—it's the same country—and it was easy enough to see where you had been."

"Good God!—It joins on—of course it does; but—I have been—you have been— Oh, let's walk, please, or I shall fall off!"

Georgie ranged alongside, and laid a hand that shook below her bridle-hand, pulling Dandy into a walk. Miriam was sobbing as he had seen a man sob under the touch of the bullet.

"It's all right—it's all right," he whispered feebly. "Only—only it's true, you know."

"True! Am I mad?"

"Not unless I'm mad as well. *Do* try to think a minute quietly. How could any one conceivably know anything about the Thirty-Mile Ride having anything to do with you, unless he had been there?"

"But where? But *where*? Tell me!"

"There—wherever it may be—in our country, I suppose. Do you remember the first time you rode it—the Thirty-Mile Ride, I mean? You must."

"It was all dreams—all dreams!"

"Yes, but tell, please; because I know."

"Let me think. I—we were on no account to make any noise—on no account to make any noise." She was staring between Dandy's ears, with eyes that did not see, and a suffocating heart.

45

"Because 'It' was dying in the big house?" Georgie went on, reining in again.

"There was a garden with green-and-gilt railings—all hot. Do *you* remember?"

"I ought to. I was sitting on the other side of the bed before 'It' coughed and 'They' came in."

"You!"—the deep voice was unnaturally full and strong, and the girl's wide-opened eyes burned in the dusk as she stared him through and through. "Then you're the Boy—my Brushwood Boy, and I've known you all my life!"

She fell forward on Dandy's neck. Georgie forced himself out of the weakness that was overmastering his limbs, and slid an arm round her waist. The head dropped on his shoulder, and he found himself with parched lips saying things that up till then he believed existed only in printed works of fiction. Mercifully the horses were quiet. She made no attempt to draw herself away when she recovered, but lay still, whispering.

"Of course you're the Boy, and I didn't know—I didn't know."

"I knew last night; and when I saw you at breakfast—"

"Oh, *that* was why! I wondered at the time. You would, of course."

"I couldn't speak before this. Keep your head where it is, dear. It's all right now—all right now, isn't it?"

"But how was it *I* didn't know—after all these years and years? I remember—oh, what lots of things I remember!"

"Tell me some. I'll look after the horses."

"I remember waiting for you when the steamer came in. Do you?"

"At the Lily Lock, beyond Hong-Kong and Java?"

"Do *you* call it that, too?"

"You told me it was when I was lost in the continent. That was you that showed me the way through the mountains?"

"When the islands slid? It must have been, because you're the only one I remember. All the others were 'Them.' "

"Awful brutes they were, too."

"I remember showing you the Thirty-Mile Ride the first time. You ride just as you used to—then. You *are* you!"

"That's odd. I thought that of you this afternoon. Isn't it wonderful?"

"What does it all mean? Why should you and I of the millions of

46

people in the world have this—this thing between us? What does it mean? I'm frightened."

"This!" said Georgie. The horses quickened their pace. They thought they had heard an order. "Perhaps when we die we may find out more, but it means this now."

There was no answer. What could she say? As the world went, they had known each other rather less than eight and a half hours, but the matter was one that did not concern the world. There was a very long silence, while the breath in their nostrils drew cold and sharp as it might have been a fume of ether.

"That's the second," Georgie whispered. "You remember?"

"It's not!"—furiously. "It's not!"

"On the downs the other night—months ago. You were just as you are now, and we went over the country for miles and miles."

"It was all empty, too. They had gone away. Nobody frightened us. I wonder why, Boy?"

"Oh, if you remember *that*, you must remember the rest. Confess!"

"I remember lots of things, but I *know* I didn't. I never have—till just now."

"You *did*, dear."

"I know I didn't, because—oh, it's no use keeping anything back!—because I truthfully meant to."

"And truthfully did."

"No; meant to; but some one else came by."

"There wasn't any one else. There never has been."

"There was—there always is. It was another woman—out there on the sea. I saw her. It was the 26th of May. I've got it written down somewhere."

"Oh, *you*'ve kept a record of your dreams, too? That's odd about the other woman, because I happened to be on the sea just then."

"I was right. How do I know what you've done when you were awake—and I thought it was only *you!*"

"You never were more wrong in your life. What a little temper you've got! Listen to me a minute, dear." And Georgie, though he knew it not, committed black perjury. "It—it isn't the kind of thing one says to any one, because they'd laugh; but on my word and honour, darling, I've never been kissed by a living soul outside my own people in all my life. Don't laugh, dear. I wouldn't tell any one but you, but it's the solemn truth."

47

"I knew! You are you. Oh, I *knew* you'd come some day; but I didn't know you were you in the least till you spoke."

"Then give me another."

"And you never cared or looked anywhere? Why, all the round world must have loved you from the very minute they saw you, Boy."

"They kept it to themselves if they did. No; I never cared."

"And we shall be late for dinner—horribly late. Oh, how can I look at you in the light before your mother—and mine!"

"We'll play you're Miss Lacy till the proper time comes. What's the shortest limit for people to get engaged? S'pose we have got to go through all the fuss of an engagement, haven't we?"

"Oh, I don't want to talk about that. It's so commonplace. I've thought of something that you don't know. I'm sure of it. What's my name?"

"Miri—no, it isn't, by Jove! Wait half a second, and it'll come back to me. You aren't—you can't? Why, *those* old tales—before I went to school! I've never thought of 'em from that day to this. Are you the original, only Annie*an*louise?"

"It was what you always called me ever since the beginning. Oh! We've turned into the avenue, and we must be an hour late."

"What does it matter? The chain goes as far back as those days? It must, of course—of course it must. I've got to ride round with this pestilent old bird—confound him!"

"'Ha! ha!' said the duck, laughing'—do you remember *that?*"

"Yes, I do—flower-pots on my feet, and all. We've been together all this while; and I've got to say good-bye to you till dinner. *Sure* I'll see you at dinner-time? *Sure* you won't sneak up to your room, darling, and leave me all the evening? Good-bye, dear—good-bye."

"Good-bye, Boy, good-bye. Mind the arch! Don't let Rufus bolt into his stables. Good-bye. Yes, I'll come down to dinner; but—what shall I do when I see you in the light!"

Bredon Hill

A. E. Housman

In summertime on Bredon
  The bells they sound so clear;
Round both the shires they ring them
  In steeples far and near,
  A happy noise to hear.

Here of a Sunday morning
  My love and I would lie,
And see the coloured counties,
  And hear the larks so high
  About us in the sky.

The bells would ring to call her
  In valleys miles away:
'Come all to church, good people;
  Good people, come and pray.'
  But here my love would stay.

And I would turn and answer
  Among the springing thyme,
'Oh, peal upon our wedding,
  And we will hear the chime,
  And come to church in time.'

But when the snows at Christmas
  On Bredon top were strown,
My love rose up so early
  And stole out unbeknown
  And went to church alone.

They tolled the one bell only,
  Groom there was none to see,
The mourners followed after,
  And so to church went she,
  And would not wait for me.

49

The bells they sound on Bredon,
   And still the steeples hum,
'Come all to church, good people,'—
   Oh, noisy bells, be dumb;
   I hear you, I will come.

With Rue My Heart Is Laden

A. E. Housman

With rue my heart is laden
   For golden friends I had,
For many a rose-lipt maiden
   And many a lightfoot lad.

By brooks too broad for leaping
   The lightfoot boys are laid;
The rose-lipt girls are sleeping
   In fields where roses fade.

White in the Moon the Long Road Lies

A. E. Housman

White in the moon the long road lies,
   The moon stands blank above;
White in the moon the long road lies
   That leads me from my love.

Still hangs the hedge without a gust,
   Still, still the shadows stay:
My feet upon the moonlit dust
   Pursue the ceaseless way.

The world is round, so travellers tell,
   And straight though reach the track,
Trudge on, trudge on, 'twill all be well,
   The way will guide one back.

But ere the circle homeward hies
   Far, far must it remove:
White in the moon the long road lies
   That leads me from my love.

My Heart Is Like a Singing Bird

Dorothy Thomas

> *In this story of young love we find a popular
> writer at her best.*

> *"My heart is like a singing bird*
> . . . .
> *Because my love is come to me."*

LOUISE woke to bird song and to happiness. The bird song
mingled rightly, assuringly, with the experimental crowing of young
roosters, the bawling of calves, and her brothers' whistling, and was
like that of the seven June mornings she had wakened to and waited
through, only better, more joyous, and the happiness—there were
words for the happiness, a woman's words. Louise had found them in
a book of poems, had learned them by heart and said them over and
over, sung them, rather, on the half-mile walk to the little country
school she taught, the mornings of the last long week of May, and
meadow larks had answered from field and fence: "Louise, Louise,
Bill's coming. It's true! It's true!" It was for this morning, now come,
the poem had been learned and saved. It was for just such a morning
in a woman's life it had been sung in the first place, Louise was sure.
It began:

> *My heart is like a singing bird*

and ended:

> *Because the birthday of my life*
> *Is come, my love is come to me.*

Beside her pillow, half under the edge of it—she would put up a
sleep-limp hand in a moment to it—was the blue cardboard box that
held Bill's letters, his eighteen letters. They were brief, matter-of-
fact, one-page letters. They began, every one of them, "Dear Louise,"

51

and ended, "So long, Bill." Every one was written on a Sunday in answer to hers of the Sunday before. The last one, the one she meant to read in a moment, though she knew it word for word, that had to do with the business of getting ready for final exams, a stock-judging contest and the modest records of tennis triumphs, closed with "Be home the second week in June. I'll be over. So long, Bill." That was all in reality, in plain fact, but there was a world of which the world of plain fact was only the beginning; a world that came into its own with the second week in June; with cherry time, haying time and Bill's homecoming.

Only the morning before, out in the side yard to see whether the cherries were really going to be ripe enough for Sunday pies, she had stood, the sun warm on her hair, watching the orphaned black lamb that the boys had brought to the house yard to bottle-feed, leaping and whirling, and had run to him and caught him up and said to him: "You think this is June? It's nice, all right, but you wait, you wait! This is nothing to what it's to be—nothing, nothing!" And she was sure in her heart that for Bill, too, the world waited, promised in every leaf shadow across a professor's desk in classrooms where he sat and listened. He had wanted, she believed, for some good reason of his own, to wait; to save their world whole, without one word said, outright, for it, until school was done for him; until he could come home to her. That was Bill, and she loved him.

She had meant to read the last letter again before she got up, but she heard her mother's step on the stair and slid the box farther under her pillow. It was from shyness only that she hid it. Her folks liked Bill, she knew; liked him and his folks. There was pride for her in her being Bill's girl in her brothers' teasing, and a kindly satisfaction in the way her father would hand her one of Bill's letters, having come in the mail while she was at school. Several mornings that spring, she had slept late and been hurried getting ready, and so forgotten to put the blue box away, only to think of it after she was well on her way or at school, and to smile, safe in knowing that her mother would put it away for her in the left-hand top dresser drawer, where its place was.

"Well," her mother said fondly, " 'bout time you got up, isn't it, sleepyhead? Your father says he's going to call you when he calls the boys, after this. He says, "What we got a girl for, anyhow?""

"I wondered how long I was going to be babied," Louise said. "It has been good not to have to get up early."

"I guess he babies you because it looks like we might not have you around much longer," her mother said, and sat down on the bed beside her.

"What?" Louise asked, startled. Never before had her mother spoken so openly about the time they all expected to see come; when Bill would take her away from them. Now her mother laughed and gave her a little spank. "Well, that's the way the land lies, isn't it? You look like you did when you were little; open those brown eyes so wide, all innocence! You get your quiet ways from father's folks. They were all like that. I suppose you'd have us think a boy like Bill would go with a girl all summer, write her all winter, and neither of you have anything serious in mind? Why, Louise! What you blushing for?"

"We didn't go together all summer," Louise said. "He didn't ask to go with me until August and—"

"Well, he certainly didn't let any grass grow under his feet, once he started coming here. He was over about every night, seemed to me."

"No, mamma; just nine nights and two Sunday afternoons," Louise said.

"Well, he's a good boy, and your father and I are both glad to see you choosing a boy from a family we know, close neighbors, like the Atwells. The only thing is, I hope they fix it for Bill to farm their place and that they don't settle him way off somewhere, like the other boys. Mrs. Atwell said, the other Sunday, Jack and Mamie hadn't been home but twice since Christmas. Papa says—"

"Mamma," Louise cried, "please! It scares me to have you and Papa talking it over like that. You don't understand—"

"Now, dear, your father's not hasty. What do you suppose Frank Atwell wants to talk to him about, if not about where Bill's to be, to settle and farm?"

"Mr. Atwell?" Louise exclaimed, and sat up in bed and grasped her mother's wrist with both hands. "Mamma, has Mr. Atwell been over here? Is—is Bill really home? Did he come over with him? Mamma, what's happened?"

"Nothing yet. He just called and asked if Papa was here, and I told him he hadn't got to the field yet, and he said I was not to call him in; that he'd be over directly; that he wanted to see him."

"He didn't say what about? He didn't say anything about Bill—he didn't say he was home?"

"No, he didn't, but he's home all right."

"Did he call?"

"No, but he's home; he's not up yet. His mother was calling his Aunt Mina. She said he got home last night; drove home with a friend from school."

"Late?"

"I guess so. I expect he got in too late to call you, and sat up late, visiting with his folks."

Louise leaned back against the pillow and clasped her hands behind her head, lost in the wonder of Bill's being home for sure, asleep still in his old room upstairs in his father's house, not quite two miles away.

"I'll get up," Louise said, and made her words honest with one quick movement.

"I guess you better, missie," her mother said. "Bill'll come, if you don't look out, and catch you not up yet, and he'll think he'll have to get his own breakfasts." Her mother left, turning in the doorway to smile fondly on her daughter as she stood stretching lazily in the bright sun from the east window.

It was possible, of course, that Bill might come early. Thinking on that, Louise put on her blue-and-white gingham with the fluted organdy collar that had taken so long a time in the ironing. It was a plain dress but for the collar; plain enough so that her brothers would not be likely to say, "H'm, what you all dolled up for, sis? Somebody coming?" but pretty, quite pretty. Gravely, in her eagerness to look her loveliest and yet not look too "fixed up," she brushed her hair to careless waviness before the dresser mirror and tied a narrow blue ribbon around her head.

It did frighten her, trouble her, to have her mother speak out so about Bill and about the future. It was one thing to treasure in her heart, in quiet happiness, every word Bill had ever said, every word he had written, and to dream of his coming, and quite another to have her mother speaking of him and of her, much as she might speak of Ruth and Art, her married sister and her husband. Love itself did not belong to the world of everyday reality, and by rights should not, until Bill had come home; until he had come over to see her and had told her he loved her—told her in words. She must ask her mother not to talk so.

There was only her mother in the kitchen when she came down, and she was busy with the breakfast dishes. "Oh, Mamma," Louise said, "why didn't you leave them for me? I'll finish them."

54

"No, there's no sense in Bill coming and finding you with your hands in the dishwater in a hot kitchen. It's going to be a warm day, don't you think? Your father's not gone to the field. When I went out and told him Atwell was coming over, he said he'd wait. There's coffee, though I guess it's pretty strong by now, and there's pancake batter on the warming oven in the crock. The boys got away with all the strawberries you stemmed last night, but there's more in the basket here. I mean to get at them, soon as I get the dishes done, and, if I can, get them put up before dinner. Help yourself."

Louise helped herself to the strawberries, idly dipping berries by their stems into a little mound of sugar in her saucer, sipping her coffee between berries.

"Was that our ring I heard while I was dressing?" she asked, trying to make her voice sound casual and not too eager.

"Yes, it was. It was Ruth. She called and said she'd be over. She's made the baby rompers. What do you think of that! Made him a good pink pair and two pair to creep in, out of the backs of Art's old work shirts. Won't he be cute? She's coming over, she said, this morning, just as soon as she can put up a lunch for Art and get her work done up. My, I don't see how she drives, with that baby. He's so wiggly now, and grabby. But she straps him in with that harness outfit Art fixed, and drives right along."

"She didn't say anything about—anybody?"

"Yes. She did. She said she heard he was home. She said Mrs. Atwell was calling her other sister, over that way, when she was trying to get the line to call us. She said she said he drove home with a friend of his, a school friend, and his sister."

"His sister?"

"Yes, this friend's sister."

"Did she say— Are they staying to visit over at Atwells', or are they going on?"

"She didn't say, and I didn't ask. Now, Louise, you dust in the front room and dining room, and keep cool. You look awfully nice. Friends are as likely to have sisters as not. You—"

"Of course," Louise said. "Bill has lots of friends. He plays tennis with girls, Home Ecs. girls. Did Ruth say anything else?"

"Not that I remember. . . . Oh, yes, she said Bill's mother said he was changed."

"Changed? How?"

"She didn't say. A boy's bound to change some, in a school year. It would be funny if he didn't. . . . What's wrong with you, Louise? You're not getting nerves, are you? You seem so—so kind of jumpy this morning. You've worked too hard, that's what. Your father said he wished he hadn't let you teach this year, not with so many enrolled in this district, and those Bowler boys in school. Don't you ever worry about any old boy's sister! If Bill was the kind to have his head turned, he'd have had it turned months ago, and wouldn't have been like he's been, written like he has, steady."

"I'm not worried, Mamma," Louise said, "and, Mamma, I wish you wouldn't talk about it."

"Well, dear, I'm talking about it. You know neither your father or I are any hand to talk about things like that, and you know we've all respected how you feel about it, all of us. You girls are as different as you can be. Why, Ruth talked everything over with me, right from the start, right from the time Art began coming here, and here Papa and I don't even know how long you and Bill have been engaged. I can understand it, because you're just like my father's people. It's all right. You have to do things your own way, and I understand. But here, when we've tiptoed around a whole year, nearly, about this, surely there's no harm in speaking of it, now Bill's home. You don't look like you feel well, Louise. If you don't feel like it, don't dust. I'll do it."

"I feel fine," Louise said, and got the dust mop and dustcloth from their place on the basement landing and went into the dining room.

"Better set the plants up on the dining table," her mother called after her. "You know what the baby did last time. Ruth was scared eating that dirt would make him awfully sick, but I told her I thought it'd not hurt him a bit, and it didn't. You know I think he really likes the plants, the color; he's so noticing. Is that someone coming? Is it Frank Atwell or Ruth?"

"It's Mr. Atwell," Louise said, and drew back from the now-bare windows to watch the Atwell car, empty of Atwells except for the gray-haired head of the house, come up the slope from the highway, pass the twin cottonwoods by the house-yard gate and turn toward the stables.

"See," her mother said, coming into the dining room, with the pancake griddle which she was washing in her hand, to see for herself, "a man busy as Frank Atwell doesn't come over the middle of the morn-

56

ing to talk about the weather. And I bet you've got a better notion of what he's come over to talk to your father about, young lady, than your father or I have. I bet Bill's drawn up and sent you the plans of his house. Be sure of one thing, dear. No, two! Be sure, while it's still on paper, that you're to have good big closets, and enough of them, and that there's east sun in the kitchen and low enough windows. A man'll stick the windows up under the ceiling where you'll get no earthly good of them, every time, if you don't watch him."

"Please, Mamma!" Louise whispered, raising both hands in a hushing gesture.

"There they are, sitting out there by the barn door," her mother said. "Your father's got him a stick to whittle. Isn't that like him?"

Louise, dusting the living room, and too far from the kitchen for her mother to talk to her, felt a little easier. She wished Bill would come soon; come before her sister Ruth came with her newly romp-ered baby. It would be fine if he would come almost at once—just as soon as she had finished dusting the piano—come to the front door instead of to the kitchen door; come and meet her, with the two of them alone in the shady, vine-covered front porch. Now that his com-ing was so near, she was afraid, with a heart-pressing, happy fear.

How would he greet her? What would his first words be? Would he be wearing the blue-checked shirt she liked best? Maybe he'd have on his white linen suit. His mother had told her, a couple of Sundays ago, while the two families stood visiting after church, that Bill had bought himself a new white linen suit. Ruth had told her mother that his mother said he had changed. "School changes a boy," her mother had said, with seeming satisfaction. She had not thought about Bill changing. He had not changed in his letters. If he changed while she stayed the same, would he change toward her?

Dusting the piano, she could see her reflection in the shining wood. Would he find her fair? How her breath had caught when her mother told her he had driven home from school with a friend and his sister! Was she one of the girls he played tennis with, she wondered. Why was it, now, now that he was home again, learning that a girl was there —a sister of a friend—could make her feel faint with anxiety? Why now, when the school-year long she had only to reread Bill's letters, to remember their parting, to feel secure? In parting, he had kissed her and said, "We'll write; and I'll see you Christmas, Louise." But he had not come home Christmas. His family had been quarantined with chicken pox. His eldest brother's children had got it while with their grandparents and he had Christmased with an aunt and uncle in a town nearer the university, and had a very dull time. It was wrong of her, and silly, too, to think of other girls now. This was the day of Bill's coming. He was home. The birds her mother was shooing with the broom from their cherry trees might be singing in the Atwell trees any minute now.

Louise whisked the dustcloth from one end of the keyboard to the other, and standing, her head thrown back, played a cord that said, for all the house to hear:

The birthday of my life is come!

Her mother came around to the front porch and stopped to shoo some pigeons from the back of the porch swing.

"I declare," she said to her daughter, through the open window, "I don't know what your father keeps them for. He likes the sound of them, he says. Go on and play something, dear. I hope you keep up your music. I've not said anything to your father about it yet, but I don't see why you can't have the piano. It was bought for you girls, and you know Ruth'll never do anything more with her music. She never did care much about it, anyway. And I know how proud Bill is you can play as well as you can. We could put Papa's roll-top desk where the piano is. He's always wanted it back in the living room. Goodness knows why. . . . Here's Ruth now!"

Louise's mother leaned the broom against a porch pillar and went to the yard gate to meet her elder daughter and take her one and only grandchild to her heart.

"Well, did he go to sleep?" she cried. "Did he go to sleep strapped in this mean old harness? Louise, come see, come see him in rompers. Fix a place for him, won't you? There! Grandma's boy can go right back to sleep again. Fix the lounge in the living room for him. Fold up that scratchy old shawl; it'd be too hot for him. Fetch that quilt from the foot of my bed, Louise, that blue-and-white one. It's folded on the foot of my bed."

Louise ran for the quilt and Ruth put down the basket of garden stuff she had brought. "Maybe you've got more radishes and onions than you can use, Mamma," she said, "but Art pulled these and we can't begin to use them all, so I brought them over."

58

"That's nice," her mother said. "There! Grandma'll take off his little shoes. We've got them, Ruth, but I've not been up to the garden in three or four days. I've told the boys to weed up there, and I hope they have. 'Deed we can use them. I've just been snowed under with work. I thought I'd have more time, with Louise home and free to help, but I declare— Isn't he sweet in that pink! And hasn't he grown, though?"

"Grown! I should say he has," his mother agreed happily. "And, Mamma, he's trying to walk! Art's folks were over Sunday and had Art's grandmother along, and she took on so about how fast he creeps. Art and his dad were coaxing baby to walk and Art had a good hold of him, of course, and you know what his grandma said to me? She said, 'Girl, you let that boy walk at his age and you'll have him so bowlegged you won't be able to get pants on him!'"

"Nonsense!" her mother laughed. "You walked at nine months, or was it Jim? And there's no bowlegs in this family. Come on out in the kitchen. I've those strawberries I'd like to get put up before time to get dinner, if I can. Louise, you don't need to help. It's too warm out there."

"I'll help," Louise said.

"What's the matter, Louise," asked her sister; "don't you feel well?"

"I feel fine," Louise replied.

"She got a little run down," her mother said, "that last month of school. It's no wonder; those Bowler kids in school, and one of them to get through the eighth-grade examinations. Well, she did it all right. All three of her eighth-graders passed with good grades. How she ever drilled that boy up to pass the spelling examination, I can't see."

"Don't I know!" exclaimed Ruth, turning to have her mother tie her apron for her. "But I think one year of teaching is enough. It was enough for me. Wasn't that the Atwell car I saw out by the barn? No need to ask if it's Bill. If it was, he'd be up here at the house."

"It's his father," her mother said, "and Louise is feathering up and shushing me all over the place for saying I bet he's come over to talk about where Bill's to live. They'll build; they'll just about have to. I don't know where they'd expect them to live, if they don't."

"Oh, say," Ruth interrupted, "did you hear about Agnes?"

"No," her mother answered; "what's happened to Agnes? I didn't know she'd got home. I was talking to her mother last Sunday and she said they didn't expect her for another week yet. Her school lets out later than Bill's does."

"Well, she's got home. She's married!"

"Why, the idea! I thought her folks were going to give her a church wedding. Were they married down there at school?"

"She didn't marry Bryan; she married somebody else!"

"She didn't! Well!"

"No, she married somebody she met down there at school. Her folks didn't know a thing about it, not until she wired yesterday."

"Well, I declare! Louise, what do you think of that? How'd Bryan take it?"

"I don't know. Art's mother talked with Agnes' mother last night and then she called me. Her folks hadn't known a thing; Bryan's either. Art's mother said to me, 'That's all right. Bryan can do better, and not have to go out of the neighborhood!' She'll say what she thinks, you know. I never did think they were suited, really, did you, Mamma?"

"They looked nice together," Louise said.

"Well, that's how it is; one here and another there," their mother said. "I'm glad Bill wasn't taking but the two-year Ag course and that he'd had one year out of the way before he started going with you, Louise. It's not a good idea to be so long apart, and so far."

"Yes," Ruth agreed. "I'm glad Art was never away. Except, it would have been nice to have had some letters from him. You know, Mamma, I've not had one single letter from Art?"

"Bill's mother said this morning, when she called her sister, that both the boys, Bill and this school friend, she didn't call him by name, were still asleep, but that the girl was up and out picking some daisies to put on the breakfast table. Town girl, I guess. She said Bill's driven half the way himself; he and the boy took turns, and they talked late, last night."

"Well, that's nice," her mother said. "Did she say— Louise, go in and have a look at the baby, will you? There's an old fly in there, I noticed when we put him down, bothering around. Here, take the swatter and see if you can get him."

Louise knew well that her mother wanted to get her out of the way, so that she could ask Ruth if Mrs. Atwell had said anything else about these friends of Bill's; about this girl who got up early to pick daisies for the breakfast table. The fly vanquished and the voices still low and guarded in the kitchen, she sat down in the chair by the lounge and fanned the baby gently with a folded newspaper.

The baby slept with his hands up either side of his head, his fists limply curled. His knees were tanned and dimpled. Louise bent and laid her lips lightly against one of them. Dear boy! Ruth was so happy, so settled, so right in her life, with her one year of teaching, her Art, her determination to make Art's people see she was a good manager, her sewing and canning, and her fine baby. There they were, her mother and sister, out in the kitchen now, plotting and planning just such a life, just such a secure happiness for her, with Bill.

Agnes Marshall? Why, she was to have married Bryan Haywood toward the end of June! She and Bryan had gone together the last two summers while Agnes was home from school. True, they had more than one quarrel the summer before, and it was said they had "quit for good," but Agnes and Bryan had written, while Agnes was away—that she knew. And they had been engaged; Agnes had Bryan's ring. "Not a good idea to be so long apart, and so far," her mother had said. What had she done! What had she done, to stake her whole happiness on those short and impersonal letters? Bill had been in school, like Agnes; been where he had met hundreds of pretty, attractive girls. He had written her about them; had said, "I played doubles this afternoon with a couple of Home Ecs. and Ed Fischer."

A couple of Home Ecs.! This sister of Bill's friend was likely one of them. Well, why didn't she stay in the house and help Mrs. Atwell get breakfast then, if she knew so much about cooking? Maybe there was a course in flower arrangement. Likely there was. Likely this girl was one Bill knew very well. Maybe, oh, maybe she was Bill's girl down at school! He'd never mentioned any girl, by name. Maybe he had brought this girl home, so his folks could meet her and see how pretty and how clever she was, with all she had learned in cooking and sewing classes. Maybe he had brought her home to show her the place, to let her pick out a spot where she would like a house. Maybe it was with her he had drawn the plans for a house, with plenty of closets and low enough windows in the kitchen.

How could Bill do this to her? How could he write to her the winter through, every other Sunday, as he had written; how could he look at her as he had looked down at her in saying good-bye, and other times, too; how could he kiss her, in parting, as though she were the most precious thing in life, and not love, not—? But maybe she was

61

the one in the wrong. What did she know about men and about love anyway? Maybe men did look at girls like that, did kiss them like that, and mean nothing at all. Other men, maybe, but not Bill, surely, surely! His letters; they were not love letters. What was there real in them, to build on? Only to a foolish, heart-willed girl could they mean anything. What was true then? The world of facts—"cold facts" her father always called them—was true, and not that other world of the heart's making.

He was home. He had been home over twelve hours now, and he had not called, had not come over. Breakfast was not a meal to be lingered over. And he was lingering, with the girl and the daisies she had picked.

Was he staying away because he didn't know what to say to her, because he was astonished to come home and find how things stood for him? Likely his folks talked them over, just as hers did. What would he think of her? He would think she was a dishonest simpleton, that's what he would think. He would not know that she had said nothing, but had only kept still and let them think what they would. Likely Bill didn't love her. He had only written to her; written good friendly letters and remembered her kindly. Now, now his people and hers and all their neighbors would think he had treated her as Agnes Marshall had treated Bryan Haywood, and blame him and pity her. Bryan would be all right. He would go back to Art's younger sister, Fran. He had had a hard enough time making up his mind between Fran and Agnes. He would be all right, better off, surely. Fran would make a better farm wife than Agnes. But for her, Louise, there would be no consolation, no comfort. Let her heart ache! It deserved to ache, it had been so stupid. She would not let them go on thinking she and Bill were sweethearts. She would go out in the kitchen, no matter how hard it was now, and tell her mother and sister how it really was, and then, then she would go right out to the barn, where her father and Mr. Atwell were talking, and tell them.

She got up, pushing her hair back, and the baby wakened, looked up at her with his round blue eyes and sleepily held up his arms to be taken. The feel of him, the utterly confiding way he nestled to her and drooped his warm head on her shoulder, gave her courage. She walked with him into the kitchen, where his mother and grandmother were still busy with the strawberries, still talking.

"Well," her mother cried, "did grandma's boy have a dood seep?

Did him? Bless his heart! Grandma will fix him something. Grandma will fix him some nice strawberries."

"Oh, Mamma, do you think you should?" Ruth asked anxiously. "He's never eaten strawberries!"

"I'll crush them good. Crush them and put a little cream on them, and some sugar. They won't hurt him at all. He's nearly a year old, isn't he? Grandma wouldn't do anything to hurt her boy, now, would she?" She leaned toward the baby, smiled at him and then chortled lovingly.

"Well, I don't know," Ruth said. "Mamma, I feel so responsible! If I took him over here and gave him something to eat that made him sick, Art's mother and grandmother would never forgive me. Honestly, Mamma, I think they think I don't know how to take care of a baby! They make such a fuss when they see him. They're afraid I let him sit in the sun too long, they're afraid—"

"Well, he's our first grandchild just as much as he's theirs, and they don't care an iota more for him than we do, so there! If you think it might hurt him, I won't give it to him, Ruth, but I'm sure it wouldn't."

"I'm sure it wouldn't either, he's so well," Ruth said. "Go ahead, Mamma, but just a little."

"Mamma," Louise said, "listen, I want to—I've got to tell you something!"

"There goes Mr. Atwell now, and here's Papa coming to the house," Louise's mother said, and with a dish of berries in her hand, she went to the screen door to open it for him. "Well," she said brightly, "having rather early morning callers, aren't you?"

"Nope, just one," he said. "Well, hello! How are you, scalawag! Come over to see your old granddad, did you? Well, well! Come to granddad! Golly, Ruth, just heft this boy! And good and hard too! No sissy, are you, scalawag? Want to go up? Want grandpa to toss you up?"

"Now, Papa," his wife said anxiously, "be careful how you toss him up. He's only a baby, even if he is in rompers; you might make him bite his tongue. If you hurt that child, Art's folks— Papa, what was Atwell over here about?"

"Nothing. Nothing much. Up d'go! Up d'go! Whee! See, he likes it! Knows his granddad wouldn't drop him, don't he? Hear him laugh?"

"Yes," his wife said, "he sounds just like Jim did when he was a

63

baby, doesn't he? Did you hear me? Why was Atwell over here?"

"I told you, nothing much. He just wanted to know what I thought about Bill building on that rise there on our cornfield between our places."

"On our cornfield?"

"Yes, that's what he wanted to know about. He don't want the whole field, Mamma, he just wants two acres, there by the road. There's that row of cottonwoods there, along the road, and it really makes a better place for a house than any they got on their land, unless they built right up by their house, and he thinks the places would be better a little farther apart. He aims Bill to pretty well take over their place, I guess. Both the other boys have settled quite a piece off. He'd like Bill there, near, but not right on the doorstep. He thinks Bill wouldn't like that."

"But," his wife asked, "what about Bill? Why didn't he come over to see you about it himself, if that's the place he'd like to build? It's all right with me, Papa. I always did think that would be a good place for a house. But why—"

"Well, now, hold your horses, Mamma! He just wanted to look into this before he said anything to Bill about it. He said the boy wasn't up yet, when he came over. He said he wanted to know what I'd think about it too. He knew the boy'd want to build, all right. He's been counting on that. He said he remembered Bill saying, last fall, he thought that would be a good site for a house. What do you think about it, sister?" He had put the baby down and now he came and put an arm about his younger daughter and patted her shoulder. "I guess they, Bill or any of them, wouldn't put up a house without being pretty sure you liked the site. After all, you're the one's to live in it. What do you say about that place?"

"Papa, did Mr. Atwell say anything about me?" Louise asked.

"No, honey, not 'specially, but—"

"Did he mention me; did he say anything at all about me?"

"No, that's not his way, Louise, but that's understood. He'd leave it for Bill to talk to you about it. You know that."

"Of course," Louise's mother said with—Louise felt—not quite enough conviction in her voice. "Louise, he'll be over soon as those people are gone, you know that. A person can't jump up and run off and leave company, especially after they've brought him home. You're just nervous. I know—"

"Oh, Mamma, look!" Ruth cried. "Oh, Mamma, how many do you suppose he's eaten?"

The baby stood, braced against a chair, helping himself with both hands to unstemmed strawberries. The berries were all over his cheeks and some in his hair. His grandmother caught him up and thrust a searching forefinger into his mouth. "Spit it out, dear; 'pit it out for grandma!"

"Stems and all!" wailed Ruth. "Mamma, how many do you suppose he got down? Will they hurt him? Do you think they'll hurt him? Oh, darling, why did you eat them?"

His grandmother was able to extract only one berry stem from the baby's mouth. His grandfather took him, howling and kicking, and talked him into going up again. "Up? Want to go up?" he cried. "That's it, don't cry. Few old berries won't hurt you. What do all these women think you are, a sissy? At-a-boy—up he goes!"

"Papa, don't! You'll upset his stomach. Those berries!" Ruth cried.

"Well, if they come up, all the better. But they won't hurt him. Say, last time he was over here he pulled a pot off the plant shelf and ate fistfuls of dirt before you caught him, and it didn't hurt him a lick." He set the baby down again, heading him toward his mother. "Sister, how about it? I asked you what do you think of that knoll for a house site? Won't be a big place, I guess, but I think it'll be pretty nice. Atwell says Bill's had a course in building down at school. He mention that to you, sister?"

"Yes," Louise said, "he did. He made good grades in it, too, and the teacher—he's a real architect—picked a barn Bill planned, to put up to show them all. But, Papa, you mustn't think—"

"My goodness," her mother wailed, "Ruth, I thought you were looking after this baby! Here, lamb, let grandma get them. Here, 'pit it out. Stems! Both hands full—his mouth full of stems! Ruth, why'd you set that pan down on that chair? Well, he couldn't have swallowed many before I got him. Louise, take him, won't you? Hold him. Don't let him down."

Louise took the baby; now he squirmed in her arms and kicked to be let down for further ventures. "Papa," she began again. "Please! It's all a mistake. Bill's not going to build a house for me!"

"Now, Mamma, what'd I tell you?" her father asked sternly. "I told you Louise was getting run down, worn out. We shouldn't ever have let her teach; she's not husky like you, Ruth. She's not herself,

65

talking like that."

"I know just how you feel," Ruth consoled. "Mamma, do you remember what a goose I was? I felt just like you do, Louise. The morning of the day I married Art, with all the folks downstairs, I think it was hearing his grandmother down there talking about the things Art would and wouldn't eat. I told Mamma I was scared to pieces, that I didn't want to get married, that I was afraid I didn't love Art! Think of that! It's because you've not seen him for so long. I know just how you feel. The minute he walks in the door, you'll see how—"

"There! That's our ring!" her mother cried triumphantly. "That'll be Bill now. I bet anything. Louise, you answer it, dear."

"All right," Louise said. "I will." She handed the still-squirming baby to her sister but her mother cried, "No, you answer it, Papa. Look at her! Child, you're white! You're in no shape to answer the phone and talk with Bill. What would he think? Go on, Papa. Now, you just get hold of yourself, dear." She was pushing her husband toward the door that led to the dining room and the telephone.

They all, even the baby, feeling the tenseness, quieted and listened. Louise's mother put an arm about her and whispered, "Now, you just brace up."

"Hello," her father shouted in his telephone voice. "Well, hello, Bill, how are you? . . . Your dad? He just left. Must be home, 'bout now. . . . Sure, thought he oughta be— Well, we'll be glad to see you. Good-bye."

"There!" Louise's mother said, again. "Now run upstairs, dear, and put on your blue linen. That's not too dressed up and it looks so nice. And put a little color on."

"Papa," Louise asked gravely, "what did he say? Is he coming over here?"

"Sure, he's coming over here."

"Did he say he was?"

"Of course he said so," her sister said, trotting the baby. "Go on and get dressed, Louise. Can I help you any?"

"Papa, did he say he was coming over here?"

"Louise, what's got into you?" her father asked. "Give me a chance to get my breath and I'll tell you every word he said."

"Well, go ahead," his wife impatiently urged. "How many times must she ask you?"

"I asked him how he was. He said he was all right. Then he asked if his dad was over here, and I said he had been, and that he oughta be home by now. He said there he was, driving in right now, and I said we'd be glad to see him. There! Now I'm goin' on out to the field. I've wasted the whole morning. Might bring him on out to the field, Louise, if you get around to it."

"He didn't say he was coming over here, Papa?"

"No, not in so many words, but why else would he want the car?"

"Did he say he wanted the car?"

Her father stood looking at her, shaking his head. "Mamma," he said, "I think you better put this girl to bed. She's not herself. Louise, I'd have sworn you had the best head in the family; that you had more good sense than any child we got, but I don't know what's got into you. What's the matter, anyway?"

"There's nothing the matter, except she's a little nervous, with Bill coming home when he's been away so long. Go on, Papa. And, Louise, run change your dress, dear, do! It's not but two miles; he'll be over here. Go on!"

"And I'll change the baby's rompers," Ruth said. "I should have put the blue ones on him first and saved the pink until Bill came, but I don't suppose he'll be noticing the baby much. . . . Look, darling, grandpa's waving you good-bye. Wave to grandpa! Want your clean rompers on?"

Louise went upstairs to her room. She took the blue dress from its hanger in the closet, and looking on the perfection of its smoothness, and remembering the good half hour she had spent ironing its pleats, tears came to her eyes and a tiredness came into her knees.

She sat down on the bed. He had not said he was coming over, but he was, likely; he had not even asked to speak to her. He would be there in a minute, and she would go down to meet him; and somehow, when they were alone, she would tell him how, through just keeping still, she had let her folks come to believe, and had let them go on believing, that, that—how could she ever say it? But she would, she must.

What would he think, in his astonishment, in his embarrassment? He would understand, though. Why should she doubt him in that? He would say, "That's all right, Louise. People get notions. We can still be good friends, can't we? Don't you worry about it." And then, maybe then, he would tell her about this girl, this girl at his house, and

67

she would tell him she was glad for him, and wish him happiness.

She went to the dresser and picked up the brush and brushed the hair back from her face and adjusted the blue ribbon around her hair.

A car! There it was, coming up the lane, dappled with leaf shadow and sun from the cottonwoods, and Bill was in it. He had come. She must go down to him. Her heart beat hard. "My heart is like a singing bird!" the words came to her mind. Well, it was true, still, still! Even though she had been a fool, even though all she had dreamed and hoped for was not to be, still her heart was like a singing bird, because Bill had come; because, after a near-year of waiting, she should see him, she should hear him saying, "How are you, Louise?"

There was no time to put on the blue linen dress. She heard the car door close while she was on the stair. There he was, coming up the front walk, hurrying. Scarcely knowing what she did, her hand went out to the screen door, then she was on the porch, and then on the walk, going to meet him, for she had seen his face even while she was on the stairs, seen his face lifted to see her coming down, coming to meet him, and in it was the answer to every promise her heart had ever known. Bill was home.

Afflatus

Anthony Lane

The wind
With a breath for beauty
Blew my song away from me
And let it soar . . .

A Birthday

Christina Georgina Rossetti

My heart is like a singing bird
    Whose nest is in a watered shoot;
My heart is like an apple-tree
    Whose boughs are bent with thick-set fruit;
My heart is like a rainbow shell
    That paddles in a halcyon sea;
My heart is gladder than all these,
    Because my love is come to me.

Raise me a dais of silk and down;
    Hang it with vair and purple dyes;
Carve it in doves and pomegranates,
    And peacocks with a hundred eyes;
Work it in gold and silver grapes,
    In leaves and silver fleur-de-lys;
Because the birthday of my life
    Is come, my love is come to me.

Flowering Night

Scharmel Iris

The sky hurls down a hundred stars
    Above a lake of amethyst;
Beyond the blooming lilac hills
    Wanders a thin blue mist.

This beauty is too great that one
    Should bear it all alone;
The night has flowered as has flowered
    My heart that was a stone.

Night Bus

Samuel Hopkins Adams

Gathering most of the Academy awards during the year it appeared as the motion picture "It Happened One Night," this gay story also made film stars of Clark Gable and Claudette Colbert.

THROUGH THE RESONANT cave of the terminal, a perfunctory voice boomed out something about Jacksonville, points north, and New York. The crowd at the rail seethed. At the rear, Mr. Peter Warne hoisted the battered weight of his carryall, resolutely declining a porter's aid. Too bad he hadn't come earlier; he'd have drawn a better seat. Asperities of travel, however, meant little to his seasoned endurance.

Moreover, he was inwardly fortified by what the advertisement vaunted as "The Best Fifteen-cent Dinner in Miami; Wholesome, Clean and Plentiful." The sign knew. Appetite sated, ticket paid for, a safe if small surplus in a secure pocket; on the whole, he was content with life.

Behind him stood and, if truth must be told, shoved a restive girl. Like him she carried her own luggage, a dressing case, small and costly. Like him she had paid for her ticket to New York. Her surplus, however, was a fat roll of high-caste bills. Her dinner at the ornate Seafoam Club had cost somebody not less than ten dollars. But care sat upon her somber brow, and her expression was a warning to all and sundry to keep their distance. She was far from being content with life.

All chairs had been filled when Peter Warne threaded the aisle, having previously tossed his burden into an overhead bracket. Only the rear bench, stretching the full width of the car, offered any space. Three passengers had already settled into it; there was accommodation for two more, but the space was piled full of baled newspapers.

70

"Hi!" said the late arrival cheerfully to the uniformed driver, who stood below on the pavement looking bored. "I'd like one of these seats."

The driver turned a vacant gaze upon him and turned away again.

"Have this stuff moved, won't you?" requested the passenger, with unimpaired good humor.

The official offered a fair and impartial view of a gray-clad back.

Mr. Warne reflected. "If you want a thing well done, do it yourself," he decided. Still amiable, he opened the window and tossed out four bundles in brisk succession.

Upon this, the occupant of the uniform evinced interest. "Hey! What d'you think you're doin'?" He approached, only to stagger back under the impact of another bale which bounded from his shoulder. With a grunt of rage, he ran around to the rear door, yanked it open and pushed his way in, his face red and threatening.

Having, meantime, disposed of the remainder of the papers, Mr. Warne turned, thrust his hand into his rear pocket, and waited. The driver also waited, lowering but uncertain. Out popped the hand, grasping nothing more deadly than a notebook.

"Well, come ahead," said its owner.

"Come ahead with what?"

"You were figuring to bust me in the jaw, weren't you?"

"Yes; and maybe I *am* goin' to bust you in the jor."

"Good!" He made an entry in the book. "I need the money."

The other goggled. "What money?"

"Well, say ten thousand dollars damages. Brutal and unprovoked assault upon helpless passenger. It ought to be worth that. Eh?"

The official wavered, torn between caution and vindictiveness. A supercilious young voice in the aisle behind Peter Warne said: "Do you mind moving aside?"

Peter Warne moved. The girl glided into the corner he had so laboriously cleared for himself. Peter raised his cap.

"Take my seat, madam," he invited, with empressement. She bestowed upon him a faintly speculative glance, indicating that he was of a species unknown to her, and turned to the window. He sat down in the sole remaining place.

The bus started.

Adjustment to the motion of ten tons on wheels is largely a matter of technique and experience. Toughened traveler as he was, Peter

71

Warne sat upright, swaying from the hips as if on well-oiled hinges. Not so the girl at his side. She undertook to relax into her corner with a view to forgetting her troubles in sleep. This was a major error. She was shuttled back and forth between the wall and her neighbor until her exasperation reached the point of protest.

"Tell that man to drive slower," she directed Peter.

"It may surprise you, but I doubt if he'd do it for me."

"Oh, of course! You're afraid of him. I could see that." Leaning wearily away, she said something not so completely under her breath but that Peter caught the purport of it.

"I suspect," he observed unctuously and with intent to annoy, "that you are out of tune with the Infinite."

Unwitherable though his blithe spirit was, it felt the scorch of her glare. Only too obviously he was, at that moment, the focal point for a hatred which included the whole universe. Something must have seriously upset a disposition which, he judged, was hardly inured to accepting gracefully the contrarieties of a maladjusted world.

She looked like that. Her eyes were dark and wide beneath brows that indicated an imperious temper. The long, bold sweep of the cheek was deeply tanned and ended in a chin which obviously expected to have its own way. But the mouth was broad, soft and generous. Peter wondered what it would look like when, as, and if it smiled. He didn't think it likely that he would find out.

Beyond Fort Lauderdale the bus was resuming speed when the feminine driver of a sports roadster, disdaining the formality of a signal, took a quick turn and ran the heavier vehicle off the road. There was a bump, a light crash, a squealing of brakes, the bus lurched to a stop with a tire ripped loose. After a profane inspection, the driver announced a fifteen-minute wait.

They were opposite that sign manual of Florida's departed boom days, a pair of stone pillars leading into a sidewalked wilderness and flanked by two highly ornamental lamp-posts without glass or wiring. The girl got out for a breath of air, set her dressing case at her feet and leaned against one of the monuments to perishable optimism. As she disembarked, her neighbor, in a spirit of unappreciated helpfulness, had advised her to walk up and down; it would save her from cramps later on.

Just for that she wouldn't do it. He was too officious, that young man. Anyway, the fewer human associations she suffered, the better

72

she would like it. She had a hate on the whole race. Especially men. With a total lack of interest, she observed the parade of her fellow wayfarers up and down the road, before shutting them out from her bored vision.

A shout startled her. The interfering stranger on the opposite side of the road had bounded into the air as if treacherously stabbed from behind, and was now racing toward her like a bull at full charge. At the same time she was aware of a shadow moving away from her elbow and dissolving into the darkness beyond the gates. Close to her, the sprinter swerved, heading down the deserted avenue. Beyond him she heard a crash of brush. His foot caught in a projecting root and he went headlong, rising to limp forward a few yards and give it up with a ruefully shaken head.

"Lost him," he said, coming opposite her.

"I don't know why that should interest me." She hoped that she sounded as disagreeable as she felt. And she did.

"All right," he replied shortly, and made as if to go on, but changed his mind. "He got your bag," he explained.

"Oh!" she ejaculated, realizing that that important equipment was indeed missing. "Who?" she added feebly.

"I don't know his name and address. The thin-faced bird who sat in front of you."

"Why didn't you catch him?" she wailed. "What'll I do now?"

"Did it have much in it?"

"All my things."

"Your money and ticket?"

"Not my ticket; I've got that."

"You can wire for money from Jacksonville, you know."

"Thank you. I can get to New York all right," she returned, with deceptive calm, making a rapid calculation based on the six or eight dollars which she figured (by a considerable overestimate) were still left her.

"Shall I report your loss at the next stop?"

"Please don't." She was unnecessarily vehement. One might almost suppose the suggestion had alarmed her.

Joining the others, she climbed aboard. The departed robber had left a chair vacant next the window. One bit of luck, anyway; now she could get away from that rear seat and her friendly neighbor. She transferred herself, only to regret the change bitterly before ten miles

73

had been covered. For she now had the chair above the curve of the wheel, which is the least comfortable of bus seats. In that rigorously enforced distortion of the body she found her feet asleep, her legs cramped. Oh, for the lesser torments of the place she had so rashly abandoned!

Twisting her stiffening neck, she looked back. The seat was still vacant. The chatty young man seemed asleep.

Lapsing into the corner, she prepared for a night of heroism. The bus fled fast through the dark and wind. Exigencies of travel she had known before; once she had actually slept in the lower berth of a section, all the drawing-rooms and compartments being sold out. But that was less cramped than her present seat. Just the same, she would have stood worse rather than stay at home after what had happened!

If only she had brought something to read. She surveyed her fellow passengers, draped in widely diverse postures. Then the miracle began to work within her. She grew drowsy. It was not so much sleep as the reflex anaesthetic of exhaustion. Consciousness passed from her.

Sun rays struck through the window upon her blinking lids. White villas slid by. A milk cart rattled past. Stiff and dazed, she felt as if her legs had been chilled into paralysis, but all the upper part of her was swathed in mysterious warmth. What were those brown, woolly folds?

The tanned, quick-fingered hands explored, lifted a sleeve which flopped loose, discovered a neatly darned spot; another; a third. It had seen hard service, that garment which wrapped her. She thought, with vague pleasure of the senses, that it had taken on a sturdy personality of its own connected with tobacco and wood smoke and strong soap; the brisk, faintly troubling smell of clean masculinity. She liked it, that sweater.

From it, her heavy eyes moved to her neighbor who was still asleep. By no stretch of charity could he be called an ornament to the human species. His physiognomy was blunt, rough and smudgy with bristles; his hair reddish and uncompromisingly straight.

Nevertheless, a guarded approval might be granted to the setting of the eyes under a freckled forehead, and the trend of the mouth suggested strong, even teeth within. Nose and chin betokened a careless good humor. As for the capable hands, there was no blinking the stains upon them.

His clothing was rough and baggy, but neat enough except for a

74

gaping rent along one trouser leg which he had come by in chasing her thief. For the first time in her life, she wished that she knew how to sew. This surprised her when she came to consider it later.

For the moment she only smiled. It was a pity that Peter Warne could not have waked up at the brief, warm interval before her lips drooped back to weariness.

Nearly an hour later, he roused himself at the entrance to Jacksonville where a change of lines was due, and his first look rested upon a wan and haggard face.

"Breakfast!" said he, with energy and anticipation.

The face brightened. "The Windsor is a good place," stated its owner.

"I wouldn't doubt it for a minute. So is Hungry Joe's."

"Do you expect me to eat at some horrid beanery?"

"Beans have their virtue. But oatmeal and coffee give you the most for your money."

"Oh, money! I'd forgotten about money."

"If you want to change your mind and wire for it—"

"I don't. I want to eat."

"With me?"

She speculated as to whether this might be an invitation; decided that it probably wasn't. "If the place is clean."

"It's cleaner than either of us at the present moment of speaking," he grinned.

Thus recalled to considerations of femininity, she said: "I'll bet I look simply *terrible!*"

"Well, I wouldn't go as far as that," was the cautious reply.

"Anyhow, there's one thing I've got to have right away."

"What's that?"

"If you must know, it's a bath."

"Nothing doing. Bus leaves in fifty minutes."

"We can tell the driver to wait."

"Certainly, we can tell him. But there's just a possibility that he might not do it."

This was lost upon her. "Of course he'll do it. People always wait for me," she added with sweet self-confidence. "If they didn't, I'd never get anywhere."

"This is a hard-boiled line," he explained patiently. "The man would lose his job if he held the bus, like as not."

75

She yawned. "He could get another, couldn't he?"

"Oh, of course! Just like that. You haven't happened to hear of a thing called unemployment, have you?"

"Oh, that's just socialistic talk. There are plenty of jobs for people who really want to work."

"Yes? Where did you get that line of wisdom?"

She was bored and showed it in her intonation. "Why, everybody knows that. Bill was saying the other day that most of these people are idle because they're just waiting for the dole or something."

"Who's Bill?"

"My oldest brother."

"Oh! And I suppose Bill works?"

"We-ell; he plays polo. Almost every day."

Mr. Warne made a noise like a trained seal.

"What did you say?"

"I said, 'here's the eatery.' Or words to that effect."

The place was speckless. Having a healthy young appetite, the girl disdained to follow the meager example of her escort, and ordered high, wide and handsome. Directing that his fifteen-cent selection be held for five minutes, Peter excused himself with a view to cleaning up. He returned to find his companion gone.

"At the Windsor, having my bath," a scrawl across the bill of fare enlightened him. "Back in half an hour."

That, he figured after consultation of his watch, would leave her just four minutes and twenty seconds to consume an extensive breakfast and get around the corner to the terminal, assuming that she lived up to her note, which struck him as, at the least, doubtful. Well, let the little fool get out of it as best she could. Why bother?

Peter ate slowly, while reading the paper provided free for patrons. At the end of twenty-five minutes, he was craning his neck out of the window. A slight figure turned the corner. Relief was in the voice which bade the waiter rush the order. The figure approached—and passed. Wrong girl. Peter cursed.

Time began to race. Less than five minutes to go now. Half of that was the minimum allowance for getting to the starting place. Peter bore his grip to the door, ready for a flying take-off, in case she appeared. In case she didn't. . . . People always waited for her, did they? Well, he'd be damned if he would! In one short minute he would be leaving. Thirty seconds; twenty; fifteen; five. Sister Ann, do you see

76

anything moving? *Malbrouck s'en va-t'en guerre.* No dust along the road? We're off!

Such was the intention. But something interfered; an intangible something connected with the remembrance of soft contours on a young, sleeping face, of wondering eyes slowly opened. Peter dashed his valise upon the floor, kicked it, cast himself into a chair and sulked. His disposition was distinctly tainted when the truant made triumphal entrance. She was freshened and groomed and radiant, a festal apparition. Up rose then Mr. Warne, uncertain where to begin. She forestalled him.

"Why, how nice you look!" By virtue of his five minutes, the freedom of the washroom, and a pocket kit, he had contrived to shave, brush up, and make the best of a countenance which, if by strict standards unbeautiful, did not wholly lack points. "How much time have I for breakfast?"

"Plenty," barked Peter.

"Swell! I'm starving. I *did* hurry."

"Did you?" he inquired, between his teeth.

"Of course I did. Didn't you just say I had plenty of time?"

"You certainly have. All day."

She set down her coffee cup. "Why, I thought our bus—"

"Our bus is on its way to New York. The next one leaves at eight tonight."

"I do think you might have telephoned them to wait," she protested. A thought struck her impressionable mind. "Why, you missed it, too!"

"So I did. Isn't that extraordinary!"

"Because you were waiting for me?"

"Something of the sort."

"It was awfully nice of you. But why?"

"Because the poor damfool just didn't have the heart to leave a helpless little hick like you alone," he explained.

"I believe you're sore at me."

"Oh, not in the least! Only at myself for getting involved in such a mix-up."

"Nobody asked you to miss the old bus," she stated warmly. "Why did you?"

"Because you remind me of my long-lost angel mother, of course. Don't you ever go to the movies? Now, do you still want to go to New York?"

77

"We-ell; I've got my ticket. I suppose that's still good."

"Up to ten days. At this rate, it'll take us all of that to get there. The thing is to figure out what to do now."

"Let's go to the races," said she.

"On what?" he inquired.

"I've got some money left."

"How much?"

She examined her purse. "Why, there's only a little over four dollars," she revealed in disappointed accents.

"How far d'you think that'll take you?"

"I could bet it on the first race. Maybe I'd win."

"Maybe you'd lose, too."

"I thought you had that kind of disposition the minute I set eyes on you," she complained. "Pessimist!"

"Economist," he corrected.

"Just as bad. Anyway, we've got a whole day to kill. What's your dashing idea of the best way to do it?"

"A park bench."

"What do you do on a park bench?"

"Sit."

"It sounds dumb."

"It's cheap."

"I hate cheap things, but just to prove I'm reasonable I'll try it for a while."

He led her a block or so to the area of palms and flowers facing the Windsor where they found a bench vacant and sat down. Peter slouched restfully. His companion fidgeted.

"Maybe the band will play by and by," said he encouragingly.

"Wouldn't that be nah-ice!" murmured the girl, and Peter wondered whether a hard slap would break her beyond repair.

"How old are you, anyway?" he demanded. "Fifteen?"

"I'm twenty-one, if you want to know."

"And I suppose it cost your family a bunch of money to bring you to your present fine flower of accomplished womanhood."

"You shouldn't try to be poetic. It doesn't, somehow, go with your face."

"Never mind my face. If I take you to the station and buy you a ticket to Miami—day coach, of course," he interpolated, "will you go back, like a sensible girl?"

"No, I won't. Think how silly I'd look, sneaking back after having—"

"You'd look sillier trying to get to New York at your present rate of expenditure," he warned, as she failed to complete her objection.

"If you can put up the price of a ticket to Miami," said she, with a luminous thought, "you might better lend me the money. I'll pay you back—twice over."

"Tha-anks."

"Meaning you won't?"

"Your powers of interpretation are positively uncanny."

"I might have known you wouldn't." She turned upon him an offended back.

"My name," he said to the back, "is Peter Warne."

A shrug indicated her total indifference to this bit of information. Then she rose and walked away.

He called after her: "I'll be here at six-thirty. Try not to keep me waiting *more* than half an hour."

Just for that—thought the girl—I'll be an hour late.

But she was not. It annoyed her to find how a day could drag in a town where she knew nobody. She went to a movie. She lunched. She went to another movie. She took a walk. Still, it was not yet six o'clock.

At six-thirty-one she started for the park. At six-thirty-four she was at the spot, or what she had believed to be the spot, but which she decided couldn't be, since no Peter Warne was visible. Several other benches were in sight of the vacant band stand. She made the rounds of all. None was occupied by the object of her search. Returning to the first one, she sat down in some perturbation. Perhaps something had happened to Peter Warne. Nothing short of an accident could explain his absence.

There she sat for what seemed like the better part of an hour, until an ugly suspicion seeped into her humiliated mind that she had been left in the lurch. And by a man. A clock struck seven. She rose uncertainly.

"Oh!" she said, in a long exhalation.

Peter Warne was strolling around the corner of the stand.

"Where have you been?" she demanded, like an outraged empress. He remained unstricken. "You were late," he observed.

"I wasn't. What if I was? Only a minute."

79

"Nearer five."

"How do you know? You must have been watching. You were here all the time. And you let me think you'd gone away. Oh! Oh! *Oh!*"

"You're pretty casual about keeping other people waiting, you know."

"That's different." She spoke with a profound conviction of privilege.

"I'm not going to argue that with you. Have you any money left?"

"A dollar and four cents," she announced, after counting and recounting.

Cooly he took her purse, transferred the coins to his pocket, and handed it back. "Confiscated for the common necessity," he stated, and she refrained from protest. "Come along."

She fell into step with him. "Could I please have something to eat?"

"Such is the idea. We'll try Hungry Joe's again."

This time he did the ordering for both of them: soup, hash, thick, pulpy griddle cakes and coffee. Total, sixty-five cents. Fortified by this unfamiliar but filling diet, she decided to give Mr. Peter Warne a more fitting sense of their relative status. Some degree of respect was what her soul demanded to bolster her tottering self-confidence. She had heard that a married woman was in a better position to assert herself than a girl. On that basis she would impress Peter.

"You've been treating me like a child," she complained. "You may as well understand right now that I'm not. I'm a married woman. I'm Mrs. Corcoran Andrews." She had selected this name because Corcoran, who was her third or fourth cousin, had been pestering her to marry him for a year. So he wouldn't mind. The effect was immediate.

"Huh?" jerked out the recipient of the information. "I thought Corker Andrews married a pink chorine."

"They're divorced. Do you *know* Corker?"

"Sure I know Corker."

"You're not a *friend* of his?" The implication of her surprise was unflattering.

"I didn't say that." He grinned. "The fact is, I blacked his boots once for three months."

"What did you do that for?"

"What does a man black boots for? Because I had to. So you're Cor—Mr. Andrews' wife." His regard rested upon her small, strong, deeply browned left hand. She hastily pulled it away.

"My ring's in the bag that was stolen."

"Of course," he remarked. (What did he mean by that?) "Time to be moving."

They emerged into a droning pour of rain. "Can't you get a taxi?" she asked.

"We walk," was the uncompromising reply, as he tucked his hand beneath her arm. They caught the bus with little to spare, and again drew the rear seat.

Outside, someone was saying: "Since Thursday. Yep; a hundred miles up the road. There'll be bridges out."

Feeling sleepy and indifferent, she paid no heed. She lapsed into a doze which, beginning bumpily against the wall, subsided into the unrealized comfort of his shoulder.

Water splashing on the floor boards awakened her; it was followed by the whir of the wheels, spinning in reverse.

"Got out by the skin of our teeth," said Peter Warne's lips close to her ear.

"What is it?"

"Some creek or other on the rampage. We'll not make Charleston this night."

He went forward, returning with dreary news. "We're going to stay in the nearest village. It looks like a night in the bus for us."

"Oh, no! I can't stand this bus any longer. I want to go to bed," she wailed.

He fetched out his small notebook and fell to figuring. "It'll be close reckoning," he said, scowling at the estimate. "But if you feel that way about it—" To the driver he shouted: "Let us off at Dake's place."

"What's that?"

"Tourist camp."

"Aren't they awful places? They look it."

"The Dake's chain are clean and decent enough for anybody," he answered in a tone so decisive that she followed him meekly out into the night.

Leading her to a sort of waiting room, he vanished into an office, where she could hear his voice in colloquy with an unseen man. The latter emerged with a flash light and indicated that they were to follow. Her escort said to her, quick and low: "What's your name?"

81

"I told you," she returned, astonished. "I'm Mrs. Cor—"

"Your first name."

"Oh. Elspeth. Why? What's the matter?" She stared at him.

"I had to register as Mr. and Mrs.," he explained nervously. "It's usual for a husband to know his wife's first name."

She asked coldly: "What is the idea?"

"Do you mind," he urged, "talking it over after we get inside?"

Their guide opened the door of a snug cabin, lighted a light and gave Elspeth a shock by saying: "Good night, Mrs. Warne. Good night, Mr. Warne. I hope you find everything comfortable."

Elspeth looked around upon the bare but neat night's lodging: two bunks separated by a scant yard of space, a chair, four clothes hooks, a shelf with a mirror above it. Peter set down his carryall and sat at the head of a bunk.

"Now," said he, "you're free to come or go."

"Go where?" she asked blankly.

"Nowhere, I hope. But it's up to you. You're a lot safer here with me," he added, "than you would be by yourself."

"But why did you have to register that way? To save appearances?"

"To save two dollars," was his grim correction, "which is more to the point. That's the price of a cabin."

"But *you're* not going to stay *here*."

"Now, let me explain this to you in words of one syllable. We've got darn little money at best. The family purse simply won't stand separate establishments. Get that into your head. And I'm not spending the night outside in this storm!"

"But I—I don't know anything about you."

"All right. Take a look." He held the lamp up in front of what developed into a wholly trustworthy grin.

"I'm looking." Her eyes were wide, exploring, steady, and—there was no doubt about it in his mind—innocent.

"Well; do I look like the villain of the third act?"

"No; you don't." She began to giggle. "You look like a plumber. A nice, honest, intelligent, high-principled plumber."

"The washroom," he stated in the manner of a guidebook, "will be found at the end of this row of shacks."

While she was gone, he extracted a utility kit from his bag, tacked two nails to the end walls, fastened a cord to them and hung a spare blanket, curtain-wise, upon it.

"The walls of Jericho," was his explanation, as she came in. "Solid porphyry and marble. Proof against any assault."

"Grand! What's this?" She recoiled a little from a gaudy splotch ornamenting the foot of her bed.

"Pajamas. My spare set. Hope you can sleep in them."

"I could sleep," she averred with conviction, "in a straitjacket." She had an impulse of irrepressible mischief.

"About those walls of Jericho, Peter. You haven't got a trumpet in that big valise of yours, have you?"

"Not even a mouth organ."

"I was just going to tell you not to blow it before eight o'clock."

"Oh, shut up and go to sleep."

So they both went to sleep.

Something light and small, falling upon her blanket, woke Elspeth.

"Wha' za'?" she murmured sleepily.

"Little present for you," answered Peter.

"Oh-h-h-h-h-h!" It was a rapturous yawn. "I never slept so hard in my *whole* life. What time is it?"

"Eight o'clock, and all's well before the walls of Jericho."

She ripped the small package open, disclosing a toothbrush. "What a snappy present! Where did it come from?"

"Village drug store. I'm just back."

"How nice of you! But can we afford it?" she asked austerely.

"Certainly not. It's a wild extravagance. But I'm afraid to cut you off from all luxuries too suddenly. Now, can you get bathed and dressed in twenty minutes?"

"Don't be silly! I'm not even up yet."

"One—two—three—four—"

"What's the count about?"

"On the stroke of ten I'm going to break down the wall, drag you out and dress you myself if neces—"

"Why, you big bum! I believe you wou—"

"—five—six—seven—"

"Wait a *minute!*"

"—eight—ni-i-i-i—"

A blanket-wrapped figure dashed past him and down to the showers. After a record bath she sprinted back to find him squatted above a tiny double grill which he had evidently extracted from that wonder-box of a valise.

83

"What we waste on luxuries we save on necessities," he point out. "Two eggs, one nickel. Two rolls, three cents. Tea from the Warne storehouse. Accelerate yourself, my child."

Odors, wafted from the cookery to her appreciative nostrils, stimulated her to speed. Her reward was a nod of approval from her companion and the best egg that had ever caressed her palate.

"Now you wash up the dishes while I pack. The bus is due in ten minutes."

"But they're greasy," she shuddered.

"That's the point. Get 'em clean. Give 'em a good scraping first."

He vanished within. Well, she would try. Setting her teeth, she scraped and scrubbed and wiped and, at the end, invited his inspection, confident of praise. When, with a pitying glance, he silently did over two plates and a cup before stacking and packing them, she was justifiably hurt. "There's no suiting some people," she reflected aloud and bitterly.

Flood news from the northward, they learned on boarding the bus, compelled a re-routing far inland. Schedules were abandoned. If they made Charleston by nightfall they'd do pretty well, the driver said. Elspeth, refreshed by her long sleep, didn't much care. Peter would bring them through, she felt. . . .

Yellow against the murk of the night sky shone the lights of Charleston. While Peter was at the terminal office making inquiries, Elspeth, on the platform, heard her name pronounced in astonishment. From a group of company chauffeurs a figure was coming toward her.

"Andy Brinkerhoff! What are you doing in that uniform?"

"Working. Hello, Elspie! How's things?"

"Working? For the bus company?"

"Right," he chirped. "This being the only job in sight and the family having gone bust, I grabbed it. What-ho!"

"How awful!"

"Oh, I dunno. I'd rather be the driver than a passenger. What brought you so low, Elspie?"

"Sh! I've beat it from home."

"Gee! Alone?"

"Yes. That is—yes. Oh, Andy! I never dreamed how awful this kind of travel could be."

"Why don't you quit it, then?"

"No money."

The lad's cherubic face became serious. "I'll raise some dough from the bunch. You could catch the night plane back."

For a moment she wavered. In the distance she sighted Peter Warne scanning the place. There was a kind of expectant brightness on his face. She couldn't quite picture him going on alone in the bus with that look still there. She flattered herself that she had something to do with its presence.

"I'll stick," she decided to herself, but aloud: "Andy, did you ever hear of a man named Peter Warne?"

"Warne? No. What about him?"

"Nothing. What's a telegram to Miami cost?"

"How much of a telegram?"

"Oh, I don't know. Give me a dollar." And then she wrote out a message:

Mr. Corcoran D. Andrews, Bayside Place, Miami Beach, Fla.

Who what and why is Peter Warne Stop Important I should know Stop On my way somewhere and hope to get there some time Stop This is strictly confidential so say nothing to nobody Stop Having a helluvaruff time and liking it Stop Wire Bessie Smith, Western Union, Raleigh, N. C.

El

"Oh, here you are," said Peter, barely giving her time to smuggle the paper into Brinkerhoff's hand. "We're going on. Think you can stand it?"

"I s'pose I've got to," replied Elspeth.

Incertitude had discouraged about half the passengers. Consequently, the pair secured a window chair apiece. At the moment of starting there entered a spindly young male all aglow with self-satisfaction which glossed him over from his cocky green hat to his vivid spats.

By the essential law of his being it was inevitable that, after a survey of the interior, he should drop easily into a seat affording an advantageous view of the snappy-looking girl who seemed to be traveling alone. He exhumed a magazine from his grip and leaned across.

"Pardon *me*. But would you care to look at this?"

Elspeth wouldn't but she looked at Mr. Horace Shapley with attention which he mistook for interest. He transferred himself with suitable preliminaries to the vacant chair at her side and fell into confidential discourse.

85

His line, so Elspeth learned, was typewriter supplies and he hailed from Paterson, New Jersey. Business was punk but if you knew how to make yourself solid with the girl behind the machine (and that was his specialty, believe *him*), you could make expenses and a little bit on the side.

Elspeth glanced across at Peter to see how he regarded this development. Peter was asleep. All right, then; if he wanted to leave her unprotected against the advances of casual strangers. Unfamiliar with this particular species, she was mildly curious about its hopeful antics.

She smiled politely, asked a question or two, and Mr. Shapley proceeded to unfold romantic adventures and tales of life among the typewriters. The incidents exhibited a similarity of climax: "And did *she* fall for me! Hot momma!"

"It must be a fascinating business," commented his listener.

"And how! I'll bet," said Mr. Shapley, with arch insinuation, "you could be a naughty little girl yourself, if nobody was lookin'." He offered her a cigaret. She took it with a nod and tossed it across the aisle, catching the somnolent Peter neatly in the neck. He woke up.

"Hi!"

"Come over here, Peter." He staggered up. "I want you to know" (with a slight emphasis on the word) "Mr. Shapley."

"Pleezetomeetcha," mumbled that gentleman in self-refuting accents.

"He thinks," pursued Elspeth, "that I'm probably a naughty little girl. Am I?"

"You can't prove it by me," said Peter.

"Say, what's the idea?" protested the puzzled Mr. Shapley.

"I don't like him; he nestles," stated Elspeth.

"Aw, now, sister! I was just nicin' you along and—"

"Nicing me along!" Elspeth repeated the phrase with icy disfavor. "Peter; what are you going to do about this?"

Peter ruminated. "Change seats with you," he said brightly.

"Oh!" she choked as she rose. As she stepped across her neighbor to gain the aisle, he gave a yelp and glared savagely, though it was presumably an accident that her sharp, high heel had landed upon the most susceptible angle of his shin. After a moment's consideration, Peter followed her to her new position.

So entered discord into that peaceful community. Mr. Shapley sulked in his chair. Elspeth gloomed in hers. Discomfort invaded

Peter's amiable soul. He perceived that he had fallen short in some manner.

"What did you expect me to do about that bird?" he queried.

"Nothing."

"Well, that's what I did."

"I should say you did. If it had been me, I'd have punched his nose."

"And got into a fight. I never could see any sense in fighting unless you have to," he argued. "What happens? You both get arrested. If I got arrested and fined here, how do we eat? If they jug me, what becomes of you? Be sensible."

"Oh, you're sensible enough for both of us." It was plain, however, to the recipient of this encomium, that it was not intended as a compliment. "Never mind. What are we stopping for?"

The halt was occasioned by evil reports of the road ahead, and the chauffeur's unwillingness to risk it in darkness.

"I'll do a look-see," said Peter, and came back, pleased, to announce that there was a cheap camp around the turn. Without formality, the improvised Warne family settled in for the night.

Silence had fallen upon the little community when an appealing voice floated across the wall of their seventy-five-cent Jericho. "Peter. Pe-*ter!*"

"Mmpff."

"You're not a very inquisitive person, Peter. You haven't asked me a single question about myself."

"I did. I asked you your name."

"Because you had to. In self-protection."

"Do you want me to think up some more questions?"

She sniffed. "You might show a *little* human interest. You know, I don't like you much, Peter. But I could talk to you, if you'd let me, as freely as if you were—well, I don't know how to put it."

"Another species of animal."

"No-o-o-o. You mustn't belittle yourself," said she kindly.

"I wasn't. And I didn't say an inferior species."

It took her a moment to figure this out, and then she thought she must have got it wrong. For how could his meaning possibly be that her species was the inferior? . . . Better pass that and come to her story. She began with emphasis:

"If there's one thing I can't stand, it's unfairness."

"I thought so."

"You thought *what?*"

"Somebody's been interfering with your having your own sweet way, and so you walked out on the show. What was the nature of this infringement upon the rights of American womanhood?"

"Who's making this stump speech; you or me?" she retorted. "It was about King Westley, if you want to know."

"The headline aviator?"

"Yes. He and I have been playing around together."

"How does friend husband like that?"

"Huh? Oh! Why, he's away, you see. Cruising. I'm staying with Dad."

"Then he's the one to object?"

"Yes. Dad doesn't understand me."

"Likely enough. Go ahead."

"I'll bet you're going to be dumb about this, too. Anyway, it was all right till King got the idea of finding the lost scientific expedition in South America. Venezuela, or somewhere. You know."

"Professor Schatze's? South of the Orinoco. I've read about it."

"King wants to fly down there and locate them."

" 'S all right by me. But where does he figure he'll land?"

"Why, on the prairie or the pampas."

"Pampas, my glass eye! There isn't any pampas within a thousand miles of the Orinoco."

"What do you know about it?"

"I was there myself, five years ago."

"You were! What doing?"

"Oh, just snooping around."

"Maybe it wasn't the same kind of country we were going to."

"*We?*" She could hear a rustle and judged that he was sitting upright. She had him interested at last.

"Of course. I was going with him. Why, if we'd found the expedition I'd be another Amelia Earhart."

Again the cot opposite creaked. Its occupant had relaxed. "I guess your family needn't have lost any sleep."

"Why not?" she challenged.

"Because it's all a bluff," he returned. "Westley never took a chance in his life outside of newspaper headlines."

"I think you're positively septic. The family worried, all right. They tried to keep me from seeing him. So he took to nosing down

88

across our place and dropping notes in the swimming pool, and my father had him arrested and grounded for reckless flying. Did you ever hear anything like that?"

"Not so bad," approved Peter.

"Oh-h-h-h! I might know you'd side against me. I suppose you'd have had me sit there and let Dad get away with it."

"Mmmmm. I can't exactly see you doing it. But why take a bus?"

"All the cars were locked up. I had to sneak out. I knew they'd watch the airports and the railroad stations, but they wouldn't think of the bus. Now you've got the whole story, do you blame me?"

"Yes."

"I do think you're unbearable. You'd probably expect me to go back."

"Certainly."

"Maybe you'd like to send me back."

"You wouldn't go. I did try, you know."

"Not alive, I wouldn't! Of *course* you wouldn't think of doing anything so improper as helping me any more."

"Sure, I will," was the cheerful response. "If you've got your mind set on getting to New York, I'll do my best to deliver you there intact. And may God have mercy on your family's soul! By the way, I suppose you left some word at home so they won't worry too much."

"I did not! I hope they worry themselves into convulsions."

"You don't seem to care much about your family," he remarked.

"Oh, Dad isn't so bad. But he always wants to boss everything. I—I expect I didn't think about his worrying. D'you think he will— much?" The query terminated in a perceptible quaver.

"Hm. I wonder if you're really such a hard-boiled little egg as you make out to be. Could you manage with a bag of pecans for dinner tomorrow?"

"Ouch! Do I have to?"

"To wire your father would come to about the price of two dinners."

"Wire him? And have him waiting in New York for me when we get there? If you do, I'll jump through the bus window and you'll never see me again."

"I see. Westley is meeting you. You don't want any interference. Is that it?"

"I left him a note," she admitted.

"Uh-huh. Now that you've got everything movable off your mind, what about a little sleep?"

"I'm for it."

Silence settled down upon the Warne menage.

Sunup brought Peter out of his bunk. From beyond the gently undulant blanket he could hear the rhythm of soft breathing. Stealthily he dressed. As he opened the door, a gust of wind twitched down the swaying screen. The girl half turned in her sleep. She smiled. Peter stood, bound in enchantment.

In something like panic he bade himself listen to sense and reason. That's a spoiled child, Peter. Bad medicine. Willful, self-centered—and sweet. (How had that slipped in?) Impractical, too. Heaven pity the bird that takes her on! Too big a job for you, Peter, my lad, even if you could get the contract. So don't go fooling with ideas, you poor boob.

Breakfast necessities took him far afield before he acquired at a bargainer's price what he needed. Elspeth had already fished the cooking kit out of the bag and made ready in the shelter of the shack. Not a word did she say about the fallen blanket. This made Peter self-conscious. They breakfasted in some restraint.

A wild sky threatened renewal of the storm. Below the hill a shallow torrent supplanted the road for a space. Nevertheless, the bus was going on. Elspeth washed the dishes—clean, this time.

"You get out and stretch your legs while I pack," advised Peter.

As she stepped from the shack, the facile Mr. Shapley confronted her.

"The cream off the milk to you, sister," said he, with a smile which indicated that he was not one to bear a grudge. "I just want to square myself with you. If I'd known you was a married lady—"

"I'm not," returned Elspeth absently.

Mr. Shapley's eyes shifted from her to the shack. Peter's voice was raised within: "Where are your pajamas, Elspeth?"

"Airing out. I forgot 'em." She plucked them from a bush and tossed them in at the door.

"*Oh*-oh!" lilted Mr. Shapley, with the tonality of cynical and amused enlightenment. He went away, cocking his hat.

Warning from the bus horn brought out Peter with his bag. They took their seats and were off.

The bus' busy morning was spent mainly in dodging stray watercourses. They made Cheraw toward the middle of the afternoon. There Peter bought two pounds of pecans; a worthy nut and one which satisfies without cloying. They were to be held in reserve, in case. In case of what? Elspeth wished to be informed. Peter shook his head and said, darkly, that you never could tell.

North of Cheraw, the habits of the bus became definitely amphibian. The main route was flowing in a northeasterly direction, and every side road was a contributory stream. A forested rise of land in the distance held out hope of better things, but when they reached it they found cars parked all over the place, waiting for a road-gang to strengthen a doubtful bridge across the swollen river.

"Let's have a look at this neck of the woods," Peter suggested.

To determine their geographical circumstances was not difficult. Rising waters had cut off from the rest of the world a ridge, thinly oval in shape, of approximately a mile in length, and hardly a quarter of a mile across. On this were herded thirty or forty travelers, including the bus passengers.

There was no settlement of any sort within reach; only a ramshackle farmhouse surrounded by a discouraged garden. Peter, however, negotiated successfully for a small box of potatoes, remarking to his companion that there was likely to be a rise in commodity prices before the show was over.

A sound of hammering and clinking interspersed with rugged profanity, led them to a side path. There they found a well-equipped housekeeping van, the engine of which was undergoing an operation by its owner while his motherly wife sat on the steps watching.

"Cussin' never done you any good with that machine, Abner," said she. "It ain't like a mule."

"It is like a mule. Only meaner." Abner sighted Peter. "Young man, know anything about this kind of critter?"

"Ran one once," answered Peter. He took off his coat, rolled up his sleeves, and set to prodding and poking in a professional manner. Presently the engine lifted up its voice and roared.

Elspeth, perched on a log, reflected that Peter seemed to be a useful sort of person to other people. Why hadn't he done better for himself in life? Maybe that was the reason. This was a new thought and gave her something to mull over while he worked. From the van she borrowed a basin of water, a bar of soap and a towel, and was standing by when he finished the job.

91

"What do I owe you, young man?" called Abner Braithe, from the van.

"Noth-*uh!*" Elspeth's well-directed elbow had reached its goal in time.

"Don't be an idiot!" she adjured him.

A conference took place.

"You see," said Peter at its close, "my—uh—wife doesn't sleep well outdoors. If you had an extra cot, now—"

"Why, we can fix that," put in Mrs. Braithe. "We haven't got any cot, but if you can sleep in a three-quarter bed—"

"We can't," said both hastily.

"We're used to twin beds," explained Elspeth.

"My wife's quite nervous," put in Peter, "and—and I snore."

"You don't," contradicted Elspeth indignantly, and got a dirty look from him.

It was finally arranged that, as payment for Peter's services, the Braithes were to divide the night into two watches; up to and after one A.M., Elspeth occupying the van bed for the second spell while Peter roosted in the bus.

This being settled, the young pair withdrew to cook a three-course dinner over a fire coaxed by Peter from wet brush and a newspaper; first course, thin potato soup; second course, boiled potatoes with salt; dessert, five pecans each.

"We've been Mr. and Mrs. for pretty near three days now, Peter," remarked the girl suddenly, "and I don't know the first darn thing about you."

"What d'you want to know?"

"What have you got in the line of information?"

"Not much that's exciting."

"That's too bad. I hoped you were an escaped con or something, traveling incog."

"Nothing so romantic. Just a poor but virtuous specimen of the half-employed."

"Who employs you?"

"I do. I'm a rotten employer."

"Doing what? Besides blacking boots."

"Oh, I've nothing as steady as that since. If you want to know, I've been making some experiments in the line of vegetable chemistry; pine tar, to be exact. I'm hoping to find some sucker with money to take

92

it up and subsidize me and my process. That's what I'm going to New York to see about. Meantime," he grinned, "I'm traveling light."

"What'll the job be worth if you do get it?"

"Seven or eight thousand a year to start with," said he, with pride.

"Is *that* all?" She was scornful.

"Well, I'll be—Look here, Elspeth, I said per year."

"I heard you. My brother Bill says he can't get along on *ten* thousand. And," she added thoughtfully, "he's single."

"So am I."

"You didn't tell me that before. Not that it matters, of course. Except that your wife might misunderstand if she knew we'd been sl—traveling together."

"I haven't any wife, I tell you."

"All right; all *right!* Don't bark at me about it. It isn't my fault."

"Anything else?" he inquired with careful politeness.

"I think it's going to rain some more."

They transferred themselves to the bus and sat there until one o'clock, when he escorted her to the Braithe van. He returned to join his fellow passengers, leaving her with a sensation of lostness and desertion.

Several small streams, drunk and disorderly on spring's strong liquor, broke out of bounds in the night, came brawling down the hills and carried all before them, including the bridge whereby the marooned cars had hoped to escape.

"I don't care," said Elspeth, when the morning's news was broken to her. She was feeling gayly reckless.

"I do," returned Peter soberly.

"Oh, you're worrying about money again. What's the use of money where there's nothing to buy? We're out of the world, Peter. I like it, for a change. What's that exciting smell?"

"Fish." He pointed with pride to his fire, over which steamed a pot. Dishing up a generous portion he handed it to her on a plate. "Guaranteed fresh this morning. How do you like it?"

She tasted it. "It—it hasn't much personality. What kind of fish is it?"

"They call it mudfish, I believe. It was flopping around in a slough and I nailed it with a stick. I thought there'd be enough for dinner, too," said he, crestfallen by her lack of appreciation.

"Plenty," she agreed. "Peter, could I have four potatoes? Raw ones."

93

"What for?"

"I'm going marketing."

"Barter and exchange, eh? Look out that these tourists don't gyp you."

"Ma feyther's name is Alexander Bruce MacGregor Andrews," she informed him in a rich Scottish accent. "Tak' that to heart, laddie."

"I get it. You'll do."

Quenching his fire, he walked to the van. A semicircle of men and women had grouped about the door. Circulating among them, Abner Braithe was taking up a collection. Yet, it was not Sunday. The explanation was supplied when the shrewd Yankee addressed his audience.

"The morning program will begin right away. Any of you folks whose money I've missed, please raise the right hand. Other news and musical ee-vents will be on the air at five-thirty this P.M. and eight tonight. A nickel admission each, or a dime for the three performances."

Having no nickel to waste on frivolities, Peter moved on. Elspeth, triumphant, rejoined him with her booty.

Item: a small parcel of salt.

Item: a smaller parcel of pepper.

Item: a half pound of lard.

Item: two strips of fat bacon.

Item: six lumps of sugar.

"What d'ye ken about that?" she demanded. "Am I no the canny Scawtswumman?"

"You're a darn bonny one," returned Peter, admiring the flushed cheeks and brilliant eyes.

"Is this the first time you've noticed that?" she inquired impudently.

"It hadn't struck in before," he confessed.

"And now it has? Hold the thought. I can't hurt you." (He felt by no means so sure about that.) "Now Mr. Shapley"—her eyes shifted to the road up which that gentleman was approaching—"got it right away. I wonder what's his trouble."

Gratification, not trouble, signalized his expression as he sighted them. His bow to Elspeth was gravely ceremonious. He then looked at her companion.

"Could I have a minute's conversation apart with you?"

"Don't mind me," said Elspeth, and the two men withdrew a few paces.

94

"I don't want to butt into your and the lady's private affairs," began Mr. Shapley, "but this is business. I want to know if that lady is your wife."

"She is. Not that it's any concern of yours."

"She said this morning that she wasn't married."

"She hasn't got used to the idea yet," returned Peter, with great presence of mind. "She's only been that way a few days. Honeymoon trip."

"That's as may be," retorted the other. "Even if it's true, it wouldn't put a crimp in the reward."

"What's this?" demanded Peter, eying him in surprise. "Reward? For what?"

"Come off. You heard the raddio this morning, didn'cha?"

"No."

"Well, is that lady the daughter of Mr. A. B. M. Andrews, the yachting millionaire, or ain't she? 'Cause I know she is."

"Oh! You know that, do you! What of it?"

"Ten grand of it. That's what of it," rejoined Mr. Shapley. "For information leadin' to the dis—"

"Keep your voice down."

"Yeah. I'll keep my voice down till the time comes to let it loose. Then I'll collect on that ten thou'. They think she's kidnaped."

"What makes you so sure of your identification?"

"Full description over the air. When the specifications came across on the raddio I spotted the garments. Used to be in ladies' wear," he explained.

"If you so much as mention this to Mi—to Mrs. Warne, I'll—" began Peter.

"Don't get rough, now, brother," deprecated the reward-hunter. "I ain't lookin' for trouble. And I'm not sayin' anything to the little lady, just so long as you and me understand each other."

"What do you want me to understand?"

"That there's no use your tryin' to slip me after we get out of this place. Of course, you can make it hard or easy for me. So, if you want to play in with me and be nice, anyway—I'm ready to talk about a little cut for you . . . No? Well, suit yourself, pal. See you in the mornin'."

He chuckled himself away. Peter, weighing the situation, discovered in himself a violent distaste at the thought of Mr. Horace Shapley collecting Elspeth's family's money for the delivering up of Elspeth. In fact, it afflicted him with mingled nausea and desire for manslaughter. Out of this unpromising combination emerged an idea. If he, Peter, could reach a wire before the pestilent Shapley, he could get in his information first and block the reward.

Should he tell Elspeth about the radio? Better not, he concluded.

It was characteristic of her and a big credit mark in his estimate of her, that she put no questions as to the interview with Shapley. She did not like that person; therefore, practically speaking, he did not exist. But the mudfish did. With a captivating furrow of doubt between her eyes, she laid the problem before her partner: could it be trusted to remain edible overnight?

"Never mind the fish. Can you swim?"

She looked out across the brown turbulence of the river, more than two hundred yards now to the northern bank. "Not across that."

"But you're used to water?"

"Oh, yes!"

"I've located an old boat in the slough where I killed the fish. I think I can patch her up enough to make it."

"Okay by me; I wouldn't care to settle here permanently. When do we start?"

"Be ready about ten."

"In the dark?"

"We-ell, I don't exactly want the public in on this. They might try to stop us. You know how people are."

"Come clean, Peter. We're running away from something. Is it that Shapley worm?"

"Yes. He thinks he's got something on me." This explanation which he had been at some pains to devise, he hoped would satisfy her. But she followed it to a conclusion which he had not foreseen.

"Is it because he knows we're not married?"

"He doesn't know ex—"

"I told him we weren't. Before I thought how it would look."

"I told him we were."

"Did he believe you?"

"Probably not."

"Then he thinks you're abducting me. Isn't that priceless!"

"Oh, absolutely. What isn't so funny is that there are laws in some states about people—er—traveling as man and wife if not married."

She stared at him, wide-eyed. "But so long as—Oh, Peter! I'd *hate* it if I got you into any trouble."

"All we have to do is slip Shapley. Nobody else is on." He sincerely hoped that was true.

The intervening time he occupied in patching up the boat as best he might. He had studied the course of various flotsam and thought that he discerned a definite set of the current toward the northern bank which was their goal. With bailing they ought to be able to keep the old tub afloat.

Through the curtain of the rushing clouds the moon was contriving to diffuse a dim light when they set out. The opposite bank was visible only as a faint, occasional blur. Smooth with treachery, the stream at their feet sped from darkness into darkness.

Peter thrust an oar into Elspeth's hand, the only one he had been able to find, to be used as a steering paddle. For himself he had fashioned a pole from a sapling. The carryall he disposed aft of amidships.

Bending over Elspeth as she took the stern seat, he put a hand on her shoulder.

"You're not afraid?"

"No." Just the same, she would have liked to be within reach of that firm grasp through what might be coming.

"Stout fella! All set? Shove!"

The river snatched at the boat, took it into its secret keeping—and held it strangely motionless. But the faintly visible shore slipped backward and away and was presently visible no more. Peter, a long way distant from her in the dimness, was active with his pole, fending to this side and that. It was her job to keep them on the course with her oar. She concentrated upon it.

The boat was leaking profusely now. "Shall I bail?" she called.

"Yes. But keep your oar by you."

They came abreast of an island. As they neared the lower end, an uprooted swamp maple was snatched outward in the movement of the river. Busy with her pan, Elspeth did not notice it until a mass of leafy branches heaved upward from the surface, hovered, descended, and she was struggling in the grasp of a hundred tentacles.

"*Peter!*" she shrieked.

They had her, those wet, clogging arms. They were dragging her out into the void, fight them as she would in her terror and desperation. Now another force was aiding her; Peter, his powerful arms tearing, thrusting, fending against this ponderous invasion. The boat careened. The water poured inboard. Then, miraculously, they were released as the tree sideslipped, turning again, freeing their craft. Elspeth fell back, bruised and battered.

"Are you all right?"

"Yes. It t-t-tried to drag me overboard!"

"I know." His voice, too, was unsteadied by that horror.

"Don't go away. Hold me. Just for a minute."

The skiff, slowly revolving like a ceremonious dancer in the performance of a solo waltz, proceeded on its unguided course. The girl sighed.

"Where's my oar?" It was gone.

"It doesn't matter now. There's the shore. We're being carried in."

They scraped and checked as Peter clutched at a small sapling, growing at the edge of a swampy forest. From trunk to trunk he guided the course until there was a solid bump.

"Land ho!" he shouted, and helped his shipmate out upon the bank.

"What do we do now?"

"Walk until we find a road and a roost."

Valise on shoulder, he set out across the miry fields, Elspeth plodding on behind. It was hard going. Her breath labored painfully after the first half-mile, and she was agonizingly sleepy.

Now Peter's arm was around her; he was murmuring some encouraging foolishness to her who was beyond courage, fear, hope, or any other emotion except the brutish lust for rest. . . . Peter's voice, angry and harsh, insisting that she throw more of her weight on him and *keep* moving. How silly! She hadn't any weight. She was a bird on a bough. She was a butterfly, swaying on a blossom. She was nothing. . . .

Broad daylight, spearing through a paneless window, played upon her lids, waking her. Where was the shawl of Jericho? In its place were boards, a raw wall. Beneath her was fragrant hay. She was actually alive and rested. She looked about her.

"Why, it's a barn!" she exclaimed. She got up and went to the door. Outside stood Peter.

"How do you like the quarters?" he greeted her. "Room"—he pointed to the barn—"and bath." He indicated a huge horse trough fed by a trickle of clear water. "I've just had mine."

She regarded him with stupefaction. "And now you're *shaving*. Where's the party?"

"Party?"

"Well, if not, why the elaborate toilet?"

"Did you ever travel on the thumb?"

She looked her incomprehension. He performed a digital gesture which enlightened her.

"The first rule of the thumb," explained Peter, "is to look as neat and decent as you can. It inspires confidence in the passing motorist's breast."

"Is that the way we're going to travel?"

"If we're lucky."

"Without eating?" she said wistfully.

"Tluck-tluck!" interposed a young chicken from a near-by hedge, the most ill-timed observation of its brief life.

A handy stick, flung deftly, checked its retreat. Peter pounced. "Breakfast!" he exulted.

"Where do we go now?" inquired his companion, half an hour later, greatly restored.

"The main highways," set forth Peter, thinking of the radio alarm and the state police, "are not for us. Verdant lanes and bosky glens are more in our line. We'll take what traffic we can."

Hitch-hiking on sandy side roads in the South means slow progress. Peter finally decided that they must risk better-traveled roads, but select their transportation cautiously. It was selected for them. They had not footed it a mile beside Route 1, when a touring car, battered but serviceable, pulled up and a ruddy face emitted welcome words.

"Well, well, well! Boys *and* girls! Bound north?"

"Yes." It was a duet, perfect in accord.

"Meet Thad Banker, the good old fatty. Throw in the old trunk."

"What's the arrangement?" queried Peter, cautious financier that he was.

"Free wheeling," burbled the fat man. "You furnish the gas and I furnish the spark." They climbed in with the valise. "Any special place?" asked the obliging chauffeur.

"Do we go through Raleigh?" asked the girl, and upon receiving an affirmative, added to Peter: "There may be a wire there for me."

Which reminded that gentleman that he had something to attend to. At the next town he got a telegraph blank and a stamped envelope.

99

After some cogitation, he produced this composition, addressed to Mr. A. B. M. Andrews, Miami Beach, Fla.

Daughter taking trip for health and recreation. Advise abandonment of efforts to trace which can have no good results and may cause delay. Sends love and says not to worry. Undersigned guarantees safe arrival in New York in a few days. Pay no reward to any other claimant as this is positively first authentic information.

Peter Warne

To this he pinned a dollar bill and mailed it for transmission to Western Union, New Orleans, Louisiana, by way of giving the pursuit, in case one was instituted, a pleasant place to start from. Five cents more of his thin fortune went for a newspaper. Reports from the southward were worth the money; there was no let-up in the flood. Competition from Mr. Shapley would be delayed at least another day.

Mr. Thad Banker was a card. He kept himself in roars of laughter with his witty sallies. Peter, in the rear seat, fell peacefully asleep. Elspeth had to act as audience for the conversational driver.

At Raleigh she found the expected telegram from Corcoran, which she read and thrust into her purse for future use. Shortly after, a traffic light held them up and the policeman on the corner exhibited an interest in the girl on the front seat quite disturbing to Peter.

The traffic guardian was sauntering toward them when the green flashed on. "Step on it," urged Peter.

Mr. Banker obliged. A whistle shrilled.

"Keep going!" snapped Peter.

Mr. Banker still obliged, slipping into a maze of side streets. It did not occur to Peter that their driver's distaste for police interference was instinctive. Also successful, it began to appear; when a motor cop swung around unexpectedly and headed them to the curb. The license was inspected and found in order.

"Who's the lady?" the officer began.

"My niece," said Mr. Banker, with instant candor.

"Is that right, ma'am?"

"Yes, of course it is." (Peter breathed again.)

"And this man behind?"

"Search me."

"He thumbed us and Uncle Thad stopped for him." (Peter's ad-

100

miration became almost more than he could bear.)

"Have you got a traveling bag with you, ma'am?" (So the radio must have laid weight on the traveling bag, now probably in some Florida swamp.)

"No. Just my purse."

The cop consulted a notebook. "The dress looks like it," he muttered. "And the description sort of fits. Got anything on you to prove who you are, ma'am?"

"No; I'm afraid—Yes; of course I have." She drew out the yellow envelope. "Is that enough?"

"Miss Bessie Smith," he read. "I reckon that settles it. Keep to your right for Greensboro at Morrisville."

"Greensboro, my foot! Us for points east," announced the fat man, wiping his brow as the motorcycle chugged away. "Phe-e-ew! What's it all about? Been lootin' a bank, you two?"

"Eloping," said Peter. "Keep it under your shirt."

"Gotcha." He eyed the carryall. "All your stuff in there?"

"Yes."

"How about a breath of pure, country air? I'm not so strong for all this public attention."

They kept to side roads until long after dark, bringing up before a restaurant in Tarboro. There the supposed elopers consulted and announced that they didn't care for dinner. "Oh, on me!" cried Mr. Banker. "Mustn't go hungry on your honeymoon."

He ordered profusely. While the steak was cooking, he remarked, he'd just have a look at the car; there was a rattle in the engine that he didn't like. As soon as he had gone, Elspeth said:

"Wonder what the idea is. I never heard a sweeter-running engine for an old car. What's more, he's got two sets of license cards. I saw the other one when that inquiring cop—"

But Peter was halfway to the door, after slamming some money on the table and snapping out directions for her to wait, no matter how long he took. Outside, she heard a shout and the rush of a speeding engine. A car without lights sped up the street.

With nothing else to do, Elspeth settled down to leisurely eating. . . .

At nine-thirty, the waiter announced the closing hour as ten, sharp. Beginning to be terrified for Peter and miserable for herself, she ordered more coffee. The bill and tip left her a dollar and fifteen cents.

At nine-fifty, the wreckage of Peter entered the door. Elspeth arose and made a rush upon him, but recoiled.

"Peter! You've been fighting."

"Couldn't help it."

"You've got a black eye."

"That isn't all I've got," he told her.

"No; it isn't. What an *awful*-looking ear!"

"*That* isn't all I've got, either." His grin was bloody, but unbowed.

"Then it must be internal injuries."

"Wrong. It's a car."

"Whose car?"

"Ours now, I expect. I had to come home in something."

"Where's the fat man?"

The grin widened. "Don't know exactly. Neither does he, I reckon. That big-hearted Samaritan, my child, is a road-pirate. He picks people up, plants 'em, and beats it with their luggage. Probably does a little holdup business on the side."

"Tell me what happened, Peter. Go on and eat first."

Between relishing mouthfuls, he unfolded his narrative. "You didn't put me wise a bit too quick. He was moving when I got out but I landed aboard with a flying tackle. Didn't dare grab him for fear we'd crash. He was stepping on it and telling me that when he got me far enough away he was going to beat me up and tie me to a tree. That was an idea! So when he pulled up on some forsaken wood road in a swamp, I beat him up and tied him to a tree."

"Why, Peter! He's twice as big as you."

"I can't help that. It wasn't any time for half measures. It took me an hour to find my way. But here we are."

"I'm glad," she said with a new note in her voice.

"Jumping Jehoshaphat! Is *that* all we've got left?" Aghast, he stared at the sum she put in his hands. "And it's too cold to sleep out tonight. It's an open car, anyhow. Oh, well; our transportation's going to be cheap from now on. What price one more good night's rest? Torney's Haven for Tourists is three miles up the highway. Let's get going."

Torney's provided a cabin for only a dollar. Before turning in, Peter returned to the car, parked a few rods away against a fence, to make a thorough inspection. His companion was in bed on his return.

"I've changed the plates to another set that I found under the seat. Indiana, to match the other set of licenses. It'll be safer in case our friend decides to report the loss, after he gets loose from his tree.

There's a nice robe, too. We've come into property. And by the way, Elspeth; you're Mrs. Thaddeus Banker till further notice."

Elspeth pouted. "I'd rather be Mrs. Peter Warne. I'm getting used to that."

"We've got to live up to our new responsibilities." Seated on his cot, he had taken off his shoes, when he started hastily to resume them.

"Where are you going?" she asked plaintively. "Looking for more trouble?"

"Walls of Jericho. I forgot. I'll get the robe out of the car."

"Oh, darn the robe! Why bother? It's pouring, too. Let it go. I don't mind if you don't." All in a perfectly matter-of-fact tone. She added: "You can undress outside. I'm going to sleep."

As soon as he withdrew she got out Corcoran's reply to "Miss Bessie Smith," and read it over again before tearing it into fragments. It ran as follows:

What's all this about P. W.? Watch out for that bird. Dangerous corner, blind road, and all that sorta thing. At any given moment he might be running a pirate fleet or landing on the throne of the Kingdom of Boopadoopia. Ask him about the bet I stuck him on in college, and then keep your guard up. I'm off for a week on the Keys so you can't get me again until then. Better come back home and be a nice little girl or papa spank. And how!

                                                    Cork

The scraps she thrust beneath her pillow and was asleep almost at once. But Peter lay, wakeful, crushing down thoughts that made him furious with himself. At last peace came, and dreams. . . . One of them so poignant, so incredibly dear, that he fought bitterly against its turning to reality.

Yet reality it was; the sense of warmth and softness close upon him; the progress of creeping fingers across his breast, of seeking lips against his throat. His arms drew her down. His mouth found the lips that, for a dizzying moment, clung to his, then trembled aside to whisper:

"No, Peter. I didn't mean— Listen!"

Outside sounded a light clinking.

"Somebody's stealing the car!"

Elspeth's form, in the lurid pajamas, slid away from Peter like a ghost. He followed to the window. Silent as a shadow the dim bulk of the Banker automobile moved deliberately along under a power not its own. Two other shadows loomed in its rear, propelling it by hand.

"Shall I scream?" whispered the girl.

He put a hand on her mouth. "Wait."

Another of his luminous ideas had fired the brain of Peter Warne. In his role of Thad Banker, he would let the robbers get away, then report the theft to the police and, allowing for reasonable luck, get back his property (or Mr. Banker's) with the full blessing of the authorities.

"I'm going to let 'em get away with it," he murmured. "As soon as they really start, I'll telephone the road patrol."

The dwindling shadow trundled out on the pike, where the engine struck up its song and the car sped southward. Simultaneously Peter made a rush for the camp office. It was all right, he reported, on getting back. He'd been able to get the police at once.

"But suppose they don't catch 'em."

"That'll be just too bad," admitted Peter. He yawned.

"You're sleepy again. You're always sleepy."

"What do you expect at three o'clock in the morning?"

"I'm wide awake," complained Elspeth.

Something had changed within her, made uncertain and uneasy, since she had aroused Peter and found herself for one incendiary moment in his arms. She didn't blame him; he was only half awake at the time. But she had lost confidence in him. Or could it be herself in whom she had lost confidence? In any case, the thought of sharing the same room with him the rest of that night had become too formidable.

"Please go outside again, Peter. I'm going to get dressed. I'm restless."

"Oh, my gosh!" he sighed. "Can't you count some sheep or something?"

"No; I can't." A brilliant idea struck her. "How'd you expect me to sleep when they may be back with the car any minute?"

"And then again, they may not be back till morning."

But Elspeth had a heritage of the immovable Scottish obstinacy. In a voice all prickly little italics she announced that she was *going to get up*. And she was going to walk off her nervousness. It needn't make any difference to Peter. He could go back to bed.

"And let you wander around alone in this blackness? You might not come back."

"What else could I do?"

The forlorn lack of alternative for her struck into his heart. Absolute dependence upon a man of a strange breed in circumstances wholly new. What a situation for a girl like her! And how gallantly, on the whole, she was taking it! How sensible it would be for him to go back to that telephone; call up her father (reverse charges, of course) and tell him the whole thing. *And* get himself thoroughly hated for it.

No; he couldn't throw Elspeth down. Not even for her own good. Carry on. There was nothing else for it, especially now that luck was favoring them. The car, if they got it back, was their safest obtainable method of travel. Her dress was the weak spot and would be more of a danger point after Horace Shapley contributed his evidence to the hunt. Couldn't something be done about that? . . . The dress appeared in the doorway, and Peter went in to array himself for the vigil.

The two state police found the pair waiting at the gate. Apologetically they explained that the thieves had got away into the swamp. Nothing could have suited Peter better, since there would now be no question of his being held as complaining witness. To satisfy the authorities of his ownership was easy. They took his address (fictitious), wished him and his wife good luck, and were off.

"Now we can go back to bed," said Peter.

"Oh, dear! Can't we start on?"

"At this hour? Why, I suppose we could, but—"

"Let's, then." In the turmoil of her spirit she wanted to be quit forever of Torney's Haven for Tourists and its atmosphere of unexpected emotions and disconcerting impulses. Maybe something of this had trickled into Peter's mind, too, for presently he said:

"Don't you know it's dangerous to wake a sound sleeper too suddenly?"

"So I've heard."

"You can't tell what might happen. I mean, a man isn't quite responsible, you know, before he comes quite awake."

So he was apologizing. Very proper.

"Let's forget it."

"Yes," he agreed quietly. "I'll have quite a little to forget."

"So will I," she thought, startled at the realization.

They packed, and chugged out, one cylinder missing. "I hope the old junk-heap holds together till we reach New York," remarked Peter.

"Are we going all the way in this?"

"Unless you can think of a cheaper way."

"But it isn't ours. It's the fat man's."

"I doubt it. Looks to me as if it had been stolen and gypped up with new paint and fake numbers. However, we'll leave it somewhere in Jersey if we get that far, and write to both license numbers to come and get it. How does that set on an empty conscience?"

"Never mind my conscience. That isn't the worst emptiness I'm suffering from. What's in the house for breakfast? It's nearly sunup."

"Potatoes. Pecans." He investigated their scanty store and looked up. "There are only three spuds left."

"Is that all?"

Something careless in her reply made him scan her face sharply. "There ought to be five. There are two missing. You had charge of the larder. Well?"

"I took 'em. You see—"

"Without saying a word about it to me? You must have pinched them out when we were on the island and cooked them for yourself while I was working on the boat," he figured somberly. Part of this was true, but not all of it. The rest she was saving to confound him with. "Do you, by any chance, still think that this is a picnic?"

Now she *wouldn't* tell him! She was indignant and hurt. He'd be sorry! When he came to her with a potato now, she would haughtily decline it—if her rueful stomach didn't get the better of her wrathful fortitude.

In resentment more convincing than her own, he built the wayside fire, boiled the water and inserted one lone potato; the smallest at that. He counted out five pecans, added two more, and handed the lot to her. He then got out his pocketknife, opened it, and prodded the bubbling tuber. Judging it soft enough, he neatly speared it out upon a plate. Elspeth pretended a total lack of interest. She hoped she'd have the resolution to decline her half with hauteur. She didn't get the chance.

Peter split the potato, sprinkled on salt, and ate it all.

With difficulty, Elspeth suppressed a roar of rage. That was the kind of man he was, then! Selfish, greedy, mean, tyrannical, unfair, smug, bad-tempered, uncouth—her stock ran thin. How idiotically she had overestimated him! Rough but noble; that had been her formula for his character. And now look at him, pigging down the last delicious fragments while she was to be content with a handful of nuts. Nuts! She rose in regal resentment, flung her seven pecans into the fire, and stalked back to the car.

Somewhere in the vicinity of Emporia, eighty miles north of their breakfast, he spoke. "No good in sulking, you know."

"I'm *not* sulking." Which closed that opening.

Nevertheless, Elspeth was relieved. An oppressive feeling that maybe his anger would prove more lasting than her own had tainted her satisfaction in being the injured party. One solicitude, too, he exhibited. He kept tucking her up in the robe.

This would have been less reassuring had she understood its genesis. He was afraid her costume might be recognized. He even thought of suggesting that she might effect a trade in some secondhand store. In her present state of childish petulance, however, he judged it useless to suggest this. Some other way must be found.

Some money was still left to them. Elspeth saw her companion shaking his head over it when their gas gave out, happily near a filling station. His worried expression weakened her anger, but she couldn't bring herself to admit she was sorry. Not yet.

"There's a cheap camp seventy miles from here," he said. "But if we sleep there we can't have much of a dinner."

"Potatoes," said the recalcitrant Elspeth. She'd teach him!

They dined at a roadside stand which, in ordinary conditions, she would have considered loathsome. Every odor of it now brought prickly sensations to her palate.

The night presented a problem troubling to her mind. No shared but unpartitioned cabin for her! Last night's experience had been too revelatory. What made things difficult was that she had told him she needed no more walls of Jericho to insure peaceful sleep. Now if she asked him to put up the curtain, what would he think?

Pursuant to his policy of avoiding large cities and the possible interest of traffic cops, Peter had planned their route westward again, giving Richmond a wide berth. They flashed without stop through towns with hospitable restaurants only to pull up at a roadside stand of austere menu, near Sweet Briar.

Never had Elspeth seen the important sum of twenty-five cents laid out so economically as by Peter's method. Baked beans with thick, fat, glorious gollups of pork; a half-loaf of bread, and bitter coffee. To say that her hunger was appeased would be overstatement. But a sense of returned well-being comforted her. She even felt that she could face the morning's potato, if any, with courage. Meantime, there remained the arrangements for the night.

Peter handled that decisively, upon their arrival at the camp. Their cabin was dreary, chill, and stoveless. When he brought in the robe from the car, she hoped for it over her bunk. Not at all; out came his little tool kit; up went the separating cord, and over it was firmly pinned the warm fabric.

With a regrettable though feminine want of logic, Elspeth nursed a grievance; he needn't have been at such pains to raise that wall again without a request from the person most interested. She went to sleep crossly but promptly.

In the morning the robe was tucked snugly about her. How long had that been there? She looked around and made a startling discovery. Her clothes were gone. So was Peter. Also, when she looked out, the car. The wild idea occurred to her that he had stolen her outfit and run away, *à la* Thad Banker. One thing was certain: to rise and wander forth clad in those grotesque pajamas was out of the question. Turning over, she fell asleep again.

Some inner sensation of his nearness awoke her, or perhaps it was, less occultly, his footsteps outside, approaching, pausing. She craned upward to bring her vision level with the window. Peter was standing with his side face toward her, a plump bundle beneath his arm. Her clothes, probably, which he had taken out to clean. How nice of him!

He set down his burden and took off his belt. With a knife he slit the stitches in the leather, carefully prying something from beneath the strips. It was a tight-folded bill.

So he had been holding out on her! Keeping her on a gnat's diet. Letting her go hungry while he gorged himself on boiled potato and salt, and gloated over his reserve fund. Beast! This knowledge, too, she would hold back for his ultimate discomfiture. It was a composed and languid voice which responded to his knock on the door.

"Hello! How are you feeling, Elspeth?"

"Very well, thank you. Where have you been?"

"Act two, scene one of matrimonial crisis," chuckled Peter. "Hubby returns early in the morning. Wife demands explanation. Husband is ready with it: 'You'd be surprised.'" There was a distinct trace of nervousness in his bearing.

"Well, surprise me," returned Elspeth, with hardly concealed hostility. She sat up in bed. "Where are my clothes?"

"That's the point. They're—uh—I—er—well, the fact is, I pawned 'em in Charlottesville."

"You—pawned—my—clothes! Where's the money?" If that was the bill in the belt, she proposed to know it.

"I spent most of it. On other clothes. You said your feet hurt you."

"When we were walking. We don't have to walk any more."

"How do you know? We aren't out of the woods yet. And you don't need such a fancy rig, traveling with me. And we do need the little bit extra I picked up on the trade."

Stern and uncompromising was the glare which she directed upon his bundle. "Let me see."

Her immediate reaction to the dingy, shoddy, nondescript outfit he disclosed was an involuntary yip of distress.

"Don't you like 'em?" he asked.

"They're terrible! They're ghastly!"

"The woman said they were serviceable. Put 'em on. I'll wait outside."

It would have taken a sturdier optimism than Peter's to maintain a sun-kissed countenance in the face of the transformation which he presently witnessed. Hardly could he recognize her in that horrid misfit which she was pinning here, adjusting there.

"Hand me the mirror, please."

"Perhaps you'd better not—"

"Will you be so good as to do as I ask?"

"Oh, all *right!*"

She took one long, comprehensive survey and burst into tears.

"Don't, Elspeth," he protested, appalled. "What's the difference? There's no one to see you."

"There's me," she gulped. "And there's you."

"I don't mind." As if he were bearing up courageously under an affliction.

"I'm a *sight*," she wailed. "I'm hideous! Go and get my things back."

"It can't be done."

"I won't go out in these frightful things. I won't. I won't. I *won't!*"

"Who's going to pay the rent if you stay?"

Obtaining no reply to this pertinent inquiry, he sighed and went out. Down the breeze, there presently drifted to Elspeth's nostrils the tang of wood smoke. Her face appeared in the window.

"About those missing potatoes," said she. (How mean she was going to make him feel in a minute!) "Are you interested in knowing what became of them?"

"It doesn't matter. They're gone."

"They're gone where they'll do the most good," she returned with slow impressiveness. "I gave them away."

"Without consulting me?"

"Do I have to consult you about everything I do?"

"We-ell, some people might figure that I had an interest in those potatoes."

"Well, I gave them to a poor old woman who needed them. She was hungry."

"Umph! Feeling sure, I suppose, that your generosity would cost you nothing, as I'd share the remainder with you. Error Number One."

"Peter, I wouldn't have thought anyone could be so des-des-despicable!"

This left him unmoved. "Who was the starving beneficiary? I'll bet it was that old creature with the black bonnet and gold teeth in the bus."

"How did you know?"

"She's the sort you would help. In case you'd like to know, that old hoarder had her bag half full of almond chocolates. I saw her buy 'em at Charleston."

"Hoarder, yourself!" Enraged at the failure of her bombshell, she fell back on her last ammunition. "What did you take out of your belt this morning?"

"Oh, you saw that, did you? Watchful little angel!"

"I'm not! I just happened to see it. A bill. A big one, I'll bet. You had it all the time. And you've starved me and bullied me and made me walk miles and sleep in barns, while you could just as well have—"

"Hired a special train. On ten dollars."

"Ten dollars is a lot of money." (Ideas change.)

"Now, I'll tell you about that ten dollars," said he with cold precision. "It's my backlog. It's the last resort. It's the untouchable. It's the dead line of absolute necessity."

"You needn't touch it on my account." (Just like a nasty-tempered little brat, she told herself.) "Of course, starvation isn't absolute necessity."

"Can you do simple arithmetic?"

110

"Yes. I'm not quite an idiot, even if you do think so, Peter."

"Try this one, then. We've got something over five hundred miles to go. Gas will average us seventeen cents. This old mudcart of Banker's won't do better than twelve miles on a gallon. Now, can any bright little girl in this class tell me how much over that leaves us to eat, sleep and live on, not counting oil, ferry charge and incidentals?"

"I can't. And I don't want to," retorted Elspeth, very dispirited. A long, dull silence enclosed them like a globe. She shattered it. "Peter!"

"What?"

"D'you know why I hate you?"

"I'll bite," said he, wearily. "Why?"

"Because, darn you! you're always right and I'm always wrong. Peter! Peter, dear! A potato, Peter. Please, Peter; one potato. Just one. The littlest. I know I don't deserve it, but—"

"Oh, what's the *use!*" vociferated Peter, throwing up both hands in abject and glad surrender. And that quarrel drifted on the smoke of their fire down to the limbo of things become insignificant, yet never quite to be forgotten.

Two young people, haggard, gaunt, shabby, bluish with the chill of an April storm, drove their battered car aboard the Fort Lee ferry as the boat pulled out. They were sharing a bag of peanuts with the conscientious exactitude of penury: one to you; one to me. Quarter of the way across, both were asleep. At the halfway distance the whistle blared and they woke up.

"We're nearly there," observed the girl without any special enthusiasm.

"Yes," said the man with still less.

A hiatus of some length. "Why didn't you tell me about blacking Corker's boots?"

"What about it?"

"It was on a bet, wasn't it?"

"Yes. In college. I picked the wrong team. If I'd won, the Corker would have typed my theses for the term. What put you on?"

"A telegram from Cork."

"Oh! The one to Bessie Smith that saved our lives in Raleigh?"

She nodded. "Anyway, I knew all the time you weren't a valet," she asserted.

He cocked a mild, derisive eye at her. "You're not building up any

111

rosy picture of me as a perfect gentleman, are you?"

"No-o. I don't know what you are."

"Don't let it worry you. Go back to sleep."

"You're always telling me to go to sleep," she muttered discontentedly. She rubbed her nose on his shoulder. "Peter."

He sighed and kissed her.

"You needn't be so solemn about it."

"I'm not feeling exactly sprightly."

"Because we're almost home? But we'll be seeing each other soon."

"I thought that headliner of the air was waiting to fly you somewhere."

"Who? Oh-h-h-h, King." She began to laugh. "Isn't that funny! I'd absolutely forgotten about King. He doesn't matter. When am I going to see you?" As he made no reply, she became vaguely alarmed. . . . "You're not going right back?"

"No. I've got that possible contract to look after. Down in Jersey."

"But you'll be in town again. And I'll see you then."

"No."

"Peter! Why not?"

"Self-preservation," he proclaimed oracularly, "is the first law of nature."

"You don't want to see me again?"

"Put it any way you like," came the broad-minded permission, "just so the main point gets across."

"But I think that's absolutely lousy!" Another point occurred to her. "There's no reason why you shouldn't if it's because—well, that business about my being married was a good deal exaggerated. If that makes any difference."

"It does. It makes it worse."

"Oh! . . . You don't seem surprised, though."

"Me? I should say not! I've known from the first that was all bunk."

"Have you, Smarty? How?"

"You tried to put it over that you'd been wearing a wedding ring. But there was no band of white on the tan of your finger."

"Deteckative! I haven't had a bit of luck trying to fool you about anything, have I, Peter? Not even putting across the superior-goddess idea. And now you're the one that's being snooty."

"I'm not. I'm being sensible. See here, Elspeth. It may or may not have been called to your attention that you're a not wholly unattractive young person—and that I myself am not yet beyond the age of—"

"Consent," broke in the irrepressible Elspeth.

"—damfoolishness," substituted Peter, with severity. "So," he concluded, with an effect of logic, "we may as well call it a day."

"Not to mention several nights." She turned the brilliance of mirthful eyes upon him. "Wouldn't it be funny if you fell in love with me, Peter?"

"Funny for the spectators. Painful for the bear."

"Then don't mention it, Bear!" Another idea occurred to her. "How much money have you got left?"

"Forty-odd cents."

"Now that you're in New York you can get more, of course."

"Yes? Where?"

"At the bank, I suppose. Where does one get money?"

"That's what I've always wanted to know," he grinned.

"I can get all I want tomorrow. I'll lend you a hundred dollars. Or more if you want it."

"No; thank you."

"But I borrowed yours!" she cried. "At least, you paid for me."

"That's different."

"I don't see how." Of course she did see, and inwardly approved. "But—but I owe you money!" she cried. "I'd forgotten all about that. You'll let me pay that back, of course."

If she expected him to deprecate politely the idea she was swiftly undeceived. "The sooner, the better," said Peter cheerfully.

"I'll bet you've got it all set down in that precious notebook of yours."

"Every cent." He tore out a leaf which he handed to her.

"Where can I send it?"

He gave her an address on a street whose name she had never before heard; Darrow, or Barrow, or some such matter.

In the splendor of the great circular court off Park Avenue, the bedraggled automobile looked impudently out of place. The doorkeeper almost choked with amazement as the luxurious Miss Elspeth Andrews, clad in such garments as had never before affronted those august portals, jumped out, absently responding to his greeting.

"I think your father is expecting you, miss," said he.

"Oh, Lord!" exclaimed Elspeth. "Now, what brought him here?"

Peter could have told her, but didn't. He was looking straight

113

through the windshield. She was looking at him with slightly lifted brows.

"Good-bye, Elspeth," said he huskily.

"Good-bye, Peter. You've been awfully mean to me. I've loved it."

Why, thought Peter as he went on his way, did she have to use that particular word in that special tone at that unhappy moment?

Between Alexander Bruce MacGregor Andrews and his daughter, Elspeth, there existed a lively and irritable affection of precarious status, based upon a fundamental similarity of character and a prevalent lack of mutual understanding. That she should have willfully run away from home and got herself and him on the front pages of the papers, seemed to him an outrage of the first order.

"But it was your smearing the thing all over the air that got us into the papers," pointed out Elspeth, which didn't help much as a contribution to the *entente cordiale*. Both sulked for forty-eight hours.

Meantime, there arrived by special delivery a decidedly humid shoe-box addressed in an uncompromisingly straight-up-and-down hand— just exactly the kind one would expect, thought the girl, knowing whose it was at first sight—full of the freshest, most odorous bunch of arbutus she had ever beheld. Something about it unmistakably defined it as having been picked by the sender.

Elspeth searched minutely for a note; there was none. She carried the box to her room and threw three clusters of orchids and a spray of gardenias into the scrapbasket. After that she went to a five-and-ten-cent store, made a purchase at the toy counter, had it boxed, and herself mailed it to the address given her by Peter Warne. The shipment did not include the money she owed him. That detail had escaped her mind.

"Scotty, dear." She greeted her father in the style of their companionable moods. "Do let's be sensible."

Mr. Andrews grunted suspiciously. "Suppose you begin."

"I'm going to. Drink your cocktail first." She settled down on the arm of his chair.

"Now what devilment are you up to?" demanded the apprehensive parent.

"Not a thing. I've decided to tell you about my trip."

Having her narrative all duly mapped out, she ran through it smoothly enough, hoping that he would not notice a few cleverly glossed passages. Disapproval in the paternal expression presently yielded to amused astonishment.

"Nervy kid!" he chuckled. "I'll bet it did you good."

"It didn't do me any harm. And I certainly found out a few things I'd never known before."

"Broadening effect of travel. Who did you say this young man was that looked after you?"

"I'm coming to that. The question is, what are you going to do for him?"

"What does he want?"

"I don't know that he exactly wants anything. But he's terribly poor, Scotty. Why, just think! He had to reckon up each time how much he could afford to spend on a meal!"

"Yes? I'm told there are quite a few people in this country in the same fix," observed Mr. Andrews dryly. "How much'll I make out the check for?"

"That's the trouble. I don't believe he'd take it. He's one of those inde-be-goshdarn-pendent birds. Wouldn't listen to my lending him some money."

"Humph! That probably means he's fallen for your fair young charms. Be funny if he hadn't."

"I'll tell you what would be funnier."

"What?"

"If I'd fallen for him," was the brazen response.

"Poof! You're always imagining you're in love with the newest hero in sight. Remember that young Danish diplo—"

"Yes; I do. What of it? I always get over it, don't I? And I'll get over this. You'd think he was terrible, Dad. He's sure rough. You ought to have seen Little Daughter being bossed around by him and taking it."

"Is that so?" said her father, spacing his words sardonically. "Bossed you, did he? He and who else?"

"Oh, Peter doesn't need any help."

The grin was wiped off the Andrews face. "Who?"

"Peter. That's his name. Peter Warne."

"*What?*"

"Gracious! Don't yell so. Do you know him?"

"I haven't that pleasure as yet. Just let me make sure about this." He went into the adjoining room, whence he emerged with a sheaf of papers. "Peter Warne. So he's poor, is he?"

"Desperately."

"Well, he won't be, after tomorrow."

"Oh, Scotty! How do you know? Is he going to get some money? I'm so glad!"

"Some money is correct. Ten thousand dollars, to be exact."

"From his tar-pine or something process? How did *you* know about it?"

"From me. I don't know anything about—"

"From you?" Her lips parted; her eyes were wide and alarmed. "What for?"

"Information leading to the discovery and return of Elspeth, daughter of—"

"The reward? For me? Peter? I don't believe it. Peter wouldn't do such a thing. Take money for—"

"He has done it. Put in his claim for the reward. Do you want to see the proof?"

"I wouldn't believe it anyway."

Alexander Andrews studied her defiant face with a concern that became graver. This looked serious. Selecting a letter and a telegram from his dossier, he put them into her reluctant hand. At sight of the writing her heart sank. It was unmistakably that of the address on the box of arbutus. The note cited the writer's telegram of the fourteenth ("That's the day after we got off the island," thought Elspeth. "He was selling me out then.") and asked for an appointment.

"He's coming to my office at ten-thirty Thursday morning."

"Are you going to give him the money?"

"It looks as if I'd have to."

"He certainly worked hard enough for it," she said bitterly. "And I expect he needs it."

"I might be able to work a compromise," mused the canny Scot. "Though I'm afraid he's got the material for a bothersome lawsuit. If any of the other claimants"—he indicated the sheaf of letters and telegrams—"had a decent case, we could set off one against the other. The most insistent is a person named Shapley."

"Don't let him have it," said the girl hastily. "I'd rather Peter should get it, though I'd never have believed— Sold down the river!" She forced a laugh. "I brought a price, anyway."

"I've a good mind to give him a fight for it. It would mean more

116

publicity, though."

"Oh, no!" breathed Elspeth.

"Enough's enough, eh? Though it couldn't be worse than what we've had."

"It could. Much worse. If you're going to see Pe—Mr. Warne, I'd better tell you something, Father. I've been traveling as Mrs. Peter Warne."

"Elspeth!"

"It isn't what you think. Purely economy—with the accent on the 'pure.' But it wouldn't look pretty in print. Oh, damn!" Her voice broke treacherously. "I thought Peter was so straight."

Her father walked up and down the room several times. He then went over and put his arm around his daughter's shoulders. "It's all right, dawtie. We'll get you out of it. And we'll find a way to keep this fellow's mouth shut. I'm having a detectaphone set up in my office, and if he makes one slip we'll have him by the short hairs for blackmail."

"Peter doesn't make slips," returned his daughter. "It's his specialty not to. Oh, well, let's go in to dinner, Scotty."

Resolutely, she put the arbutus out of her room when she went up to bed that night. But the spicy odor from far springtime woodlands clung about the place like a plea for the absent.

Stern logic of the morning to which she sorrowfully awoke filled in the case against Peter. Nevertheless and notwithstanding, "I don't believe it," said Elspeth's sore heart. "And I won't believe it until—until—"

Severe as were the fittings of Mr. Alexander Bruce MacGregor Andrews' spacious office, they were less so than the glare which apprised Peter Warne, upon his entry, that this spare, square man did not like him and probably never would. That was all right with Peter. He was prepared not to like Mr. Andrews, either. On this propitious basis the two confronted each other.

After a formidable silence which the younger man bore without visible evidence of discomposure, his host barked:

"Sit down."

"Thank you," said Peter. He sat down.

"You have come about the money, I assume."

"Yes."

117

"Kindly reduce your claim to writing."

"You'll find it there." He handed over a sheet of paper. "Itemized."

"What's this?" Mr. Andrews' surprised eye ran over it.

"Traveling expenses. Elsp—your daughter's."

The father gave the column of figures his analytical attention. "Boat, twenty dollars," he read. "You didn't take my daughter to Cuba, did you?"

"I had to steal a boat to get through the flood. The owner ought to be reimbursed. If you think that's not a fair charge, I'll assume half of it. Everything else is split."

"Humph! My daughter's share of food, lodging and gasoline, excluding the—er—alleged boat, seems to figure up to eighteen dollars and fifty-six cents. Where did you lodge?"

"Wherever we could."

With the paper before him, Mr. Andrews began to hammer his desk. "You have the temerity, the impudence, the effrontery, the—the—anyway, you come here to hold me up for ten thousand dollars and on top of that you try to spring a doctored expense account on me!"

"Doctored!" echoed Peter. "Maybe you think you could do it for less?"

Taken aback, Mr. Andrews ceased his operations on the desk. "We'll pass that for the main point," he grunted. "Upon what do you base your claim for the ten thousand dollars?"

"Nothing," was the placid reply. "I made no claim."

"Your telegram. Your letter—"

"You couldn't have read them. I simply warned you against paying anybody else's claim. You had others, I suppose."

"Others! A couple of hundred!"

"One signed Horace Shapley?"

"I believe so."

"I don't like him," observed Peter, and explained.

"Then your idea," interposed Mr. Andrews, "was to get in first merely to block off this other person. Is that it?"

"Yes."

"And you aren't claiming any part of the reward?"

"No."

"You're crazy," declared the other. "Or maybe I am. What *do* you want?"

118

Peter gently indicated the expense account. Mr. Andrews went over it again.

"You mean to tell me that you kept my daughter for five days and more on a total of eighteen dollars and fifty-six cents?"

"There are the figures."

Mr. Andrews leaned forward. "Did she kick much?"

Peter's grin was a bit rueful. "There were times when—"

"You'd have liked to sock her. I know. Why didn't you present your bill to her?"

"I did. I reckon she just forgot it."

"She would! . . . Have a cigar." As the young fellow lighted up, his entertainer was writing and entering a check.

"As a matter of correct business, I ought to have Elspeth's O.K. on this bill. However, I'll pass it, including the boat. Receipt here, please." The amount was $1,038.56.

Shaking his head, Peter pushed the check across the desk. "Thank you, but I can't take this, Mr. Andrews."

"Bosh! Elspeth told me you were broke."

"I am . . . No; I'm not, either. I forgot. I've just made a deal on a new process of mine. Anyway, I couldn't take that—that bonus."

"That's funny. If you're no longer broke, I should think you'd be above bringing me a trifling expense account for—er—entertaining my daughter."

"It's a matter of principle," returned Peter firmly.

Mr. Andrews rose and smote his caller on the shoulder. "I begin to see how you made that little spitfire of mine toe the mark. More than I've been able to do for the past ten years. Eighteen dollars and fifty-six cents, huh?" He sank back in his chair and laughed. "See here, my boy; I like you. I like your style. Will you take that money as a present from me?"

"Sorry, sir, but I'd rather not."

The older man stared him down. "Because I'm Elspeth's father, eh? You're in love with her, I suppose."

Peter grew painfully red. "God forbid!" he muttered.

"What do you mean, God forbid?" shouted the magnate. "Better men than you have been in love with her."

"All right, Mr. Andrews," said Peter in desperation. "Then I am, too. I have been from the first. Now, you tell me—you're her father —what's the sense of it with a girl like Elspeth? I'm going back to

Florida with a contract for eight thousand a year, to complete my process."

"That's more than I was making at your age."

"It's more than I expect to be making at yours," said Peter with candor. "But how far would that go with her? Look me over, sir. Even if I had a chance with Elspeth, would you advise a fellow like me to try to marry her?"

"No, I wouldn't!" roared the father. "You're too darn good for her."

"Don't talk like a fool," snapped Peter.

"Just for that," reflected Mr. Andrews as his caller withdrew, jamming a substituted check into his pocket, "I'll bet you'll have little enough to say about it when the time comes."

He sent for Elspeth and left her alone with the detectaphone. What that unpoetic cylinder spouted forth rang in her heart like the music of the spheres with the morning and evening stars in the solo parts. So *that* was how Peter felt about it.

Memory obligingly supplied the number on Darrow or Farrow or Barrow or whatever strange street it was. The taxi man whom she hailed earned her admiration by knowing all about it.

Peter said: "Come in," in a spiritless manner. With a totally different vocal effect he added: "What are *you* doing *here?*" and tacked onto that "You oughtn't to be here at all."

"Why not?" Elspeth sat down.

He muttered something wherein the word "proper" seemed to carry the emphasis, and in which the term "landlady" occurred.

"Proper!" jeered his visitor. "You talk to me about propriety after we've been traveling together and sharing the same room for nearly a week!"

"But this is New York," he pointed out.

"And you're packing up to leave it. When?"

"Tonight."

"Without the ten thousand dollar reward?"

"How did you know about that? Your fath—"

"I've just come from his office. You might better have taken the check."

"Don't want it."

"That's silly. What," she inquired reasonably, "have you got to get married on?"

"Eight thousand a ye—I'm not going to get married," he inter-

120

rupted himself with needless force.

"Not after compromising a young and innocent—"

"I haven't compromised anyone." Sulkily and doggedly.

"Peter! I suppose registering me as your wife all over the map isn't compromising. Did you ever hear of the Mann Act?"

"B-b-b-but—"

"Yes; I know all about that 'but.' It's a great big, important 'but,' but there's another bigger 'but' to be considered. We know what happened and didn't happen on our trip, *but* nobody else would ever believe it in this world. I certainly wouldn't."

"Nor I," he agreed. "Unless," he qualified hastily, "the girl was you."

"Or the man was you."

They laughed with dubious heartiness. When they had done laughing, there seemed to be nothing to follow, logically. Elspeth got up slowly.

"Where are you going?" demanded Peter, in a panic.

"If you don't like me any more"—she put the slightest possible stress on the verb, leaving him to amend it if he chose—"I'm sorry I came."

To this rueful observation, Peter offered no response.

"You did like me once, you know. You as much as admitted it."

Peter swore.

"Did you or did you not tell my father that you would never get over it?"

"It?"

"Well—me."

"Your father," said Peter wrathfully, "is a human sieve."

"No; he isn't. There was a detectaphone listening in on everything you said. I got it all from that."

"In that case," said the now desperate and reckless Peter, "I may as well get it off my chest." And he repeated what he had earlier said about his feelings, with a fervor that wiped the mischief from Elspeth's face.

"Oh-h-h-h!" she murmured, a little dazed. "That's the way you feel."

"No, it isn't. It isn't half of it."

"Where do we go from here?" thought the girl. The atmosphere of sprightly combat and adventure had changed. She was not breathing quite so easily. Her uncertain look fell upon an object at the top of

121

the half-packed carryall. "Oh!" she exclaimed. "You got my present."

"Yes; I got it."

"I hope you liked it." Politely.

"Not particularly."

Her eyes widened. "Why not?"

"Well, I may be oversensitive where you're concerned, but I don't care so much about being called a tinhorn sport, because—well, I don't know, but I suppose it's because I let you pay back the money for our trip," he concluded morosely.

The girl was looking at him with a mixture of contempt, amusement, pity, and something stronger than any of these. "Oh, you boob!" she breathed. "That isn't a tinhorn. That's a trumpet."

"A *trumpet?*"

"The kind What's-his-name blew before the walls of Jericho, if you have to have a diagram. Oh, *Pee*-ter; you're such a dodo!" sighed Elspeth. "What am I ever going to do about you? Would you like to kiss me, Peter?"

"Yes," said Peter. And he did.

"This means," he informed her presently, and dubiously, "our having to live in a Florida swamp—"

"On eighteen dollars and fifty-six cents?"

"On eight thousand a year. That isn't much more, to you. You'll hate it."

"I'll love it. D'you know where I'd like to land on our wedding trip, Peter?"

"Yes. Dake's Two-dollar Cabins; Clean; Comfortable; Reasonable."

"*And* respectable. You're too clever, Peter, darling."

"Because that's exactly what I'd like. Social note: Mr. and Mrs. Peter Warne are stopping in Jaw-jaw on their return trip South."

"Let's go," said Elspeth joyously.

Mrs. Dake, in the wing off the tourist-camp office, yawned herself awake of an early May morning and addressed her husband. "That's a funny couple in Number Seven, Tim. Do you reckon they're respectable?"

"I should worry. They registered all right, didn't they?"

"Uh-huh. Wouldn't take any other cabin but Seven. And wanted an extra blanket. This hot night."

"Well, we could spare it."

"That isn't the only queer thing about 'em. After you was asleep, I looked out and there was the young fellah mopin' around. By and by he went in, and right soon somebody blew a horn. Just as plain as you ever heard. What do you think about that, Tim?"

Mr. Dake yawned. "What they do after they're registered and paid up is their business, not our'n."

Which is the proper and practical attitude for the management of a well-conducted tourist camp.

May Night

Adelaide Love

Speak only of our love tonight;
Let all the problems be
Of books and art, of wrong and right,
Of wars and destiny.

There will be time enough to come
In which to solve each thing;
For souls there is millennium,
For lips this night of spring!

Poem in Prose

Archibald MacLeish

This poem is for my wife
I have made it plainly and honestly
The mark is in it
Like the burl on the knife

I have not made it for praise
She has no more need for praise
Than summer has
On the bright days

123

In all that becomes a woman
Her words and her ways are wonderful
Love's lovely duty
The well-swept room

Wherever she is there is sun
And time and a sweet air
Peace is there
Work done

There are always curtains and flowers
And candles and baked bread
And a cloth spread
And a clean house

Her voice when she sings is a voice
At dawn by a freshening sea
Where the wave leaps in the
Wind and rejoices

Wherever she is it is now
It is here where the apples are
Here in the stars
In the quick hour

The greatest and richest good—
My own life to live—
This she has given me

If giver could

Simple Life

Rose Franken

Young married love pictured realistically, humorously, yet tenderly. Rose Franken has achieved tremendous popularity with her well-loved books, her play and her films about Claudia. Here is a story that is a favorite with many.

THE new maid got off the train and looked like a halibut. Claudia's heart sank. She would have preferred her to look like almost anything but a halibut. A bulldog, an anteater, a horse—a horse would have been fine—but not a halibut.

"I'm Mrs. Naughton," Claudia introduced herself.

Hardly anybody ever believed she was old enough to be a married woman, but the new maid registered neither surprise nor interest in the fact that her prospective mistress was not a middle-aged lady with the beginnings of a double chin.

"What's your name?" Claudia pursued, as she led the way to the car.

"Emma Kastey."

The girl's voice was faint and watery, just as a fish might talk if a fish talked, and her shoulder sagged bonelessly beneath the weight of the straw valise. Claudia couldn't help feeling a little disappointed. She had never engaged anyone sight unseen before, and waiting for the train had been rather exciting, particularly since the agency had given such a glowing account of Emma's unusual capabilities. "She sounds marvelous, we're in luck," Claudia had exulted to David that morning. "I bet we have finger bowls at every meal."

"I'd rather have good coffee at every meal," said David, who felt that bad coffee—or no coffee—was the basis of many unhappy marriages. "We haven't had a decent cup of coffee since Bertha," he added gloomily.

"Bertha was a joy," Claudia readily conceded. But Bertha was not the sort of servant to complement the remodeled perfection of the salt-box house. Secretly, Claudia dreamed of a trim, beautifully trained maid in a pastel uniform, and although she hadn't found one up to date, she had a feeling that the Elite Agency was going to send her the answer to that dream.

"Did you ever live on a farm?" she queried, as she moved the grocery bundles aside in order to make room on the front seat.

"Not on a farm," said Emma, with no expression whatsoever.

Claudia pondered the possibilities implied in the provocative rejoinder.

"Where *did* you live?" she invited brightly.

"For a Mrs. Morris," said Emma, looking vague.

Claudia tried to bear in mind that David, who had known Coolidge personally, had often told her what a wonderful person he was underneath—very dynamic and strong, although you'd never have suspected it. Perhaps the Halibut was the same type as Coolidge. Claudia drew a deep breath and began all over again.

"Where, for a Mrs. Morris?"

"Flatbush."

"Oh."

Claudia felt let down. Flatbush was probably as good as any place and the Morrises might have been a wonderful family, but they sounded like children and paper napkins. Not that she objected to paper napkins, and children were all to the good, but she had rather set her heart on one-plate-at-a-time service, for Julia was stopping off for lunch the following day on one of her chronic trips to Boston.

It was funny how Julia always roused in Claudia a slightly competitive spirit. David said he couldn't understand it, for Claudia's values were pretty straight, but Claudia said not to worry about it, it was perfectly natural for in-laws to feel that way about each other and had nothing to do with anybody's real character.

Now, brooding doubtfully upon the fresh shrimps she had just bought as the main luncheon dish, Claudia wondered whether the Halibut had ever ventured very far afield from steaks and chops.

"This is different from Flatbush," she judiciously gave warning.

Emma made no reply.

"A lot more lovely," ended Claudia lamely, waving her hand toward the bleak countryside fanning past. (Pretty pretty garbage to carry

126

out to the incinerator every day, and butter to churn, and milk pails to clean, she inwardly elaborated.)

Emma continued to say nothing. Her silence made Claudia nervous. "We're almost there," she offered hastily, and stepped on the gas so that the last five miles might seem as nothing.

As they neared the house she felt that she must, at any cost, clear up certain major issues that would have to be faced sooner or later. As a matter of fact, there was a small mountain of rompers and bibs awaiting Emma's immediate arrival. "I suppose," she essayed in her most casual voice, "that the agency told you about laundry?"

"They said light wash," the Halibut specified feebly but firmly.

Claudia debated the moot point of whether Bobby's frequent change of linen—black of knee and soggy of bosom—could justly be classed in the category of light wash. She glanced at the Halibut's face, which had settled into a mask of obdurate inactivity, and decided to let well enough alone. Perhaps Emma would become so devoted to Bobby—as Bertha had been—that nothing would be too much for her. "It's mostly just the baby's few little things," she murmured. "Do you like babies?"

Emma gave an imperceptible shrug. "I don't mind them," she said without enthusiasm.

Claudia's heart lifted. At least Emma didn't mind them, which was a relief after Sophie and Annie-before-Sophie. She would probably prove quite satisfactory after all. True, she didn't have much magnetism, but it was just as well, because there was no sense in having a lot of magnetism when you couldn't go out nights anyway. Magnetism, or something like it, had been the trouble with Katie.

Abruptly they came upon the house, sitting like a small surprise in the lap of the bend. Claudia always found it difficult to realize that it was the same crude tumbledown building that she had looked at on that raw March day less than a year ago. Yes, David and Roger had been right. Beauty dwelt in its simple ancient dignity, but who, except a brace of architects, could have suspected it? And who besides a seasoned veteran, could have lived through those grueling months of restoration, when the carpenters didn't show up during fishing season, and the plumbers went to the town meeting, and the stonemasons threw down their trowels every now and again to maintain their social standing on the relief rolls. Claudia tore her hair out. But David told her it wouldn't get her anywhere. "It's New England," he summed up philosophically.

At long last, many weeks after the glib finishing date set by the contractor, the workmen gathered up their tools and left the Naughtons to a paradise of exquisite peace and order. Claudia missed them, "Like a toothache," she amended. Still, she missed them and she was always touched when, on Sundays, they drove past with their wives or sweethearts and slowed up before the gate, with a proprietary air. Sometimes, utter strangers also stopped to look. David always raised a howl and threatened to use a shotgun on them. "Those blasted busybodies!" he'd cry, just as if he meant it. "Go on," Claudia would nudge him wickedly, "you know you love it, invite them in, show them around, offer them a cigar."

She was so used to having people rave about the place, that she expected the Halibut to at least change her expression as the car drew to a stop in the driveway. By this time she'd resigned herself to the fact that Emma wasn't the sort to go into convulsions of joy over anything on earth, but certainly the picture-book quality of the salt-box house should have elicited some faint reaction.

"It's nice, isn't it?" she prompted.

The Halibut glanced out of the window. Her opinion was to remain an eternal mystery in Claudia's life, for at that instant Emma froze in terror and she uttered a shrill scream for help, as Bluff and Bluster dashed to the running board in welcome, and raked at the glass with their Gargantuan paws. "What are they?" she gasped.

"Only dogs," said Claudia, which was somewhat of an understatement, for Bluff and Bluster were probably the biggest and most ferocious-looking great Danes in existence. Claudia, herself, had approached them with considerable trepidation the night David had brought them home, but he had explained that they were probably a great deal more frightened of her than she was of them. "Danes are very sensitive," he cautioned her. "Never speak loudly to them, or make any sudden move to startle them."

"I won't," Claudia had promised. "I'll be very gentle."

Fortunately, no one in Eastbrook suspected that the dogs were sissies, and David said it wasn't necessary to carry burglar insurance, or to worry about the baby being kidnaped. Only last week, however, a tree surgeon from Redbury came very near guessing the truth. Having discovered that he remained quite unscarred after the vicious hullabaloos that attended his previous visits, he slyly inquired why the dogs were named as they were. It was a Saturday and David happened to be at home. David didn't like the tree surgeon, who had thrown Claudia into a panic by intimating that all their priceless old maples would languish if not braced and filled and pruned at once.

"What's wrong with the names Buff and Buster?" David belligerently demanded.

"Oh," the tree surgeon apologized, "I thought it was Bluff and Bluster."

"You thought wrong," said David shortly. He whistled to them. "Hi, Bluff, Hi, Bluster!" he called and walked off to the barn with the dogs prancing at his heels.

The tree surgeon turned to Claudia with a bewildered shrug. Claudia blushed. "My husband's a Chinaman," she murmured, and the tree surgeon took to his heels and was never heard from again.

Expediency as well as pride constrained them to foster the legend of ferocity, but in the case of the Halibut, Claudia knew that at this point, a false front might prove fatal. "Don't be upset," she shouted above the volley of barking, "they just like to make believe they're fierce, but they wouldn't hurt a fly."

Emma, however, didn't believe the story for an instant and sidled fearfully into the house, glued to Claudia's side. It was unfortunate that Shakespeare should have chosen the very moment of their entrance to pull his tiger act. From an unseen vantage point of the kitchen window sill, he leapt through the air and landed with a heavy plop at the newcomer's feet.

Emma shrieked, dropping her suitcase.

"It's only the cat," Claudia hastened to explain.

Emma didn't like cats, but Shakespeare didn't know it. He edged his beautiful supple body against her legs and with a deft paw, plucked a single thread of her stocking and started a runner.

"Oh, I'm terribly sorry," Claudia murmured in abject apology.

Emma said nothing. She stood in the middle of the blue-and-white tiled floor, looking more than ever like a halibut, with her heavy lips an inverted arc of unvoiced disapproval.

"It's a lovely kitchen, everything so nice and clean and modern," Claudia pointed out encouragingly.

Emma continued to say nothing.

"I'll show you to your room," Claudia went on. "We built on this ell and it's a lovely room with three exposures."

She moved invitingly toward a small passageway leading from the pantry, but Emma made no pretense of following. Her flaccid face developed unsuspected planes of firm decision. She picked up her suitcase.

"I don't like the place," she stated with flat finality. "I wouldn't stay."

Claudia called for David on the 6:14, reluctantly leaving Bobby to the care of a neighboring schoolgirl. "How is she?" he asked elliptically, the first thing after he kissed her.

"Simply marvelous," Claudia returned out of the welling bitterness in her heart.

"That's a break.—Move," he said, and shoved her along to the other end of the seat.

Her anger flared. "What's the matter, doesn't my driving suit you?"

"Nope," he admitted pleasantly.

The tears came. She had been trying to hold them back for the last hour, but now they came, running down her cheeks and flooding her voice. "That's the most unjust thing I ever heard of. Just because I got one little ticket and banged one little fender, you keep making remarks about it and I won't stand for it!"

He stared at her and then turned off the ignition. "What's the matter, darling?" he said gently. "Didn't she come?"

Claudia nodded and gulped. "She's gone."

It was too fast for him. "You mean she never showed up?"

"I said she's gone," Claudia reiterated shrilly. "She came and she didn't like it and she's gone, and you should have married someone who could manage servants and run your house and drive your car."

He took her in his arms and held her just like she always held Bobby when he bumped his head. He gave her his handkerchief.

She mumbled, "Everybody can see us."

He said, "Let them, who cares?—Look, darling, cheer up, she couldn't have been much good anyway."

"She looked like a fish," sobbed Claudia.

"Well, then," he placated her, drying her eyes with his handkerchief. "You certainly wouldn't have wanted her.—Blow. That's a good girl."

He was simply darling and did his best to help her with supper, only he wasn't a very good help. She asked him to open a can of tomatoes, but instead of doing it, he discovered that the automatic opener lacked a screw. "What damn fool," he demanded furiously, "used this for a hammer?"

"Nobody used it for a hammer. If you don't mind, I'm waiting for the tomatoes."

He said something uncomplimentary about females not having any mechanical ability, opened the can and then got under her feet while he looked for the screw.

"Listen," she suggested with veiled irony, wanting to kill two birds with one stone, "how about getting out of the kitchen? Take Bobby's supper upstairs and feed him for me."

She should have known better. Bobby was at an age where he wouldn't swallow what he didn't like. David shortly reappeared with blazing eyes and practically the whole dish of cereal on his coat. He was also full of theories on child training.

"Oh, hush up," said Claudia, under her breath.

"—And don't help me with the dishes for heaven's sake," she anticipated him after supper.

He wasn't in the least offended. "All right," he said, "I'll go out and take a look at the cow, if you're sure you don't need me."

She said, "I was never so sure of anything in all my life."

The dogs, whom she had banished from the kitchen, were waiting for him outside the door. She could hear his voice rising loud and full above the frenzy of their greeting. "Wouldn't the boss let you in? Oh, the bad woman. Good old Bluffy! Good old Bluster!" She wondered if he knew how silly he sounded, more like a half-wit than a grown man. She loved him when he acted that way.

Through the window, as she stacked the dishes, she saw the light go up in the barn and hang like a jewel in the dead winter blackness. It gave her suddenly the same sort of lost and lonely feeling as the scream of a train whistle sounding through the night. It made her want David to come quickly back to her. It made her want to run upstairs to look at Bobby, fast asleep in bed. It made her want to telephone her mother in New York. She thought, "Maybe I just don't like living in the country—"

The knowledge came as a shock to her. She was no better, really, than Annie or Sophie or even Emma. They all had the same thing in common—they couldn't face the solitude and the vastness.

By the time David returned, her nerves were on edge. His cheek was cool against her hot one and there was the lingering odor of barn and dogs about him.

"Nothing doing with the cow," he said, pulling off his jacket.

131

He felt the radiator. "Not any too much heat. I'd better have a look at the furnace." He departed, whistling, to the cellar.

"He doesn't mind anything he does around the place," thought Claudia. He didn't mind feeding the stock, or sweeping off the paths, or cleaning out the chicken coops. Although they had a farmer down the road come in to do the milking and the chores, he was drunk more often than not and, during ducking season, scarcely showed up at all. David wanted to find someone else, but the community offered very little that was better in the way of hired help. "Don't worry about it," he told Claudia. "I can get home earlier, nights, and do the job myself, particularly since the cow's gone dry."

He had spent summers on his grandfather's farm and knew things that were Greek to Claudia, who had been brought up to regard with closed eyes the basic functions of the animal kingdom. It was still a source of wonder to her how he had known the proper time to have the cow bred. "A little birdie told me," he informed her gravely.

As a matter of fact, she was only vaguely interested in the life that lay outside the house. There was too much to keep her busy indoors.

Tonight, as she lay in bed, she wondered how on earth she could plow through the thousand and one things that had to be done before Julia's arrival the next morning. Julia hadn't seen the house since it was finished. She had driven up once, with Hartley, while it was still in the process of construction, with no doors hung anywhere at all, which was a great disadvantage, especially to visitors who had come a long distance. Hartley had said, looking all around the garden and the new fences, and the copper piping that was going in, "This is great. Put your money in the ground. But—" he had amended knowingly, "don't put too much in. A couple of years and you'll be back in New York like the rest of them."

"Never!" Claudia and David had cried in a single breath. And indeed it had been wonderful in the beginning. She would never forget the day that David scythed the meadow, with his shirt off, and came in to lunch looking and smelling like a hired man out of a book. She'd fallen in love with him all over again. "Darling," she'd marveled, putting her arms around him, "you're so wonderfully sweaty." It was a very special, very stirring kind of sweat and had given her exactly the same feeling as the first time she'd watched him bathe the baby. "I adore it here," she'd breathed out of the fullness of her heart.

"Glad we bought the place?" His voice was almost as husky as hers.

"Oh, but am I," she'd whispered back. "Are you?"

"You bet," he'd whispered in return.

She had often looked back to that day, trying to recapture the simple flowing rhythm of existence. She had lost it, somehow. Life had become complicated all at once and everything seemed to go wrong. The roof leaked, the rhododendrons lost their leaves in a blight and the cow developed pneumonia, for which the veterinary came four times at ten dollars a visit. A day or so later, Bobby broke out with the mumps, but the local doctor only charged three dollars a visit which was a vague source of disgruntlement to Claudia. "You could pay him ten dollars a visit, too, if it would make you feel any better," David mildly proposed.

"That's not the point," Claudia had argued hotly. "I actually think you're more concerned for Louella than for your own child."

"Louella's a swell cow," said David.

Claudia made no reply. She was grateful, of course, for all the milk and cream and butter—and also for the not inconsiderable by-product of lovely roses—but when Louella went dry on account of the calf that was soon to be born, it was heavenly simple just to buy two quarts of milk every day from the grocery store. "What's the matter?" David had demanded suspiciously. "Don't you like having your own dairy products?"

She had wanted suddenly to cry out, "No, I don't, it's a terrible damned nuisance," but she couldn't bear to hurt him. She had sensed that it satisfied some deep need within him to know that he and the land were friends, and that he could work it and, in return, it would nourish and protect him. "I love having our own dairy products," she had answered gently, but in her heart she wept, for she was aware that she had always lied to him, a little, about the way she really felt about the place.

For a while, she had almost fooled herself into believing that it meant as much to her as it did to him. But now the lie was catching up with her and there was no ease within her. She was just like a hundred other housewives—ridden with servant trouble and her nails a mess. She wondered how David always managed to be so philosophical about everything—unless, of course, something like the can opener made him mad, or the way she drove the car.

He heard her tossing restlessly beside him. "What's the matter, can't you sleep?"

"I am asleep," she answered.

By half past eleven the next morning, the house literally sparkled with cleanliness and luncheon stood ready on the stove. "I'm amazing," she thought modestly. "I wonder how I did it."

It was lucky that shrimp curry stretched, because Julia brought a friend with her—Carra Beritza, the opera singer. Claudia had met her at Julia's once or twice, and remembered the enormous brown eyes in the small sallow face. Her hat was enormous, too, which made her seem even tinier than she really was. She had a helpless childlike air and, when she met people, she always looked as if she were going to kiss them, but didn't.

"Is it not naughty of me to come without an invitation?" she begged Claudia's forgiveness. "I am giving a concert in Boston thees evening so I am clever and say to Jooliaa, 'Jooliaa, I want a heetch.'"

"I'm glad you didn't," Claudia murmured, wondering how to divide one single grapefruit into three.

"Claudia, I love it," Julia interrupted in her brusque, distinguished manner. "This living room is charming, utterly charming!"

Claudia forgot the grapefruit. "Do you really think so?"

"Oh, but yes, eet is enchanting!" cried Beritza, with one of her enormous gestures.

"I must see everything from kitchen to attic," Julia went on, being her most satisfactory self and not a bit patronizing. "Beritza's interested in old houses, too; she wants to buy one before she goes to Hollywood."

"I want to buy thees one!" Beritza suddenly exclaimed. "No, but my dear I mean it, I mean it, I mean it! I am not in joking. *I want to buy thees house.*" She stood in the middle of the floor with her hands clasped and her eyes closed, like someone in a trance. Her voice dropped to a whisper. "Eet is what I have dreamed. Eet is my perfect setting, Jooliaa, is it not?"

"Don't be absurd, Carra, these youngsters are mad about their place—"

Beritza turned to Claudia. "But you will sell it to me, no? You can make yourselves another one?"

Claudia laughed. "Oh, of course. But you'd better see the rest of it, then maybe you'll change your mind and won't want it."

"No, I weel not change my mind," said Beritza. "I weel want it, I

134

am like that. I am—how you call it—all feelings and no logic—"

Claudia was arrested. "That's funny," she said. "That's exactly what my husband says that I am, too—"

"Eet is the artist in the both of us," said Beritza, sagely. "You write—or perhaps you paint—is it not?"

Claudia's heart warmed to her, even though she wasn't crazy about musicians as a rule. "I was going on the stage and then I got married," she admitted.

"Ah!" Beritza cried triumphantly.

She went into ecstasies over the upstairs. "How much?" she entreated. "How much can I have it for, furniture and everything?"

Naturally Claudia no more dreamed that she was in earnest than the man in the moon. "Thirty thousand," she glibly retorted, saying the first outrageous sum that came into her mind.

"Thirty thousand!" echoed Beritza, on a crescendo of negation.

"Why, that's cheap." Claudia broke in indignantly, feeling like an actress instead of a housewife for the first time in months. "It's absolutely nothing for a hundred acres of valuable property and a historic old house, superbly decorated and remodeled by one of the most famous young architects in America!"

She was aware that Julia was looking at her strangely. She laughed, reckless and elated. No wonder Julia was puzzled—Julia had never seen her anything but serious. "Thirty thousand," she reiterated, "is giving it away."

"But eet is *throwing* it away!" exclaimed Beritza, playing along in good style. "Why eet is nothing! It is a mere fraction of what I will get to make my first picture in Hollywood!"

"Oh, dear," mourned Claudia. "If I had known that, I would have made it fifty."

Beritza pretended to pout, but her red lips grew suddenly thin and set. "No, it is a bargain. You said it. I pay it. Thirty and not a penny more."

Claudia could be playful only so long and no longer. Even good comedy could pall and become stupid. "Sold," she acquiesced, a trifle bored.

Beritza clapped her hands. "See, Jooliaa!"

Julia caught Claudia's eye. "I want to wash up before starting off," she said.

She pulled Claudia into the bathroom after her and shut the door.

135

"Listen, you chump, are you joking about all this?"

"Oh, don't be silly, of course I am."

"Well," said Julia shortly, "Beritza's not."

"Not?" gasped Claudia.

"Not," said Julia.

"Oh, I can't believe it. Why should she imagine I'd be in earnest, asking a price like thirty thousand? Why David was reckoning out the other night, it's only cost us half that much. The woman's cuckoo!"

Julia began to laugh hysterically. "On the contrary, she's known to have one of the shrewdest business heads on two continents. Congratulations, my little financial genius, it's not everybody that can make a hundred per cent profit on a year's investment!"

Claudia sat down on the edge of the tub. Through the whirling of her senses, she realized that Julia thought she was a lot smarter than she really was.

She counted the minutes until David came home. He noticed with approval, that she looked very pretty and not at all tired for a change. "I'll be right back, Skinnymalink."

"Oh, no, you don't!" She pushed him into a chair. "Sit down, I have something to tell you."

"Can't it wait? I want to look at the cow."

"The cow's all right."

"Did you go out to see her?"

"No—" (It hadn't occurred to her to do so.)

"Then how do you know she's all right?"

"Oh, because she is," she answered impatiently. "Listen." She couldn't keep it to herself another second. "I sold the place today for thirty thousand dollars. That is," she added politely, "if you're agreeable."

"That's fine," he said.

He didn't believe her. He didn't believe her even when she told him everything that happened. He listened with one ear and then dismissed the story as a lot of nonsense. "She was taking you for a ride," he said and started up from his chair.

"David, wait a minute! She means every word of it. You see, practically all the movie stars have Connecticut farms—Madame Beritza and her favorite pig, and all that sort of thing—"

"You mean you'd leave the animals for her?" he injected on a shout.

"Not Shakespeare," said Claudia. "We can keep Shakespeare in New

136

York, but I don't see how we can keep a cow and sheep and two great Danes—"

"Doesn't she want Bobby thrown in?" he queried caustically.

"No, because she's going to adopt a baby. They all do."

David gently but firmly dislodged Claudia from his lap and stood up. He took a pipe and filled it. He puffed at it for quite a long time before he spoke.

"Listen, Claudia, I think this dame is screwy and I don't believe she'll come across. But if she should—" He tossed the match into the fireplace and looked at her—a long searching look. "Would you actually want to go ahead with it?"

Claudia felt her pulses quicken a little. "Wouldn't it be idiotic not to? After all, fifteen thousand is more than you could make in a whole year, working hard."

"A hell of a lot more," said David slowly. "But where do we go from here?"

"I've got it all planned out. A hotel until we find an apartment, and Bertha to help us out with Bobby." A note of eagerness crept into her voice. She was so sure that Beritza intended to buy the place, that she could at last unburden all that was in her heart. "Oh, David," she cried, "I'd have rather died than say anything—I'd have just stuck it out, making believe I adored it, if this hadn't happened. But people who own places are just crazy, when they can live in an apartment and let someone else do the worrying. Honestly, didn't we spend just about half in New York?"

"We had just about half, too," said David.

"That's true. Half the inconvenience, half the work, half the boredom. A farm is beautiful in theory, but it just doesn't work out as far as I can see. Burying yourself in the country all year around doesn't *give* you anything—"

"I thought it did," said David, quietly. He emptied his pipe and slipped it in his pocket. "When does she want to move in?"

"Right away, so she can have the photographers."

"Impossible."

"No, it's not! Don't we do everything quick?"

"That's right," said David.

His voice didn't sound quite natural. She sobered. "David, aren't you pleased at making a hundred per cent profit on your money, in a slump when everyone's busted?"

137

"Who wouldn't be?" he answered. "But don't count on it too much, Claudia."

"She'll take it," said Claudia confidently. "I bet you twenty cents."

Suddenly, he put his hands on her shoulders. "Gosh, dear, you should have told me that you hated it."

"Not hated it, exactly, David—"

He said, "You've been a good sport about it anyway." He left her quickly and went out to the barn.

Claudia's mother arrived the next morning, in answer to Claudia's call, with her elderly black hat slightly askew and her joy becomingly tempered with reservation. She held Bobby on her lap and spoiled him, while Claudia got ready to catch the noon train into town. "So he's coming back to his old grandma," she kept saying over and over. She looked around the many-windowed nursery, with sun pouring in from every side. "You'll never find another room like this for him in the city," she commented.

"Who wants it?" Claudia flippantly retorted. "It's three times larger than it needs be."

Luck was with her, as she had somehow known it would be. She found, immediately, a very pleasant suite in a residential hotel not very far from their old neighborhood. The rooms seemed a little cramped and stuffy but they would serve very nicely indeed until she found the right apartment. She told the manager that she was practically certain of taking them, and then hurried off to make the proper arrangements with Bertha.

The immaculate little flat smelled just the same as she remembered it—warm and comfortable, and faintly redolent of onion. "I wonder," she thought, as she rang the bell, "if all superintendents' flats smell like that."

Bertha opened the door and peered out. "Ach, my Mrs. Naughton. Come in, come in! Fritz, look only who is here!"

Fritz was just as happy to see her as Bertha. "How is the boy?" he asked, with his nice funny teeth fanning out of his broad smile.

"Fine," said Claudia.

"Big, yah?" Bertha beamed. "Und tell us about the farm—"

Claudia told them.

"Ach!" mourned Bertha. "It's too bad to sell it. Such a nice farm. We were talking only last night, Fritz und me—"

"Mamma!" Fritz sharply intervened, "lots of people don't like the

138

country, that's all right, too—"

"Of course, natürlich," Bertha agreed, getting a little red. Then she quickly changed the subject.

"Will Bertha help you out?" David asked Claudia as he rushed her along like the White Queen, to catch the last train to Eastbrook that night.

Claudia nodded. "Glad to. I imagine, though," she panted. "I mean I just sort of got the impression that Fritz doesn't want to be a superintendent any more. I imagine they'd sort of thought of coming out to us as a couple—"

David's voice was wistful. "That would have been just about perfect. I bet Fritz would have made a darn good farmer—"

"I bet so, too," Claudia concurred without regret.

They didn't talk very much on the trip home. It was too much effort to raise her voice above the clatter of the train. She had never felt so tired in her life—her head ached and each shoe felt as if it had both feet in it. "I think I'm not used to high heels and wearing a hat," she explained.

They had left the car parked at the station. It was luxurious just to climb in and drive off, with the clear night air against their faces. There was a moon that came through the trees every now and then, and looked at them. It shone on a pond and was beautiful. "David!" cried Claudia.

"I saw," said David.

The house was lit up. "It looks nice," said Claudia, "sitting there like that."

"It does," said David.

Mrs. Brown met them at the door. She had hot coffee waiting and chocolate cake. "You remind me of Bertha," Claudia told her. "And I mean it for a compliment," she added.

She sank down on the sofa and kicked off her pumps. "Bobby eat his peas? He hates them."

"I mixed them with applesauce," Mrs. Brown shamelessly admitted, and went on to tell them how smart he had been about something or other, and that she had sorted all the linens and packed them in three large boxes she had found in the storeroom.

"You did?" Claudia cried incredulously. "That was a huge job, thanks loads!"

139

"I looked at the cow, too."

David pricked up his ears. "How was she?"

"Nothing doing," said Mrs. Brown.

Claudia giggled. "You sounded just like David when you said that." She yawned and stretched. "Oh, Lord, I'm tired."

Claudia's mother said she didn't wonder. "You've had a hard day behind you, better get to bed."

She fell asleep as soon as her head touched the pillow. It seemed hours later when she awoke. She knew, before she stretched her hand to touch him, that David was no longer by her side. "David," she called softly. She put on the lamp. He was gone. "David!" she called again.

She threw her robe across her shoulders and fished for her slippers. It was freezing. She hurried to close the windows; and then she saw the light in the barn.

She couldn't help feeling annoyed. She sat on the edge of the bed waiting for him, until her impatience got the better of her.

"The idiot," she muttered and put on a heavy coat to go to fetch him.

It was black as pitch outside and the wind was bitter. She stumbled twice and a low-hung apple branch, catching her shoulder, caused her to cry out in alarm. The strange inimical blanket of the night pressed down upon her, and made her feel smothered and afraid. Her knees were trembling and her heart pounding when she pushed against the heavy unwieldy barn door, and stepped within.

The air was full of warm sweet animal smell, and the kerosene lantern gave out a flickering luminous glow. Louella was not in her stanchion. In a corner on a bed of hay, Claudia saw her standing quietly, with David on his knees beside her.

The sharp words melted from her tongue. He had thrown aside his jacket and his white pajama coat, tucked loosely into the belt of his trousers, made him seem young and vulnerable and heartbreakingly intent. "Soo girl, soo girl," he was saying in a low voice, like a croon.

With the creaking of the door, he turned. "Claudia!" He was glad to see her—not startled or angry as she had half expected him to be. Not "What are you doing out here?" or "Go back to bed, you'll catch your death of cold!" No. He acted as if he had expected her to come, as if there were nothing strange in her sudden waking to follow him. "Look!" he said.

At first she could scarcely believe it. "The calf," she whispered.

140

"Just born." There was a look on his face that held a great pride.

Claudia could not speak. She had never seen a newborn calf. She had not known that it would be this way. The calf was standing up, soft and damp, its legs freed from the mysterious confines of the womb and ready to move out into living. As she watched it, it took a few wavering steps and its brown eyes, wide open and darkly fringed—like some great mascara'd beauty, Claudia thought—reached, in unseeing vision, toward its mother's warmth. Louella's great, cavernous face was full of peace and quiet. She bent her head and gave the calf a gentle push, and then she moved away from it.

"She doesn't want it!" Claudia breathed.

"Yes, she does," said David, in a low voice. "She wants to make it strong, she wants it to come after her—"

Claudia felt the tears lump in her throat. This, that was happening to her, was her first dazzling revelation of the land. It was almost as if she were being initiated into some profound and cosmic secret—as she had been initiated into loving David, and into having Bobby, and into knowing suddenly and fully that there was God.

David's voice broke in upon her thoughts. "It's a heifer," he said. "We'll raise her and put her out to pasture, and in a couple of years she'll be giving us her own calf."

"Oh," cried Claudia, suddenly seeing the generous cycle of all life. "How wonderful—" She forgot and he forgot—that they were going back to New York to live in a hotel.

They didn't think of it until they were walking hand in hand, a little later, toward the house, looking up into the night.

"Funny," said Claudia, "I didn't know the stars were out. I'm sure there weren't any before—or maybe," she amended honestly, "I was too scared to notice them."

David was mildly astonished. "You weren't scared—" he chided.

She had to confess. "I was."

"Of what, though?" He couldn't seem to understand it.

"I don't know. But I'm not any longer. I'd be ashamed to be. I'm ashamed of almost dying with Bobby. Louella has made me feel terribly silly and inadequate all the way around."

"Louella's a very superior cow," said David.

"She's marvelous," said Claudia. "Are other cows marvelous, too? Or just Louella?"

"They're all pretty swell," admitted David. "Wait till you see how

141

the pigs and the sheep do it—" He stopped. "Maybe we'll buy another place someday," he ended lamely.

She heard the brook tumbling over the rocks and she felt the apple tree gently brush her shoulder as she passed it. "We'll never find another place like this," she said slowly. "Never."

David didn't say anything.

"I wish," she burst out suddenly, "that we were very rich."

"How rich?"

"I wish we had thirty thousand dollars, and could afford to keep Fritz and Bertha as a couple."

David drew to a stop. "What would you do?" he asked in an odd voice.

"I'd buy it back," she said.

Mrs. Brown heard them tiptoe up the steps. "What's the matter?" she called out.

"Are you awake?" asked Claudia needlessly.

Her mother's light went up. They drifted to the threshhold.

"What on earth!" Mrs. Brown exclaimed, when she saw them bundled up in coats at that hour of the night.

Claudia solemnly bent to kiss her. "Congratulations, Grandma. It's a girl!"

"You selfish things, why didn't you call me?"

"Want to go out and see it now?" asked David.

"Certainly," she said, looking almost like Claudia except that her hair was gray. "Lend me your coat, Claudia," she demanded peremptorily.

Claudia was equally peremptory. "Nothing of the kind. You need your beauty sleep. You've a hard day ahead of you."

"What doing?" Mrs. Brown demanded.

"Unpacking all the linens," Claudia pleasantly informed her.

I Thought I Heard Them Singing

Dorothy Canfield

Tender and real is this tale of an understanding mother. Here is a distinguished writer at her best.

She asked, casually, just to say something, as she handed out the four o'clock pieces of bread and peanut butter, "Well, what Christmas songs are you learning in your room this year?"

There was a moment's pause. Then the three little boys, her own and the usual two of his playmates, told her, first one speaking, then another, "We're not going to be let sing. Teacher doesn't want us in the Christmas entertainment." Their round, eight-year-old faces were grave.

"Well—" said the mother, "for goodness' sake, why not?"

Her own small David answered, looking down at his feet, "Teacher says we can't sing good enough."

"Well enough," corrected his mother mechanically.

"Well enough," he repeated, as mechanically. "She says we can't carry a tune. We'd spoil the piece our room is going to sing, she says. She's only going to let kids sing that can carry a tune."

Inwardly the mother broke into a mother's rage at a teacher, "So that's what she says, does she? What's she *for* anyhow if not to teach children what they don't know. The idea! As if she'd say she would teach arithmetic only to those who are good at it already." The downcast children stood silent. She yearned over their shamed sadness at failing to come up to the standards of their group. "Teachers are callous, that's what they are, insensitively callous. She is deliberately planting an inferior feeling in them. It's a shame to keep them from being one of those who go up on the platform and stand in the footlights. Not to let them have their share of being applauded! It's cruel."

Aloud she remarked quietly, after she had drawn a deep breath, and put the loaf of bread away, "Yes, I know. Lots of kids your age can't carry a tune. Not till they've learned. How'd you like to practise your song with me? I could play the air on the piano afternoons, after school. You'd get the hang of it that way." They brightened, and began to bite off great chunks of their snacks. They said thickly, that that would be swell.

So while the after-school bread was being eaten, washed down with gulps of milk, the mother pushed to the back of the stove the interrupted rice pudding, washed her hands at the sink, looked into the dining room where her youngest, Janey, was getting her dolls up from naps taken in the dining-room chairs, and took off her apron. Together the four went into the living room to the piano.

"What song is it, your room is to sing?"

"It came upon the midnight—" said the three little boys, speaking at once.

"That's a nice one," she commented, reaching for the battered songbook on top of the piano. "This is the way it goes." She played the air, and sang the first two lines. "That'll be enough to start on," she told them. "*Now*—" she gave them the signal to start.

They started. Happily, heartened by her interest, they opened their mouths and sang out lustily,

> *It came upon the midnight clear,*
> *That glorious song of old.*

They had evidently learned the words by heart from hearing them.

At the end of the phrase she stopped, abruptly, and for an instant bowed her head over the keys. Her feeling about Teacher made a rightabout turn.

But she was a mother, not a teacher. She lifted her head, turned a smiling face on the three sturdy, bellowing children, looking at her hopefully. "I tell you what," she said, "the way a person learns a tune, is really one note after another. The reason why a teacher can't get everybody in her room up to singing in tune is because she'd have to teach each person separately, unless they happened to be just naturally good at singing. That would take too much time, you know. A teacher has such a lot of children to see to."

They did not listen very closely, not being particularly interested in having justice done to Teacher, since they had not shared the mother's brief excursion into indignation. But they tolerated her with silent courtesy. They were used to parents and teachers and other adults, and had learned how to have a good deal of patience and self-control with their inexplicable, prosy explanations of things that did not matter.

"Listen," said the mother, "I'll strike just the two first notes on the piano—'It came——'" She struck the notes, she sang them clearly. Full of good will the little boys sang with her. She stopped. Breathed hard. "Not quite," she said, with a false smile, "pret-t-ty good. Close to it. But not quite, yet. I think we'd better take it one by one. Bill, *you* try it."

Bill was used to her, having been in and out of the house all his life, and none of the three had reached the self-conscious stage, so without hesitation Bill sang, "It ca-ame . . ." loudly.

After he had, the mother kept her eyes fixed on his still open mouth as if she were fascinated. "Try again," she said, finally. "But first, listen." Oracularly, she told them, "Half of carrying a tune is listening first."

She played the note again. And again. And again. Then, rather faintly, she said, "Peter, you sing it now."

At the notes emitted by Peter, she let out her breath, as if she had been under water and just come up. "Fine!" she said, "now we're getting somewhere! David, your turn." David, her own. "Just two notes. No, not *quite*. A little higher on 'came.' Not quite so high. Try just breathing it out, not loud at all. Maybe you can get it better."

They had come in a little after four. It was five when the telephone rang—Bill's mother asking her to send him home because his Aunt Emma was there. The mother turned from the telephone to say, "Don't you boys want to go along with Bill and play around for a while outdoors? I've got to get supper ready." Cheerful, full of confidence in her, relieved to see a door opening before them that had been slammed shut in their faces, they put on their muddy rubbers and thudded out. They had not advanced beyond those first two notes.

When she told her husband about it, that evening, after the children had gone to bed, she ended her story with a vehement, "You never heard anything like it in your life, Harry. Never. You can't *imagine* what it was like."

"Oh, yes I can too," he said over his temporarily lowered news-

145

paper. "I've heard plenty of tone-deaf kids hollering. I know what they sound like. There *are* people, you know, who really *can't* carry a tune. You probably never could teach them. Why don't you give it up?" Seeing, perhaps, in her face, the mulish mother-stubbornness, he added, with a little exasperation, "What's the use of trying to do what you *can't* do?"

That was reasonable, after all, thought the mother. Yes, the sensible thing was to give it up. She would be sensible, for once, and give it up.

So the next morning when she was downtown, doing her marketing, she turned in at the public library and asked for books about teaching music to children. Rather young children, about eight years old, she explained.

At lunch she told her husband (the children had their lunch at school), "Musical experts say there really is no such thing as a tone-deaf person. If anybody seems so, it is only because he has not had a chance to be trained."

Her husband looked at her quickly, "Oh, all right," he said, "all *right!* Have it your own way." But then he leaned to pat her hand. "You're wonderful," he told her, "I don't see how you ever keep it up as you do. Gosh, it's one o'clock already."

During the weeks between then and the Christmas entertainment, she also did not see how she could keep it up. The little boys had no difficulty in keeping it up. They had nothing else to do at four o'clock. And they were at the indestructible age, between the frailness of infancy and the taut nervous tensions of adolescence. They followed her cheerfully wherever she led.

Assiduous reading of those reference books on teaching music gave her other ideas than that frontal attack on the tune they wanted to sing. She tried out ear-experiments with them and she found that sure enough, just as the authors of the books said, the little boys could not, without seeing which keys she struck, tell whether a note was higher or lower than the one before it. She adapted and invented musical games to train their ears for this. The boys standing in a row, their backs to the piano, listening to hear whether the second note was "up hill or down hill" from the first note, thought it as good a game as any other, rather funnier than most, because so new to them. They laughed raucously over each other's mistakes, ran a contest to see who came out best, while the mother, her eyes on the clock, got up and

146

down for dashes into the kitchen where she was trying to get supper.

The two older children of the house, who had a naturally good ear for music, came in from school, listened incredulously, laughed scoffingly, and went off to skate or to rehearse a play. Little Janey, absorbed in her family of dolls, paid no attention to these male creatures of an age so far from hers that they were as negligible as grownups. Occasionally someone made a comment, "Gee, Mom, those kids are fierce. *You* can't do anything with them." "Say, Helen, an insurance man is coming to the house this afternoon. For heaven's sake keep those boys from screeching and carrying on while he is here. A person can't hear himself think."

So her task was not only to invent and adapt methods of instruction in an hour she could not spare, but also to avoid bothering the rest. After all, the home was for the whole family. They had the right to have it the background of what *they* wanted to do, needed to do.

She faltered, many was the time. She saw the ironing heaped high, or Janey was in bed with a cold, and said to herself as four o'clock drew near, "Now I'll just tell the boys today that I can *not* go on with this. We're not getting anywhere, anyhow."

But when they came storming in, hungry and cheerful and full of unquestioning certainty that she would not close that half-open door, she laid everything aside and went to the piano.

As a matter of fact, they were getting somewhere. With their backs to the piano, the boys could now tell, infallibly, whether a second note was above or below the first one. Sure. They even thought it distinctly queer that they had not been able to, at first. "Never really paid any attention to it, before," was their own accurate surmise, as to the reason.

They paid attention now, their interest aroused by their first success, by the incessant practising in their classroom, by the Christmas-entertainment thrill which filled all the schoolhouse with suspense. Although they had no part in it, they paid close attention to the drill in how to march along the aisle of the Assembly Hall, how not to knock their toes against the stairs as they climbed to the platform. They fully expected—wasn't a grownup teaching them—to climb those steps to the platform with the others, on the evening of the entertainment.

It was now not on the clock that the mother kept her eye during those daily sessions at the piano, it was on the calendar. She nervously

147

intensified her drill, but she remembered carefully not to yell at them when they went wrong, not to screw her face into the grimace which she felt, not to clap her hands over her ears and scream, "Oh, horrible! *Why* can't you get it right!" She reminded herself that if they knew how to get it right, they would of course sing it that way. She knew that she must keep them cheerful and hopeful. She smiled, she did not allow herself even to assume the blighting look of patience.

And then, just in time, along about the second week of December, they could all sound—if they remembered to sing softly and to "listen to themselves"—a note, any note, she struck on the piano.

They started again, very cautiously, to sing that tune, to begin with "It ca-ame . . ." having drawn a deep breath, and letting it out carefully. It was right. They were singing true.

She clapped her hands like a child, in an overjoyed surprise which they did not share. That was where they had been going all the time. They had got there, that was all. Why should she be surprised?

After that it went fast; the practising of the air, the repeating it for the first skeptical and then astonished teacher, their triumphant report, "She says we're all right. She says we can sing with the others. We practised going up on the platform this afternoon."

And then the Christmas entertainment. The tramping to and fro of class after class, up the aisle to the moment of footlighted glory; the big eighth graders' Christmas pantomime, the first graders' wavering performance of a Christmas dance as fairies, or were they snowflakes? Or perhaps angels? It was not clear. They were tremendously applauded, anyhow, whatever they were.

Then it was the turn of the third grade, the eight- and nine-year-olds, the boys clumping up the aisle, the girls switching their short skirts proudly. The careful tiptoeing up the steps to the platform, remembering not to knock their toes on the stair risers, the two lines of round faces, facing the audience, bland and blank in their ignorance—oh, of everything! thought David's mother, her hand clutched rather tightly on her handbag.

The crash from the piano giving them the tone, all the mouths opened,

> *It ca-ame upo-on the midnight clear*
> *That glorious song of old.*

Teacher's long drill and hers had been successful. It was not howling, it was singing. It had cost the heart's blood, thought the mother, of two women, but it was singing. It would never again be howling, not from those children.

There he stood, her little David, a fully accredited part of his corner of society, as good as anybody, the threat of the inferiority feeling averted for this time, ready to face the future with enough self-confidence to cope with what would come next. The door had been slammed in his face. She had pushed it open, and he had gone through.

The hymn ended. The burst of parental applause began clamorously. Little Janey, carried away by the festival excitement, clapped with all her might. The third grade filed down the steps from the platform and began to march back along the aisle. For a moment, the mother forgot she was no longer a girl who, when she had done something, expected some reward for it. Surely, she thought, when his class passed their seats, as they clumped down the aisle, David would turn his head to where she sat and thank her with a look.

He did turn his head as he filed by. He looked full at his family, at his father, his mother, his kid sister, his big brother and sister from the high school. He gave them a formal, small nod to let them know that he recognized them. He even smiled a little, a very little, stiffly, fleetingly. But his look was for them all.

Well, that was all right, she thought. Of course. She shifted Janey's weight a little on her knees. Did mothers ever expect to be thanked? Mothers worked—not for thanks, but to do their job. When they succeeded that was enough grounds for thanksgiving. After all, she thought, hearing very vaguely the seventh graders now on the platform (no child of hers was in the seventh grade), David was only eight. At that age they were about as completely cocoons, spiritually, as in their babyhood they had been physical cocoons. The time had not come yet for the spirit, within which was to be the core of his manhood, to stir and waken and give a sign that it lived.

The snowy weeks came and went. David rose, ravenously hungry, ate an enormous breakfast with the family, and clumped off to school with his own third graders. They stormed back after school, flinging around a cloud of overshoes, caps, mittens, windbreakers. They ate her cookies, or went to each other's houses, to eat other cookies. They gobbled, laughed raucously, kidded and joshed each other, pushed each other around. They made snow forts in their front yards, skated with awkward energy on the place where the brook overflowed the meadow, took their sleds out to Hingham Hill for coasting, made plans for a shack in the woods next summer.

If they had any souls at all at that age, thought the mother, they were certainly no more than seeds, deep inside their hard, muscular, little-boy flesh. How do souls develop, she wondered occasionally, as she washed dishes, made beds, selected carrots at the market, answered the telephone. How do souls develop out of those rough-and-ready little males? If they do develop?

David and Peter, living close to each other, frequently shared the evening play hour. They were allowed to go by themselves to each other's houses, even though it was winter-black at seven o'clock. Peter lived on the street just above theirs, up the hill. There was a short cut down across a vacant lot, which was in sight of one or the other house, all the way. It was safe enough, even for youngsters, even at night.

One evening as she sat with her mending there came a sudden perception, as physically present to her senses as if she had heard a clock strike, or the doorbell ring, that the time had passed for David's return from his evening play hour with Peter. She looked up at the clock. But she did not need to. A sixth sense told her heart, as with a blow, that he should before this have come pelting down the hill, ploughing the deep snow aside in clouds. He was late. He must have left the other house some time ago. Peter's mother always sent him home promptly.

She laid down the stocking she was darning, stepped into the dark kitchen, and put her face close to the window to look out. It was a cloudless, cold night. Every detail of the back yard world was visible, almost transparent, in the pale radiance that fell from the stars. Not a breath of wind. She could see everything, the trampled snow of the back yard, the clothes she had washed that morning and left out on the line, the deep unbroken snow beyond the yard, the path leading up the hill.

Then she saw David. He was standing on the path, halfway down, as still as the frozen night around him.

But David never stood still.

Knee-deep in the snow he stood, looking all around him. She saw him slowly turn his head to one side, to the other. He lifted his face toward the sky. It was almost frightening to see *David* stand so still. What could he be looking at? What was there he could be seeing? Or hearing? For the notion crossed her mind, as she watched him, that

150

he seemed to be listening. But there was nothing to hear. Nothing.

She did not know what was happening to her little son. Nor what to do. So she did nothing. She stood as still as he, her face at the window, lost in wonder.

She saw him, finally, stir and start slowly, slowly down the path. But David never moved slowly. Had he perhaps had a quarrel with Peter? Had Peter's mother been unkind to him?

It could do no harm now to go to meet him, she thought, and anyhow, she could not, at that moment, not go to meet him. She opened the kitchen door and stepped out into the dark, under the stars.

He saw her, he came quickly to her, he put his arms around her waist. With every fiber of her body she felt a difference in him.

She did not know what to say, so she said nothing. It was her son who spoke, "It's so still," he said in a hushed, quiet voice, a voice she had never heard before. "It's so *still!*"

He pressed his cheek against her breast, tipping his head back to look up. "All those stars," he murmured dreamily, "they shine so. But they don't make a sound. They—they're *nice*, aren't they?"

He stood a little away from her to look up into her face, "Do you remember—in the song—'the world in solemn stillness lay'?" he asked her, but he knew she remembered.

The starlight showed his clear, his honest, little-boy eyes wide, fixed trustingly on his mother's. He was deeply moved. He had not known that he had an inner sanctuary. Now he stood in it, awestruck at his first sight of beauty. And opened the door to his mother. As naturally as he breathed, he put into her hands the pure, rounded pearl of a shared joy, "I thought I heard them singing—sort of," he told her.

The Look

Sara Teasdale

Strephon kissed me in the spring,
    Robin in the fall,
But Colin only looked at me
    And never kissed at all.

Strephon's kiss was lost in jest,
    Robin's lost in play,
But the kiss in Colin's eyes
    Haunts me night and day.

151

Catalogue of Lovely Things

Richard Le Gallienne

I would make a list against the evil days
    Of lovely things to hold in memory:
First, I would set down my lady's lovely face,
    For earth has no such lovely thing as she;
    And next I add, to bear her company,
The great-eyed virgin star that morning brings;
    Then the wild rose upon its little tree—
So runs my catalogue of lovely things.

The enchanted dogwood, with its ivory trays,
    The water lily in its sanctuary
Of reeded pools, and dew-drenched lilac sprays,
    For thee, of all fair flowers, the fairest be;
    Next write I down the great name of the sea,
Lonely in greatness as the names of kings;
    Then the young moon that hath us all in fee—
So runs my catalogue of lovely things.

Imperial sunsets that in crimson blaze
    Along the hills, and, fairer still to me,
The fireflies dancing in a netted maze
    Woven of twilight and tranquillity;
    Shakespeare and Virgil, their high poesy;
Then a great ship, splendid with snowy wings,
    Voyaging on into eternity—
So runs my catalogue of lovely things.

Envoi

Prince, not the gold bars of thy treasury,
    Not all thy jeweled scepters, crowns, and rings,
Are worth the honeycomb of the wild bee—
    So runs my catalogue of lovely things.

152

A Retrieved Reformation

O. Henry

Under its other title Alias Jimmy Valentine,
*O. Henry's most famous story became both a
successful play and motion picture.*

A GUARD came to the prison shoe-shop, where Jimmy Valentine was assiduously stitching uppers, and escorted him to the front office. There the warden handed Jimmy his pardon, which had been signed that morning by the governor. Jimmy took it in a tired kind of way. He had served nearly ten months of a four-year sentence. He had expected to stay only about three months, at the longest. When a man with as many friends on the outside as Jimmy Valentine had is received in the "stir" it is hardly worth while to cut his hair.

"Now, Valentine," said the warden, "you'll go out in the morning. Brace up, and make a man of yourself. You're not a bad fellow at heart. Stop cracking safes, and live straight."

"Me?" said Jimmy, in surprise. "Why, I never cracked a safe in my life."

"Oh, no," laughed the warden. "Of course not. Let's see, now. How was it you happened to get sent up on that Springfield job? Was it because you wouldn't prove an alibi for fear of compromising somebody in extremely high-toned society? Or was it simply a case of a mean old jury that had it in for you? It's always one or the other with you innocent victims."

"Me?" said Jimmy, still blankly virtuous. "Why, warden, I never was in Springfield in my life!"

"Take him back, Cronin," smiled the warden, "and fix him up with outgoing clothes. Unlock him at seven in the morning, and let him come to the bull-pen. Better think over my advice, Valentine."

At a quarter past seven on the next morning Jimmy stood in the warden's outer office. He had on a suit of the villainously fitting,

153

ready-made clothes and a pair of the stiff, squeaky shoes that the state furnishes to its discharged compulsory guests.

The clerk handed him a railroad ticket and the five-dollar bill with which the law expected him to rehabilitate himself into good citizenship and prosperity. The warden gave him a cigar, and shook hands. Valentine, 9762, was chronicled on the books "Pardoned by Governor," and Mr. James Valentine walked out into the sunshine.

Disregarding the song of the birds, the waving green trees, and the smell of the flowers, Jimmy headed straight for a restaurant. There he tasted the first sweet joys of liberty in the shape of a broiled chicken and a bottle of white wine—followed by a cigar a grade better than the one the warden had given him. From there he proceeded leisurely to the depot. He tossed a quarter into the hat of a blind man sitting by the door, and boarded his train. Three hours set him down in a little town near the state line. He went to the café of one Mike Dolan and shook hands with Mike, who was alone behind the bar.

"Sorry we couldn't make it sooner, Jimmy, me boy," said Mike. "But we had that protest from Springfield to buck against, and the governor nearly balked. Feeling all right?"

"Fine," said Jimmy. "Got my key?"

He got his key and went upstairs, unlocking the door of a room at the rear. Everything was just as he had left it. There on the floor was still Ben Price's collar-button that had been torn from that eminent detective's shirt-band when they had overpowered Jimmy to arrest him.

Pulling out from the wall a folding-bed, Jimmy slid back a panel in the wall and dragged out a dust-covered suitcase. He opened this and gazed fondly at the finest set of burglar's tools in the East. It was a complete set, made of specially tempered steel, the latest designs in drills, punches, braces and bits, jimmies, clamps, and augers, with two or three novelties invented by Jimmy himself, in which he took pride. Over nine hundred dollars they had cost him to have made at——, a place where they make such things for the profession.

In half an hour Jimmy went downstairs and through the café. He was now dressed in tasteful and well-fitting clothes, and carried his dusted and cleaned suitcase in his hand.

"Got anything on?" asked Mike Dolan, genially.

"Me?" said Jimmy, in a puzzled tone. "I don't understand. I'm representing the New York Amalgamated Short Snap Biscuit Cracker and Frazzled Wheat Company."

This statement delighted Mike to such an extent that Jimmy had to take a seltzer-and-milk on the spot. He never touched "hard" drinks.

A week after the release of Valentine, 9762, there was a neat job of safe-burglary done in Richmond, Indiana, with no clue to the author. A scant eight hundred dollars was all that was secured. Two weeks after that a patented, improved, burglar-proof safe in Logansport was opened like a cheese to the tune of fifteen hundred dollars, currency; securities and silver untouched. That began to interest the rogue-catchers. Then an old-fashioned bank-safe in Jefferson City became active and threw out of its crater an eruption of bank-notes amounting to five thousand dollars. The losses were now high enough to bring the matter up into Ben Price's class of work. By comparing notes, a remarkable similarity in the methods of the burglaries was noticed. Ben Price investigated the scenes of the robberies, and was heard to remark:

"That's Dandy Jim Valentine's autograph. He's resumed business. Look at that combination knob—jerked out as easy as pulling up a radish in wet weather. He's got the only clamps that can do it. And look how clean those tumblers were punched out! Jimmy never has to drill but one hole. Yes, I guess I want Mr. Valentine. He'll do his bit next time without any short-time or clemency foolishness."

Ben Price knew Jimmy's habits. He had learned them while working up the Springfield case. Long jumps, quick get-aways, no confederates, and a taste for good society—these ways had helped Mr. Valentine to become noted as a successful dodger of retribution. It was given out that Ben Price had taken up the trail of the elusive cracksman, and other people with burglar-proof safes felt more at ease.

One afternoon Jimmy Valentine and his suitcase climbed out of the mail-hack in Elmore, a little town five miles off the railroad down in the black-jack country of Arkansas. Jimmy, looking like an athletic young senior just home from college, went down the board sidewalk toward the hotel.

A young lady crossed the street, passed him at the corner and entered a door over which was the sign "The Elmore Bank." Jimmy Valentine looked into her eyes, forgot what he was, and became another man. She lowered her eyes and colored slightly. Young men of Jimmy's style and looks were scarce in Elmore.

Jimmy collared a boy that was loafing on the steps of the bank as if he were one of the stockholders, and began to ask him questions about the town, feeding him dimes at intervals. By and by the young lady

155

came out, looking royally unconscious of the young man with the suitcase, and went her way.

"Isn't that young lady Miss Polly Simpson?" asked Jimmy, with specious guile.

"Naw," said the boy. "She's Annabel Adams. Her pa owns this bank. What'd you come to Elmore for? Is that a gold watch-chain? I'm going to get a bulldog. Got any more dimes?"

Jimmy went to the Planters' Hotel, registered as Ralph D. Spencer, and engaged a room. He leaned on the desk and declared his platform to the clerk. He said he had come to Elmore to look for a location to go into business. How was the shoe business, now, in the town? He had thought of the shoe business. Was there an opening?

The clerk was impressed by the clothes and manner of Jimmy. He, himself, was something of a pattern of fashion to the thinly gilded youth of Elmore, but he now perceived his shortcomings. While trying to figure out Jimmy's manner of tying his four-in-hand he cordially gave information.

Yes, there ought to be a good opening in the shoe line. There wasn't an exclusive shoe-store in the place. The dry-goods and general stores handled them. Business in all lines was fairly good. Hoped Mr. Spencer would decide to locate in Elmore. He would find it a pleasant town to live in, and the people very sociable.

Mr. Spencer thought he would stop over in the town a few days and look over the situation. No, the clerk needn't call the boy. He would carry up his suitcase, himself; it was rather heavy.

Mr. Ralph Spencer, the phœnix that arose from Jimmy Valentine's ashes—ashes left by the flame of a sudden and alterative attack of love—remained in Elmore, and prospered. He opened a shoe-store and secured a good run of trade.

Socially he was also a success, and made many friends. And he accomplished the wish of his heart. He met Miss Annabel Adams, and became more and more captivated by her charms.

At the end of a year the situation of Mr. Ralph Spencer was this: he had won the respect of the community, his shoe-store was flourishing, and he and Annabel were engaged to be married in two weeks. Mr. Adams, the typical, plodding, country banker, approved of Spencer. Annabel's pride in him almost equalled her affection. He was as much at home in the family of Mr. Adams and that of Annabel's married sister as if he were already a member.

156

One day Jimmy sat down in his room and wrote this letter, which he mailed to the safe address of one of his old friends in St. Louis:

DEAR OLD PAL:

I want you to be at Sullivan's place, in Little Rock, next Wednesday night, at nine o'clock. I want you to wind up some little matters for me. And, also, I want to make you a present of my kit of tools. I know you'll be glad to get them—you couldn't duplicate the lot for a thousand dollars. Say, Billy, I've quit the old business—a year ago. I've got a nice store. I'm making an honest living, and I'm going to marry the finest girl on earth two weeks from now. It's the only life, Billy—the straight one. I wouldn't touch a dollar of another man's money now for a million. After I get married I'm going to sell out and go West, where there won't be so much danger of having old scores brought up against me. I tell you, Billy, she's an angel. She believes in me; and I wouldn't do another crooked thing for the whole world. Be sure to be at Sully's, for I must see you. I'll bring along the tools with me.

Your old friend,

JIMMY.

On the Monday night after Jimmy wrote this letter, Ben Price jogged unobtrusively into Elmore in a livery buggy. He lounged about town in his quiet way until he found out what he wanted to know. From the drug-store across the street from Spencer's shoe-store he got a good look at Ralph D. Spencer.

"Going to marry the banker's daughter are you, Jimmy?" said Ben to himself, softly. "Well, I don't know!"

The next morning Jimmy took breakfast at the Adamses. He was going to Little Rock that day to order his wedding-suit and buy something nice for Annabel. That would be the first time he had left town since he came to Elmore. It had been more than a year now since those last professional "jobs," and he thought he could safely venture out.

After breakfast quite a family party went down town together—Mr. Adams, Annabel, Jimmy, and Annabel's married sister with her two little girls, aged five and nine. They came by the hotel where Jimmy still boarded, and he ran up to his room and brought along his suitcase. Then they went on to the bank. There stood Jimmy's horse and buggy and Dolph Gibson, who was going to drive him over to the railroad station.

All went inside the high, carved oak railings into the banking-room—

Jimmy included, for Mr. Adams's future son-in-law was welcome anywhere. The clerks were pleased to be greeted by the good-looking,
agreeable young man who was going to marry Miss Annabel. Jimmy
set his suitcase down. Annabel, whose heart was bubbling with happiness and lively youth, put on Jimmy's hat and picked up the suitcase.
"Wouldn't I make a nice drummer?" said Annabel. "My! Ralph, how
heavy it is. Feels like it was full of gold bricks."

"Lot of nickel-plated shoe-horns in there," said Jimmy, coolly, "that
I'm going to return. Thought I'd save express charges by taking them
up. I'm getting awfully economical."

The Elmore Bank had just put in a new safe and vault. Mr. Adams
was very proud of it, and insisted on an inspection by everyone. The
vault was a small one, but it had a new patented door. It fastened with
three solid steel bolts thrown simultaneously with a single handle, and
had a time-lock. Mr. Adams beamingly explained its workings to Mr.
Spencer, who showed a courteous but not too intelligent interest. The
two children, May and Agatha, were delighted by the shining metal
and funny clock and knobs.

While they were thus engaged Ben Price sauntered in and leaned on
his elbow, looking casually inside between the railings. He told the
teller that he didn't want anything; he was just waiting for a man he
knew.

Suddenly there was a scream or two from the women, and a commotion. Unperceived by the elders, May, the nine-year-old girl, in a
spirit of play, had shut Agatha in the vault. She had then shot the bolts
and turned the knob of the combination as she had seen Mr. Adams do.

The old banker sprang to the handle and tugged at it for a moment.
"The door can't be opened," he groaned. "The clock hasn't been
wound nor the combination set."

Agatha's mother screamed again, hysterically.

"Hush!" said Mr. Adams, raising his trembling hand. "All be quiet
for a moment. Agatha!" he called as loudly as he could. "Listen to
me." During the following silence they could just hear the faint
sound of the child wildly shrieking in the dark vault in a panic of
terror.

"My precious darling!" wailed the mother. "She will die of fright!
Open the door! Oh, break it open! Can't you men do something?"

"There isn't a man nearer than Little Rock who can open that door,"
said Mr. Adams, in a shaky voice. "My God! Spencer, what shall we

do? That child—she can't stand it long in there. There isn't enough air, and, besides, she'll go into convulsions from fright."

Agatha's mother, frantic now, beat the door of the vault with her hands. Somebody wildly suggested dynamite. Annabel turned to Jimmy, her large eyes full of anguish, but not yet despairing. To a woman nothing seems quite impossible to the powers of the man she worships.

"Can't you do something, Ralph—*try*, won't you?"

He looked at her with a queer, soft smile on his lips and in his keen eyes.

"Annabel," he said, "give me that rose you are wearing, will you?"

Hardly believing that she heard him aright, she unpinned the bud from the bosom of her dress, and placed it in his hand. Jimmy stuffed it into his vest-pocket, threw off his coat and pulled up his shirt-sleeves. With that act Ralph D. Spencer passed away and Jimmy Valentine took his place.

"Get away from the door, all of you," he commanded, shortly.

He set his suitcase on the table, and opened it out flat. From that time on he seemed to be unconscious of the presence of anyone else. He laid out the shining, queer implements swiftly and orderly, whistling softly to himself as he always did when at work. In a deep silence, the others watched him as if under a spell.

In a minute Jimmy's pet drill was biting smoothly into the steel door. In ten minutes—breaking his own burglarious record—he threw back the bolts and opened the door.

Agatha, almost collapsed, but safe, was gathered into her mother's arms.

Jimmy Valentine put on his coat, and walked outside the railings toward the front door. As he went he thought he heard a far-away voice that he once knew call "Ralph!" But he never hesitated.

At the door a big man stood somewhat in his way.

"Hello, Ben!" said Jimmy, still with his strange smile. "Got around at last, have you? Well, let's go. I don't know that it makes much difference, now."

And then Ben Price acted rather strangely.

"Guess you're mistaken, Mr. Spencer," he said. "Don't believe I recognize you. Your buggy's waiting for you, ain't it?"

And Ben Price turned and strolled down the street.

Garden

Anthony Lane

My heart was once a garden
  By dim, enchanted trees,
With hint of untouched violets
  And shy anemones.

I showed my love the garden
  Where April dreams I'd hide,
But heedlessly he lost the key
  And now—we're both outside!

Song

Sara Teasdale

You bound strong sandals on my feet,
  You gave me bread and wine,
And sent me under sun and stars,
  For all the world was mine.

Oh take the sandals off my feet,
  You know not what you do;
For all my world is in your arms,
  My sun and stars are you.

Love Comes to Miss Kissinger

Winfred Van Atta

An amusing tale of today.

THE Rockdale National Bank & Trust Company held its annual employes' meeting on the first Monday in June. As usual, the meeting convened at 7 A.M., disrupting the sleeping habits of fifty-seven employes, including Miss Muriel Kissinger of the checking department.

President Stone, running true to form, opened the meeting by stating unequivocally that National's greatest assets were the loyalty, honesty, and industry of its employes. There followed a lengthy summary of business progress, which, it was carefully pointed out, had been reflected in the Christmas bonus and in salary increases for the deserving. New goals for the coming fiscal year were properly identified by charts and graphs, but they could be realized, of course, only if each employe added his own extra bit of effort and courtesy. Two vice-presidents confirmed all that Mr. Stone had said, interspersing compliments for a job well done with appeals for recognition of the greater job ahead.

Miss Kissinger, wearing a new linen ensemble from Block & Kubal's spring sale, sat on a folding chair near the front of the lobby, anxious to be done with the meeting, which offered nothing new over previous years. Her new pumps were beginning to hurt, and she wanted to get to her desk upstairs, since this was the day statements went in the mail. Besides, Mr. Saddler was staring at her again from his place at the officers' table. Mr. Saddler was vice-president and manager of industrial loans. His wife had been dead for almost two years now, and his only son had recently married. For years Mr. Saddler had treated Miss Kissinger as impersonally as a piece of office furniture. Recently he had been going out of his way to be friendly. One of these days soon, she thought, she'd have to put Mr. Saddler in his place, even though he was Herbert Martin's immediate superior.

President Stone's voice suddenly penetrated Miss Kissinger's thoughts, causing her to tense.

"And so this year we decided to award gold watches to the ladies in our organization who have given twenty continuous years of loyal service. We have two such ladies. First, of course, is our lovely Miss Kissinger, whom I personally hired just twenty years ago this month, shortly after her graduation from West High. Will Miss Kissinger please step forward?"

Miss Kissinger's face was white, and she was raging inwardly. How could they be so cruel, so thoughtless? A forced smile came to her lips as she walked to the officers' table.

She listened to the presentation speech, still smiling, determined that no one should guess her true feelings. She accepted the watch, mumbled thanks, then walked back to her chair, less aware of the applause than of the knowing looks on the faces of most of the women, who could not possibly understand that circumstances rather than personal desires sometimes determined a girl's fate.

As the meeting broke up, many employes rushed up to shake Miss Kissinger's hand and offer congratulations. She thanked them politely, never once letting resentment show on her face or in her speech. Suddenly Mr. Saddler was holding her hand, looking directly into her eyes. Other employes moved discreetly away.

"You—you look lovely this morning, Miss Kissinger," he said. "I doubt whether there is anything the bank could award you that would be a true token of our affection and appreciation. Only the other Sunday I was telling my son and his wife about—"

"Thank you. Thank you very much," Miss Kissinger said, feeling the color rushing to her cheeks. She pulled free and literally ran up the marble stairway.

She turned on the lights as she entered her office, then went to her desk and sat down, putting her purse and gloves in the bottom drawer. She wanted to cry. It didn't seem possible that she could have been working here twenty years, that her thirty-eighth birthday would be coming up in another week. Where had the years gone? And the dreams?

Miss Huddleston, her assistant, came into the room humming "I'm in the Mood for Love."

162

"Statements today, Louise," said Miss Kissinger. "We'll have to hurry to get out on time tonight."

Still humming, Miss Huddleston removed the cover from the big accounting machine, then began entering final checks on the yellow statement forms. When she brought the first stack to Miss Kissinger's desk, she laid them down awkwardly with her left hand, displaying a diamond on her ring finger.

Miss Kissinger made a mental note that she would soon have to break in a new assistant, but she looked up and smiled. "How exciting, Louise."

"It happened last night," said Miss Huddleston. "Honestly, I was never so surprised in my life. I still can't imagine where Joe raised the money, but isn't the ring lovely?"

Miss Kissinger wanted to say that having met Joe several times, she was sure he would be making payments to Acme Credit Jewelers for the next fifty-two weeks. Instead she said, "It's beautiful, Louise. When?"

"Oh, not right away. Joe and I are both so young, and the folks think we should wait at least a year." Miss Huddleston hesitated, then added slyly, "I bet Mr. Martin will be giving you a ring one of these days soon, Miss Kissinger."

Miss Kissinger stiffened in her chair. So young, my eye! Louise Huddleston was twenty-five if she was a day. And just because a person happened to be friends with Herbert Martin and went out to dinner and a movie with him once a week was no reason for anyone to assume that she was waiting for him to buy her a ring.

"We must hurry now, Louise," Miss Kissinger said. "I want to get through the *R*'s by lunch."

When she settled down to the job at hand, starting with the *A* accounts, Miss Kissinger's anger passed. A smile came to her face as she checked the account of Mr. Harold Abrams, 223 Magnolia Avenue, Rolling Greens. As usual, there were five checks for the month—mortgage payment, utilities, telephone, insurance, and the regular $20 check to Dr. Oliver. Miss Kissinger had checked too many family accounts not to know what regular $20 payments to Rockdale's leading obstetrician signified.

In many ways, thought Miss Kissinger, hers was a fascinating job. It was remarkable how much one could learn about a person simply by

163

checking his bank statement each month. She had been following Harold Abrams' account for nine years, since his high-school days when he was a part-time clerk at the big supermarket on State Street. Now he managed a branch store, was buying a new home in the Rolling Greens development, and would soon become a father.

Miss Kissinger sighed wistfully, wondering what her own life would be like if she could have met and fallen in love with a steady boy like Harold Abrams shortly after graduation from high school. There had been opportunities, of course, plenty of them; but her mother had died that year, a sister was still in high school, and her father had been out of work because of the depression. One could not harbor personal ambitions in those days and still remain breadwinner for a family one loved. Now her father too was dead, her sister married and living in California, and she was alone. If the years could be erased and she again be faced with the same decision, what would she do? The answer came sharp and clear. She would do exactly as before. A person of character always faced his responsibilities with dignity and courage, holding on to his values, whatever the price. She sighed again, putting melancholy behind her, working rapidly through the *B*, *C*, and *D* accounts. A deep frown came to her face as she started on the *F*'s and came to the account of Mr. Jed Fraim, c/o The Belmont Hotel. She wondered what new cause for indignation she would find among his checks this month.

She found it immediately. The last of some sixty-odd checks drawn by Jed Fraim during the month of May was for $52.50, made out to the Individual Finance Company. Now he had taken out one of those $300 personal loans, paying heaven only knew how much interest— and him with a salary of well over $1,000 a month after withholding! It was unbelievable that any man could be so irresponsible about money. Twice each month $546.84 was deposited in his account; then a week later he was overdrawn. Most disgusting of all, thought Miss Kissinger, was the bank's attitude toward this client. A red star adorned the Fraim account card. This meant that no check could be refused without approval by an officer of the bank. During the eight-month history of this account, not a single check had been returned marked "Nonsufficient Funds."

Miss Kissinger's lips curled scornfully as she hurried through the checks. Whom did he think he was fooling by drawing them for "Cash" when they were endorsed by such places as Joe's Bar & Grill,

The Highway Inn, and other equally disreputable establishments? There was one check to Main Street Florists for $46.85. Imagine anyone spending that much money for flowers in a single month! The women who received them should know the full truth about Mr. Jed Fraim—the $50 check, for instance, that went to Dr. T. L. Dorrence each month. Miss Kissinger did not know a Dr. Dorrence in Rockdale, but she felt sure in her own mind that he must be treating Jed Fraim for dope addiction, alcoholism, or some other horrible disease. Noting that Jed Fraim had ended the month with a red debit figure of $157.60, and thinking of all the bills she had to pay out of her own meager salary each week, Miss Kissinger's teeth snapped together, and she rose from her chair. It was again time to call this account to the attention of an officer of the bank.

Mr. Saddler was the only vice-president at his desk back of the brass rail in the lobby. He looked up and smiled, catching Miss Kissinger's eye before she could turn away. He came forward with a springy step.

"Why, Miss Kissinger, how nice to see you again," he said. "I do say that is a becoming dress you are wearing."

She handed him the account card and statement. "Someone," she said, "should do something about this man. He has been consistently overdrawn for the past eight months."

Mr. Saddler looked at the account card, then smiled and handed it back with the statement. "It's quite all right, my dear," he said. "Mr. Stone is personally interested in this account. You can be absolutely sure that Mr. Fraim is responsible."

"Why?" Miss Kissinger cried. "Someone please tell me why! Mr. Stone refused to honor the overdrawn checks of his own son when the boy was in college."

"Ours not to question why, Miss Kissinger," Mr. Saddler said.

Miss Kissinger's lips came together in a straight line as she turned on her heel and pounded out her indignation on the terra-cotta floor and marble stairs.

Herbert Martin came into Miss Kissinger's office shortly before lunch. He was a short little man with a bland pink face and gentle brown eyes that blinked frequently back of thick bifocals.

"Muriel," he said excitedly, "you know that new plant The Hobart Company is building on River Street—the one the bank put up the big loan for? Well, it's being completed this morning, and they are having a party out there this evening to show it off. It's mostly for the work-men, who completed the job two months ahead of schedule, but a lot of important business people about town have been invited too. There'll be an orchestra, food, cocktails, all the trimmings. I've been given two tickets. Will you go with me?"

"But your mother, Herbert! This is her night to—"

"I've already talked to her on the telephone," he interrupted. "She understands that this is important bank business. Sister is coming over to drive her to the doctor's. We'll have fun. And it won't cost a penny. What do you say?"

At that moment Mr. Saddler came into the office and glared at Herbert Martin.

Herbert seemed to shrink back against the wall. "I—I was just check-ing an account with Miss Kissinger, Mr. Saddler," he said obsequiously. "This man has a small welding shop on West Street and has applied for a minimum loan to—"

"Yes, Martin," Mr. Saddler said coldly. "And now that you've finished—"

Herbert edged toward the door and went out with a swish.

A smile replaced the frown on Mr. Saddler's face. He glanced around the office, noting that Miss Huddleston was out; then he walked over and closed the door and, returning, sat down in the chair beside Miss Kissinger's desk.

There was a moment of silence. Mr. Saddler gave his throat a final clearing.

"I'm a direct person, Miss Kissinger," he said. "I've been wanting to talk with you alone for some time. No, don't interrupt me, please, until I've finished. As you perhaps know, it has now been two years since Mrs. Saddler, God bless her, passed away. My son agrees that I would be foolish not to consider a second marriage. I am only fifty-seven years old. Most people usually guess me younger, but there would be no point in lying. My salary here at the bank is among the top ones, and I've made many prudent investments through the years. The woman who shares my remaining years will enjoy every luxury. Indeed, I would expect to make a property settlement as a part of any marital—"

"But, Mr. Saddler! Please. I—"

"Hear me out, my dear. I've not approached this conversation

166

lightly. You are a mature, attractive, sensible woman. I've known and admired your fine qualities for many years. I doubt that you have any serious romantic interests, certainly not in Herbert Martin—not that I wish to belittle him, but—"

As if in answer to her prayer, the telephone rang. She answered it, then handed the receiver to Mr. Saddler.

"Hello," he said irritably. "Oh, Mr. Stone. Put him on, please."

There were long silences, punctuated by such statements as "Yes, sir. Yes, Mr. Stone. Of course, Mr. Stone."

He replaced the telephone and rose. "Mr. Stone wants me to go with him to a directors' meeting at The Hobart Company," he said. "I'll be away for the rest of the day, but I'd like to continue this conversation in the morning. In the meantime, my dear, please give serious thought to what I've already said."

Mr. Saddler went out, wearing an expression not unlike the one on Herbert Martin's face only a few minutes before.

Miss Kissinger stared blankly at the statement before her, tears swimming in her eyes. I'm old, she thought, really old. The past twenty years, each submerged in the routine of job, home, and, yes, boredom, had become realities. Always until this moment a real, if undefined, dream had made each new year bearable. Sooner or later she would meet a man worthy of her love, and they would marry. A home and children would naturally follow. But one year had slipped into the next, each with its special problem. Her father had been ill for so long. There had been college debts of her sister's. Now it was too late. She hadn't known, but Mr. Saddler knew. He never made propositions unless all conditions were favorable to himself. He knew that the time had come for her to consider comfort, position, and security as substitutes for romantic dreams. She buried her face in her hands, sobbing.

The sobbing stopped finally, and she straightened in her chair, reaching for her purse. After she had repaired her make-up, she phoned Herbert Martin to say she would go to the Hobart party.

That evening, at five to seven, Miss Kissinger stepped out of the bathtub into a white negligee. She went into the bedroom and loosened her silky black hair. For a long moment she gazed at herself in the mirror. Old, old, she said to herself; but it was absurd to suppose she spoke of the woman in the mirror, her skin faintly flushed from her bath, her gentle curves enhanced by the lines of the negligee. After a while Miss Kissinger picked up her brush. This time she did not pull her hair back in the severe style she ordinarily affected.

When she was dressed, she turned out the lights and walked downstairs. Herbert was waiting in his car at the curb.

"Muriel!" he cried, as she got in beside him. "You look so different. What—"

"Thank you, Herbert," she said coolly.

Herbert continued to glance at her out of the corner of his eye as he drove cautiously through town and across the Jefferson Street Bridge, turning south on River Street.

The new Hobart plant, consisting of four long, low buildings, was brightly lighted. Herbert pulled in and parked among the hundred or so cars in front.

As they got out and started toward the brightly lighted entrance, Miss Kissinger said, "Herbert, I presume Mr. Saddler will be here this evening. I do not intend to dance with him. I—I'd appreciate it if you would see to it that refusing him does not become necessary."

"But, Muriel!" Herbert cried. "He's a vice-president. He's my boss—"

"I do not intend to dance with him," she repeated decisively, then walked ahead of Herbert into the building. It had just occurred to her that she did not like Herbert Martin. She thought of the sixteen hundred dollars in her savings account. She would turn in her resignation at the end of the month. She had enough for a trip to Europe. When she came back, she'd go to New York and look for a new job there.

The long main building, not yet equipped with machinery, reverberated with music from a small orchestra on a platform erected in the center of the building. A large crowd stood about a cleared area, where several couples were dancing. Waiters from a catering service passed among the guests with cocktails and canapés. The music stopped just as Miss Kissinger and Herbert Martin came up to the edge of the crowd.

Mr. Hobart, Mr. Stone of the bank, and one of the ugliest men Miss Kissinger had ever seen mounted the platform and walked over to stand in front of a microphone. Apparently there would be speeches before dancing resumed.

"Friends and fellow workers," said Mr. Hobart. "You were invited here to have fun and inspect our wonderful new plant. Since Randolph Stone, of Rockdale National, put up most of the money for it, I'm going to turn the mike over to him and ask him to introduce the man chiefly responsible for getting it completed two months ahead of schedule. Randy Stone!"

Mr. Stone, who at the bank always looked as though he had just bit into a green persimmon, now was a picture of relaxed affability. "Friends," he said in a stentorian voice, "it is a real pleasure to introduce my good friend Jed Fraim, of the Pan-American Construction Company."

Miss Kissinger suddenly gasped. "Well, for goodness sake!" she said to no one in particular, staring at the man whose spending habits she had condemned for the past eight months.

"I would be remiss in my duty," said Mr. Stone, "if I did not say that this plant was finished ahead of schedule because Jed Fraim and his fine workmen knew that it was to manufacture a vitally needed instrument of war for our boys in Korea. That war has ended, to be sure, but may I remind you, my friends, that the threat to our security still exists."

"Hey, Jed, you old patriot," cried a rough character from the edge of the crowd, "why don't you wave a flag?"

Mr. Stone went on and on. Not only was Jed Fraim a great construction superintendent but a man of character and integrity. It was no secret that Jack Hobart was trying to get him to remain in Rockdale as plant manager of the new factory. Rockdale needed men like Jed Fraim.

"Character, my eye!" said Miss Kissinger to Herbert. "This is the most disgusting spectacle I have ever witnessed."

"Speech, Jed, you old patriot!" the same rough voice cried.

Silence came over the room as Jed Fraim raised his big hamlike hand and scowled in the direction of the voice. "There are a few knuckleheads present," he said, "who are not used to mixing in nice company. To them, I have this to say: We have exactly five days to clean and repair our equipment. On Sunday a truck-and-trailer convoy heads for New Orleans, where a ship is waiting to take it to South America. I want every man of you on the job tomorrow morning. Have fun tonight, but the first tough guy who starts a fight or makes unpleasant remarks about how this party is being run will wake up in the morning with more than a hang-over. I'm not kidding!"

"Just exactly as I've always imagined him," whispered Miss Kissinger.

"Vulgar, uncouth, disgusting, a bully—"

"And to the rest of you nice people," said Jed Fraim, "I want to say how much my men and I have enjoyed working and living among you. We are construction craftsmen with the special skills required to put up buildings in a world that needs them. If you want to thank my men for the job they did on this plant, why not buy another savings bond? Your government still needs to sell them."

"Oh, for goodness sake," said Miss Kissinger. "If he ever saved a penny for a bond, it would be a miracle!"

As the music started, Herbert took Miss Kissinger's arm and guided her to the dancing area. They had circled the floor only once when the orchestra leader came to the microphone. "Mr. Herbert Martin is wanted on the telephone."

As Herbert hurried away, Miss Kissinger waited at the edge of the crowd, watching the dancers, tapping time with her toe. A hand suddenly touched her shoulder. She turned, expecting Herbert, but it was Mr. Saddler, smiling happily.

"Martin's sister just called," he said. "She has a flat tire. He's gone to help her. I told him not to come back, that I would drive you home."

Mr. Stone, leading Jed Fraim by the arm, appeared suddenly. "Why, Miss Kissinger," he said, "how nice to find you here this evening! I want you to meet my good friend Jed Fraim. Jed, this is Miss Kissinger, one of the nicest people at our bank. You two have a dance while Saddler and I talk business."

Eager to get away from Mr. Saddler at whatever cost, Miss Kissinger permitted Jed Fraim to lead her out to the dance floor. She felt embarrassed as she opened her arms and started dancing with him. He was such a huge and ugly man. But surprisingly he was an excellent dancer, light on his feet and a gentle leader.

"Thank you," he said, as they reached the far side of the floor. "I've been trying to get away from that old windbag for the past twenty minutes. I'll take you back to your husband whenever you say."

Miss Kissinger looked into his face for the first time since they had started dancing, surprised by his directness. His face was not dissipated after all; it was the fluorescent lights above the orchestra that had made him look that way. He was simply wind-burned. "I—I doubt that you heard my name correctly," she said. "I am *Miss* Kissinger."

He smiled down at her. "There must be something wrong with the

170

men in this town," he said. "You are beautiful, and the best dancer I've ever danced with."

She knew that she should feel offended, but it seemed to be one of the nicest compliments she had ever received. Dropping her cheek against Jed Fraim's massive chest, she gave herself completely to a saxophone that was taking privileges with "Star Dust."

The music stopped just as they came alongside Mr. Saddler, who was now standing alone. He stepped out to take Miss Kissinger's arm possessively. "Just one waltz with me, my dear," he said authoritatively, "then I'll drive you home. Big day tomorrow."

Miss Kissinger looked pleadingly into Jed Fraim's eyes. He seemed to sense her feelings and deliberately moved between her and Mr. Saddler. A look of annoyance came over the vice-president's face, but he continued to smile.

"Perhaps we should go right now," said Mr. Saddler, "and we'll stop off at the Union Club for a late supper. You'll like the club, I'm sure."

"I'm sure she would, Saddler," said Jed Fraim, "but it happens that Miss Kissinger has promised to have a late supper with me. If you'll excuse us now—"

Without waiting for a reply, Jed took Miss Kissinger's arm and guided her past Mr. Saddler and toward the door that led to the parking lot. When they were outside, he said, "I don't blame you for wanting to get away from that old buzzard, but you don't have to be burdened with me either. Perhaps you'll let me drive you to wherever you want to go?"

"You are very kind, Mr. Fraim," she said, feeling grateful. "I would like a sandwich, but there's a snack bar near my apartment. If—"

"Of course," he said, guiding her toward a beat-up old convertible.

They drove slowly across the bridge and turned up Main Street. Jed Fraim suddenly pulled over to the curb, stopping in front of the Main Street Florists, where a man was working on a new window display. "I almost forgot," he said. "Will you excuse me a minute?"

The door of the store was locked, but Jed Fraim pounded on it until the man left the window and admitted him. A few minutes later he returned to the car carrying a large box of flowers and a single rose. He got into the car, placing the box on the seat between them. He remained silent for a moment, then handed her the rose. "I—I bought two dozen for a friend of mine," he said, "and there was only one left.

171

I thought you might like it."

"Why—why thank you," she said, wondering why she should feel annoyed.

"I usually have these things delivered," he said, "but the delivery boy had gone home, so I'll have to take them myself. Maybe you'd like to ride out to the hospital with me? Visiting hours are over at nine, and it's a quarter to now."

Her annoyance vanished completely as they drove toward the hospital, and Jed Fraim explained. "Mrs. Swenson had her baby this morning," he said, then added, "I think you'd like her. Why don't you come up with me? It will take only a minute."

Mrs. Swenson beamed as they came into the room. Jed opened the box and laid it on the bed beside her. "For my favorite mamma," he said. "Swenson tells me he's a fine big boy."

Mrs. Swenson reached up suddenly and pulled Jed Fraim's face down so she could kiss his cheek. "Oh, Jed, you are the sweetest person I know." She then turned to Miss Kissinger. "This big oaf tries to act like a tough guy," she said, "but don't let him fool you, Miss—"

"Miss Kissinger," Jed said, "I'm sorry I forgot to introduce you."

"He must have a hundred men in his crew, Miss Kissinger," said Mrs. Swenson, "but there's always flowers from Jed at every wedding, birth, or funeral. He must spend a fortune on flowers every month. How such a nice guy has managed to stay single for forty years—"

"We'd better go now, Miss Kissinger," said Jed Fraim. He was blushing like a schoolboy.

"Jed," said Mrs. Swenson, as they said good-bye and started to leave, "I wonder if you'd round Swenson up and send him back to the trailer. He don't have a son every day, and you know Swenson."

"Sure," said Jed, "and don't worry about catching up with us in New Orleans. Arrangements have been made to have you and the baby flown down."

After they were in the car and driving back toward town, Jed said, "You've been very kind to me this evening, Miss Kissinger, and I'd like to buy you a nice dinner at the Starlight Room in the Coronado Hotel, but I should round my gang up first and start them for the trailer camp. Would you mind riding to a couple of places? It won't take long."

The Highway Inn was a dimly lit ginmill on Route 20. Jed parked among the cars in front of it, excused himself, and went inside, coming back shortly to get his checkbook from the glove compartment. "I've got three in there," he said, "all of them with bar bills to be squared away before we leave town."

He went back inside. In a few minutes he came out, herding three husky men ahead of him. One started to turn about and go back, but Jed gave him a shove. "That's all for tonight, Gurowski," Jed said. "You are going home now, and you, Brennan, are going to take him. As for you, Swenson, if you hit another joint tonight, I'm going to tell your wife I had to make your final payment to that finance company last month. Get going."

The three men grinned sheepishly, got into a car, and drove off toward town. Jed followed slowly behind them. "They are good boys," he said, "but they play just as hard as they work. I don't know what they'd do if they didn't have me to ride herd on them and pay their bills. You wouldn't believe it, but I've got over six thousand dollars out to my men on this job alone. I must write more checks than any man in this town."

Miss Kissinger said, "I'm sure you do. I shouldn't think you could afford to."

"Oh, I always get it back," he said, "when they receive their bonus at the end of a job. There'll be a good one on this Hobart contract. I explained my situation to old man Stone at the bank when I first opened my account there. They've been very nice about letting me overdraw. I'll bet I'm overdrawn at least a hundred dollars right now."

Miss Kissinger started to say, "It's exactly a hundred fifty-seven dollars and sixty cents," but caught herself in time. Instead she said, "I can understand why you need a special arrangement with a bank in your particular job." Inwardly she felt a warm glow, remembering the look on Mrs. Swenson's face as she kissed Jed Fraim's cheek. A woman like that seldom misjudged a man.

Additional stops were made at The Lodi Restaurant, Joe's Bar & Grill, The Moose Club, and Harry's Townhouse. A total of fourteen men, several weaving unsteadily, were started for the trailer camp at the edge of town. Jed Fraim's checkbook was needed at two places.

It was eleven thirty before Jed Fraim and Miss Kissinger arrived at the beautiful Starlight Room in the Coronado Hotel. It was almost three when they left. Jed paid their bill with a check.

Miss Kissinger could not sleep after she was home and in bed. It had been the most exciting evening of her life, and it now seemed that she

173

had known Jed Fraim for years. His shyness had vanished after a couple of glasses of champagne in the dimly lighted room, and he talked freely about himself. He was the oldest of seven children and had started in the construction business when he was seventeen; he had since worked all over the world. He had helped three of his younger brothers through college, one of whom was now assistant chief engineer of his company. He'd often thought of marriage, he said, and the home he was missing, but what woman would want to share a trailer in the out-of-the-way places where he usually worked? Take this job in South America, for instance. It was to be a hospital in a small city far inland from the coast. The climate would be hard, and there would be few diversions. After this job was completed, his crew would move on to Venezuela to put up an oil-processing plant, a job that might take two years. A woman would have to be out of her mind to agree to share that kind of life. Miss Kissinger, who had never been farther from Rockdale than Chicago, wanted to say that it sounded like a fascinating life; but that, she knew, would make her appear forward.

Jed Fraim had walked with her from his car to the door of her apartment building, and he held her hand for just a moment. "You've been very kind to me, Miss Kissinger," he said. "I probably bored you with all that talk, but—"

"Not at all," she interrupted. "I enjoyed every minute of it. You— you'll be leaving soon?"

"Sunday," he said, then turned quickly and walked to his car.

It was almost nine when Miss Kissinger reached the bank next morning, late for the first time in three years. She didn't care. One thought was uppermost in her mind. Would Jed Fraim call her before he left? Mr. Saddler started to approach her in the lobby as she was going out to lunch, but she looked him coldly in the eye and walked past. At three in the afternoon Herbert Martin came into her office to apologize for not returning the previous evening. She informed him that no explanation was necessary. Then she went home two hours early.

Mrs. Nelson, who lived below her, stopped her as she came into the building and handed her a large box of flowers. She hurried up to her apartment and rapidly opened the box to find two dozen American Beauty roses and a card reading "For the best dancer I know. Called to Chicago on business, but will be back Friday. Will you have dinner with me then?" The card was signed "Jed."

Wednesday and Thursday passed slowly. On Friday she called the bank to tell them she would not be at work that day. She spent the morning touring Rockdale's leading stores, settling on a beautiful evening gown of white tulle, sprinkled with rhinestones. She purchased evening sandals and a bag to match, then, throwing away all caution, paid a hundred and fifty dollars for a fur stole. It was the most extravagant shopping spree of her life.

Jed called at six that evening to say he would be held on the job until seven and might he pick her up at eight? She tried not to appear too eager. Eight would be quite satisfactory, she told him.

Dressed and waiting, she became nervous, sure that she was too conspicuous in her new clothes. Would he think her too bold in such a low-cut dress? Her buzzer sounded at exactly eight o'clock. Her heart began to pound as she opened her door and walked to the head of the stairs to tell Jed to come up.

She stepped back into her apartment to wait, wishing she had worn her plain brown suit. Then everything was quite perfect. Jed Fraim, looking awkward and ill at ease in a new tuxedo and black tie, filled her doorway, grinning shyly as he looked about the colorful room. His eyes came to rest on her suddenly, and his square jaw sagged.

"You—you are beautiful," he said. "You are beautiful."

She felt the color rushing to her cheeks but stepped forward and guided him into the room and to a chair. "I'll be ready in just a minute," she said, and went into her bedroom to wipe away the tears.

At two A.M. they sat at a table near the dance floor in the Starlight Room, flushed and warm from dancing. The orchestra started playing again. Miss Kissinger started to get up, but Jed reached over and took her hand. "Let's sit this one out," he said. "There's something I want to tell you."

She looked down at her glass, waiting, knowing that this was the happiest moment of her life, that it could not have been more beautiful or thrilling if it had happened when she was twenty. There wasn't the slightest doubt in her mind about what Jed Fraim was going to say.

"I went to Chicago," he said, "to resign my job with Pan-American."

"But why should you resign your job?" she asked. "Surely—"

"They've offered me a good thing at Hobart's," he said. "I've been knocking around too long. I liked this little city from the first day I started work here. When I met you the other night and learned that you were unmarried, I thought—well, I thought that given a year to get acquainted, you might overlook my rough spots and find me a person worth—" He faltered, groping for words.

She looked into his eyes. "I knew what kind of person you were when I went with you to visit Mrs. Swenson." She hesitated, dropping her eyes to her glass. "But you've misjudged me. I—I wouldn't mind living in a trailer. Unless you'd prefer working and living here in Rockdale, I would love to go with you to South America. I think it would be quite the most—" She stopped suddenly, aware that she had said too much; then it didn't matter.

His happiness showed in his eyes as he rose and came around the table to take her hand and guide her onto the floor. She was in his arms, tightly held, moving slowly and rhythmically to the lilting waltz. At the far side of the floor, back of an imitation palm, he kissed her, then led her toward the checkroom to get his hat.

They were silent as they drove slowly toward her apartment. As they stopped in front of the building, he said, "I can get three weeks off before the job in South America starts. We could be married here, then stop off for ten days in Bermuda. There's just one thing."

"What?" she asked breathlessly.

"Do you like dogs?"

"I love them," she said.

"I'm glad," he replied. "I forgot to tell you about Tinker, my old boxer. I've been boarding him with Doctor Dorrence, a veterinarian who has an animal hospital out on Route Twenty."

"Oh," said Miss Kissinger, her happiness complete. And again she knew that this moment could not have been more perfect if it had happened when she was twenty.

When I Was One-and-Twenty

A. E. Housman

When I was one-and-twenty
I heard a wise man say,
'Give crowns and pounds and guineas
But not your heart away.

Give pearls away and rubies
  But keep your fancy free.'
But I was one-and-twenty,
  No use to talk to me.

When I was one-and-twenty
  I heard him say again,
'The heart out of the bosom
  Was never given in vain;
'Tis paid with sighs a plenty
  And sold for endless rue.'
And I am two-and-twenty,
  And oh, 'tis true, 'tis true.

Recuerdo

Edna St. Vincent Millay

We were very tired, we were very merry—
We had gone back and forth all night on the ferry.
It was bare and bright, and smelled like a stable—
But we looked into a fire, we leaned across a table,
We lay on the hill-top underneath the moon;
And the whistles kept blowing, and the dawn came soon.

We were very tired, we were very merry—
We had gone back and forth all night on the ferry;
And you ate an apple, and I ate a pear,
From a dozen of each we had bought somewhere;
And the sky went wan, and the wind came cold,
And the sun rose dripping, a bucketful of gold.

We were very tired, we were very merry—
We had gone back and forth all night on the ferry.
We hailed, "Good morrow, mother!" to a shawl-covered head,
And bought a morning paper, which neither of us read;
And she wept, "God bless you!" for the apples and the pears,
And we gave her all our money but our subway fares.

To Springvale for Christmas

Zona Gale

*A famous writer shows us the warm spirit of
Christmas in the heart of this mother, and her
story enriches us all.*

WHEN PRESIDENT Arthur Tilton of Briarcliff College, who
usually used a two-cent stamp, said, "Get me Chicago, please," his
secretary was impressed, looked for vast educational problems to be
in the making, and heard instead:

"Ed? Well, Ed, you and Rick and Grace and I are going out to
Springvale for Christmas. . . . Yes, well, I've got a family too, you
recall. But Mother was seventy last fall and— Do you realize that it's
eleven years since we've all spent Christmas with her? Grace has been
every year. She's going this year. And so are we! And take her the
best Christmas she ever had, too. Ed, Mother was *seventy* last fall—"

At dinner, he asked his wife what would be a suitable gift, a very
special gift, for a woman of seventy. And she said: "Oh, your mother.
Well, dear, I should think the material for a good wool dress would be
right. I'll select it for you, if you like—" He said that he would see,
and he did not reopen the subject.

In town on December twenty-fourth he timed his arrival to allow
him an hour in a shop. There he bought a silver-gray silk of a fineness
and a lightness which pleased him and at a price which made him
comfortably guilty. And at the shop, Ed, who was Edward McKillop
Tilton, head of a law firm, picked him up.

"Where's your present?" Arthur demanded.

Edward drew a case from his pocket and showed him a tiny gold
wrist-watch of decent manufacture and explained: "I expect you'll
think I'm a fool, but you know that Mother has told time for fifty
years by the kitchen clock, or else the shield of the black-marble
parlor angel who never goes—you get the idea?—and so I bought her
this."

178

At the station was Grace, and the boy who bore her bag bore also a parcel of great dimensions.

"Mother already has a feather bed," Arthur reminded her.

"They won't let you take an automobile into the coach," Edward warned her.

"It's a rug for the parlor," Grace told them. "You know it *is* a parlor—one of the very few left in the Mississippi valley. And Mother has had that ingrain down since before we left home—"

Grace's eyes were misted. Why would women always do that? This was no occasion for sentiment. This was a merry Christmas.

"Very nice. And Ricky'd better look sharp," said Edward dryly.

Ricky never did look sharp. About trains he was conspicuously ignorant. He had no occupation. Some said that he "wrote," but no one had ever seen anything that he had written. He lived in town—no one knew how—never accepted a cent from his brothers and was beloved of every one, most of all of his mother.

"Ricky won't bring anything, of course," they said.

But when the train had pulled out without him, observedly, a porter came staggering through the cars carrying two great suitcases and following a perturbed man of forty-something who said. "Oh, here you are!" as if it were they who were missing, and squeezed himself and his suitcases among brothers and sister and rug. "I had only a minute to spare," he said regretfully. "If I'd had two, I could have snatched some flowers. I flung 'em my card and told 'em to send 'em."

"Why are you taking so many lugs?" they wanted to know.

Ricky focused on the suitcases. "Just necessities," he said. "Just the presents. I didn't have room to get in anything else."

"Presents! What?"

"Well," said Ricky, "I'm taking books. I know Mother doesn't care much for books, but the bookstore's the only place I can get trusted."

They turned over his books: Fiction, travel, biography, a new illustrated edition of the Bible—they were willing to admire his selection. And Grace said confusedly but appreciatively: "You know, the parlor bookcase has never had a thing in it excepting a green curtain *over* it!"

And they were all borne forward, well pleased.

Springvale has eight hundred inhabitants. As they drove through the principal street at six o'clock on that evening of December twenty-fourth, all that they expected to see abroad was the pop-corn wagon and a cat or two. Instead they counted seven automobiles and estimated thirty souls, and no one paid the slightest attention to them as strangers. Springvale was becoming metropolitan. There was a new church on one corner and a store-building bore the sign "Public Library." Even the little hotel had a rubber-plant in the window and a strip of cretonne overhead.

The three men believed themselves to be a surprise. But, mindful of the panic to be occasioned by four appetites precipitated into a Springvale ménage, Grace had told. Therefore the parlor was lighted and heated, there was in the air of the passage an odor of brown gravy which, no butler's pantry ever having inhibited, seemed a permanent savory. By the happiest chance, Mrs. Tilton had not heard their arrival nor—the parlor angel being in her customary eclipse and the kitchen grandfather's clock wrong—had she begun to look for them. They slipped in, they followed Grace down the hall, they entered upon her in her gray gingham apron worn over her best blue serge, and they saw her first in profile, frosting a lemon pie. With some assistance from her, they all took her in their arms at once.

"Aren't you surprised?" cried Edward in amazement.

"I haven't got over being surprised," she said placidly, "since I first heard you were coming!"

She gazed at them tenderly, with flour on her chin, and then she said: "There's something you won't like. We're going to have the Christmas dinner tonight."

Their clamor that they would entirely like that did not change her look.

"Our church couldn't pay the minister this winter," she said, "on account of the new church building. So the minister and his wife are boarding around with the congregation. Tomorrow's their day to come here for a week. It's a hard life and I didn't have the heart to change 'em."

Her family covered their regret as best they could and entered upon her little feast. At the head of her table, with her four "children" about her, and Father's armchair left vacant, they perceived that she was not quite the figure they had been thinking her. In this interval they had grown to think of her as a pathetic figure. Not because their father had died, not because she insisted on Springvale as a residence, not because of her eyes. Just pathetic. Mothers of grown children, they might have given themselves the suggestion, were always pathetic. But here was Mother, a definite person with poise and with ideas, who might be proud of her offspring, but who, in her heart, never

180

forgot that they *were* her offspring and that she was the parent stock.

"I wouldn't eat two pieces of that pie," she said to President Tilton; "it's pretty rich." And he answered humbly: "Very well, Mother." And she took with composure Ricky's light chant:

> "Now, you must remember, wherever you are,
> That you are the jam, but your mother's the jar."

"Certainly, my children," she said. "And I'm about to tell you when you may have your Christmas presents. Not tonight. Christmas eve is no proper time for presents. It's stealing a day outright. And you miss the fun of looking forward all night long. The only proper time for the presents is after breakfast on Christmas morning, *after* the dishes are washed. The minister and his wife may get here any time from nine on. That means we've got to get to bed early!"

President Arthur Tilton lay in his bed looking at the muslin curtain on which the street-lamp threw the shadow of a bare elm which he remembered. He thought:

"She's a pioneer spirit. She's the kind who used to go ahead anyway, even if they had missed the emigrant party, and who used to cross the plains alone. She's the backbone of the world. I wish I could megaphone that to the students at Briarcliff who think their mothers 'try to boss' them!"

"Don't leave your windows open too far," he heard from the hall. "The wind's changed."

In the light of a snowy morning the home parlor showed the cluttered commonplace of a room whose furniture and ornaments were not believed to be beautiful and most of them known not to be useful. Yet when—after the dishes were washed—these five came to the leather chair which bore the gifts, the moment was intensely satisfactory. This in spite of the sense of haste with which the parcels were attacked—lest the minister and his wife arrive in their midst.

"That's one reason," Mrs. Tilton said, "why I want to leave part of my Christmas for you until I take you to the train tonight. Do you care?"

"I'll leave a present I know about until then too," said Ricky. "May I?"

"Come on now, though," said President Arthur Tilton. "I want to see Mother get her dolls."

It was well that they were not of an age to look for exclamations of delight from Mother. To every gift her reaction was one of startled rebuke.

181

"Grace! How could you? All that money! Oh, it's beautiful! But the old one would have done me all my life. . . . Why, Edward! You extravagant boy! I never had a watch in all my life. You ought not to have gone to all that expense. Arthur Tilton! A silk dress! What a firm piece of goods! I don't know what to say to you—you're all too good to me!"

At Ricky's books she stared and said: "My dear boy, you've been very reckless. Here are more books than I can ever read—now. Why, that's almost more than they've got to start the new library with. And you spent all that money on me!"

It dampened their complacence, but they understood her concealed delight and they forgave her an honest regret at their modest prodigality. For, when they opened her gifts for them, they felt the same reluctance to take the hours and hours of patient knitting for which these stood.

"Hush, and hurry," was her comment, "or the minister'll get us!"

The minister and his wife, however, were late. The second side of the turkey was ready and the mince pie hot when, toward noon, they came to the door—a faint little woman and a thin man with beautiful, exhausted eyes. They were both in some slight glow of excitement and disregarded Mrs. Tilton's efforts to take their coats.

"No," said the minister's wife. "No. We do beg your pardon. But we find we have to go into the country this morning."

"It is absolutely necessary to us that we go into the country," said the minister earnestly. "This morning," he added impressively.

"Into the country! You're going to be here for dinner."

They were firm. They had to go into the country. They shook hands almost tenderly with these four guests. "We just heard about you in the post office," they said. "Merry Christmas—oh, Merry Christmas! We'll be back about dark."

They left their two shabby suitcases on the hall floor and went away.

"All the clothes they've got between them would hardly fill these up," said Mrs. Tilton mournfully. "Why on earth do you suppose they'd turn their back on a dinner that smells so good and go off into the country at noon on Christmas Day? They wouldn't do that for another invitation. Likely somebody's sick," she ended, her puzzled look denying her tone of finality.

"Well, thank the Lord for the call to the country," said Ricky shamelessly. "It saved our day."

182

They had their Christmas dinner, they had their afternoon—safe and happy and uninterrupted. Five commonplace-looking folk in a commonplace-looking house, but the eye of love knew that this was not all. In the wide sea of their routine they had found and taken for their own this island day, unforgettable.

"I thought it was going to be a gay day," said Ricky at its close, "but it hasn't. It's been heavenly! Mother, shall we give them the rest of their presents now, you and I?"

"Not yet," she told them. "Ricky, I want to whisper to you."

She looked so guilty that they all laughed at her. Ricky was laughing when he came back from that brief privacy. He was still laughing mysteriously when his mother turned from a telephone call.

"What do you think!" she cried. "That was the woman that brought me my turkey. She knew the minister and his wife were to be with me today. She wants to know why they've been eating a lunch in a cutter out that way. Do you suppose—"

They all looked at one another doubtfully, then in abrupt conviction. "They went because they wanted us to have the day to ourselves!"

"Arthur," said Mrs. Tilton with immense determination, "let me whisper to you, too." And from that moment's privacy he also returned smiling, but a bit ruefully.

"Mother ought to be the president of a university," he said.

"Mother ought to be the head of a law firm," said Edward.

"Mother ought to write a book about herself," said Ricky.

"Mother's mother," said Grace, "and that's enough. But you're all so mysterious, except me."

"Grace," said Mrs. Tilton, "you remind me that I want to whisper to you."

Their train left in the late afternoon. Through the white streets they walked to the station, the somber little woman, the buoyant, capable daughter, the three big sons. She drew them to seclusion down by the baggage room and gave them four envelopes.

"Here's the rest of my Christmas for you," she said. "I'd rather you'd open it on the train. Now, Ricky, what's yours?"

She was firm to their protests. The train was whistling when Ricky owned up that the rest of his Christmas present for Mother was a brand new daughter, to be acquired as soon as his new book was off the press. "We're going to marry on the advance royalty," he said

183

importantly, "and live on—" The rest was lost in the roar of the express.

"Edward!" shouted Mrs. Tilton. "Come here. I want to whisper—"

She was obliged to shout it, whatever it was. But Edward heard, and nodded, and kissed her. There was time for her to slip something in Ricky's pocket and for the other good-byes, and then the train drew out. From the platform they saw her brave, calm face against the background of the little town. A mother of "grown children" pathetic? She seemed to them at that moment the one supremely triumphant figure in life.

They opened their envelopes soberly and sat soberly over the contents. The note, scribbled to Grace, explained: Mother wanted to divide up now what she had had for them in her will. She would keep one house and live on the rent from the other one, and "here's all the rest." They laughed at her postscript:

"Don't argue. I ought to give the most—I'm the mother."

"And look at her," said Edward solemnly. "As soon as she heard about Ricky, there at the station, she whispered to me that she wanted to send Ricky's sweetheart the watch I'd just given her. Took it off her wrist then and there."

"That must be what she slipped in my pocket," said Ricky.

It was.

"She asked me," he said, "if I minded if she gave those books to the new Springvale Public Library."

"She asked me," said Grace, "if I cared if she gave the new rug to the new church that can't pay its minister."

President Arthur Tilton shouted with laughter.

"When we heard where the minister and his wife ate their Christmas dinner," he said, "she whispered to ask me whether she might give the silk dress to her when they get back tonight."

All this they knew by the time the train reached the crossing where they could look back on Springvale. On the slope of the hill lay the little cemetery, and Ricky said:

"And she told me that if my flowers got there before dark, she'd take them up to the cemetery for Christmas for Father. By night she won't have even a flower left to tell her we've been there."

"Not even the second side of the turkey," said Grace, "and yet I think—"

"So do I," her brothers said.

To F. W.

Edith Franklin Wyatt

You are my companion
Down the silver road,
Still and many-changing,
Infinitely changing,
You are my companion.

Something sings in lives—
Days of walking on and on—
Deep beyond all singing,
Wonderful past singing.

Wonderful our road,
Long and many-changing,
Infinitely changing,
This, more wonderful—
We are here together,
You and I together,
I am your companion.
You are my companion,
My own true companion.

Let the roadside fade—
Morning on the mountain-top
Hours along the valley,
Days of walking on and on
Pulse away in silence,
In eternal silence.
Let the world all fade
Break and pass away.

Yet will this remain,
Deep beyond all singing,
My own true companion,
Beautiful past singing.

We were here together—
On this earth together.
I was your companion.
You were my companion,
My own true companion.

185

The Lesson

Pearl Buck

A young Chinese girl learns a far more important lesson than her teacher thinks she does. A tender tale by a Nobel Prize-winning author.

"I HATE to let Ru-lan go like this," said little Mrs. Stanley to her husband. "I don't believe she knows anything at all—she's not fit to be married."

She had just come in from the garden and her arms were full of roses, the swift-blooming, vivid roses of a Chinese May. Wyn Stanley looked at her, smiling, his heart caught in his throat at her loveliness. He and Mollie had been married five years but he never grew used to her. He saw her every day—how lucky he was that his work at the mission was to run the schools and not to be an itinerant evangelist! If he had had to go off on long preaching tours as Dr. Martin did, and be weeks away from Mollie, he could not have borne it. Sometimes in the night he woke to trouble and shivering, fearful lest God call him to such work, lest something happen that he and Mollie might have to be separated—suppose one of the children were to fall ill and have to be taken home across the sea to America like the Burgess child, and Mrs. Burgess away for nearly two years, or—he would put out his hand to touch Mollie's round little body lying deeply and healthfully asleep beside him. He would not wake her—but somehow she always woke and somehow he always told her his fears, and then waited to hear her laugh her sweet, contented laughter. "Oh, Wyn, as if—Anyway, God hasn't called you to evangelistic work, has he? And if I had to go home you'd come too. We'd find another job. You suppose I'd let you stay here by yourself?" He was asleep before he knew it then.

Now he looked up at her from his desk, adoring her. She dimpled and put her hand on his cheek and pretended to pout. "You haven't heard a thing I've been saying. You never listen to me."

186

He caught her hand and held it to his lips, a little firm hand, scratched with rose thorns. "It's because I can't keep from looking at you. What's going to happen to me if I keep loving you more all the time?" He drew her to him and leaned his face against her breast. Under his cheek he could feel the steady pounding of her heart. "True heart—true heart—" he murmured to the rhythm of her heart. She bent over his dark head, pressing it against her. They both forgot the girl Ru-lan. They were swept back into the summer morning five years ago in the little old churchyard behind the red brick church where her father had preached so many years, and where Wyn had come as substitute for a month of vacation. She and her mother had sent her father off for the trip to Palestine he had planned for a lifetime. What destiny it had been, that on the summer when the family did not all go away together Wyn had been the supply—just before he was to sail as a missionary to China!

They had fallen in love at once. The first moment she saw his tall, young figure mounting the steps of the pulpit she knew him and loved him. And he, when he looked over the congregation, saw her and thereafter her only. And then in just a few weeks, that July morning after church, when she was running home to the manse by the short cut through the churchyard, he came striding after her, still with his surplice on. He had, he said, meant only to ask her to—to walk with him, perhaps, in the evening. But when she turned and looked at him, under the deep shadows of the old elms and hidden by the lilacs along the path, he had taken her into his arms and enfolded her. There was no question asked and no answer given, simply meeting. Whenever they came together it was the same thing, the same deep union again— like this.

There was a small sound, and they jumped apart. The older missionaries always said, "The Chinese are not used to demonstration between the sexes." Mrs. Burgess had taken her aside very soon and said, "Try not to take your—Mr. Stanley's—hand in front of the Chinese, dear. It is—they would consider it indelicate." So she and Wyn had tried very hard to learn to wait until they were alone. But hand went so instinctively to hand, his arm was around her so naturally. Now they looked guiltily toward the door.

There she stood, Ru-lan, the girl she had come in to see Wyn about, the poor stupid girl. She was standing there in the doorway, dressed in a clean, blue cotton coat and trousers, with a blue and white print handkerchief tied full of the books she never could learn. Her father had come for her to take her home to be married, and she was ready to go.

"Come in, Ru-lan," Mollie said. She smiled, her heart full of compassion. The girl's round, placid face responded at once with a child-like pleasure. Above the large full cheeks her black eyes shone faintly. Mollie Stanley looked down at the roses and went over and took the girl's plump hand.

"I'm sorry you must go," she said in Chinese. "But your father will not consent to your staying longer. Sit down, child, and let me talk with you a little."

The girl sat down obediently, in silence. The smile had gone from her face now and she sat staring quietly at these two, observing all they did.

Mollie looked at her and was discouraged. She had so often in the schoolroom faced that dense placidity.

"Wyn, what shall we do?" she asked, turning to him. "She's seventeen and she's been here ever since we came, and I don't believe she will ever learn much. She's been through all the classes—Bible and arithmetic and hygiene—she reads a few hundred characters and that's all you can say. She just isn't fit for marriage—such a good, faithful, kind, *stupid* girl! You know she came up for baptism twice, and she just can't remember enough to answer Dr. Martin's questions, however hard I coach her. I'm sometimes afraid she's still heathen."

"No, I know," answered Wyn. "It's no good her staying here. If she had any promise at all I'd try to persuade her father to let her finish at least the grades. But I haven't the heart to let him think she ever could finish. Maybe she'd better go on and be married."

"Wyn Stanley!" his wife cried out at him, "as if it weren't serious that a girl like that is to be married and have a lot of children! Of course she will have a lot of children!"

They both looked, troubled, at Ru-lan, who meeting their eyes instantly broke into her great, beaming smile, not understanding a word of their English. They were baffled by her smile.

"Do you know whom you are going to marry, Ru-lan?" asked Mollie gently in Chinese. The girl shook her head. "It is a landowner's son," she answered simply. "My father is a landowner, too. The son of another village landlord, it is."

She seemed to put the matter aside and continued to watch them intently. Mollie Stanley sighed. She put down the roses on the desk and went over to the girl and sat down on a chair next to her and took her hand again. "Try to remember," she said, "some of the things you have been taught. Remember about keeping things clean and remember how dangerous the flies and mosquitoes are, especially to little children—and how little children should not be given cucumbers and green melons to eat, and—remember about your prayers, and about the kind Christ, who came to save our souls—remember all the things we have tried to teach about being clean and good."

"Yes, teacher," the girl replied. She was looking closely at Mollie Stanley's wedding ring. Now she asked suddenly, "Did the other teacher give you the ring?"

Mollie dropped the hand she was holding and turned to her husband, "Oh dear—" she said.

"Don't worry, dear," said Wyn instantly, "I can't bear that look in your eyes. You mustn't, mustn't try to bear on your dear self all the troubles of everyone else. We've done the best we can for this child. Now she must go home. Come—" he stood and took up the roses. "Here are your roses, darling. Run along now. I'll see that Ru-lan gets away. Where *is* her father? In the school hall? I'll go, then."

"No, but, Wyn, I can't go so lightly. Tell her—tell him we'll come to see her sometime, anyway—Ru-lan"—she turned to the girl and changed her tongue quickly—"we shall come to see you sometime— I'm coming to see if you remember everything—you must try—do not let yourself be like all the others who have never come to mission school."

"No, teacher," the girl said. She was staring at Wyn's hand resting unconsciously upon Mollie's shoulder, and he took it abruptly away.

Crossing the school lawn ahead of her, he thought to himself that Ru-lan was really a very tiresome girl. It was not only that she was so stupid, it was also that one could not be sure of what she was thinking. He would have said, for instance, that she was stolid and unfeeling; yet just now when she was about to follow him out of his study she had made one of her great, broad smiles that seemed to enwrap him and Mollie, and she had taken Mollie's hand and held it, and had said with simple, utter gratitude, "You have both taught me. Together you have taught me."

He remembered now how often they would find her staring at them in her silent persevering way, that time at supper, for instance, when

189

he had sat holding Mollie's hand as he ate—they always sat side by side —and Ru-lan had come in with a note from one of the teachers. She always contrived, he did believe, now that he thought of it, to be the one to carry notes. He'd supposed it was because she was such a faithful sort of person that they had sent her. But perhaps it was because she wanted to come. There she had stood, staring at them with that silent, beaming look—slightly feebleminded, undoubtedly. He sighed. Well, it was sad when years went into teaching someone like that, someone who could never learn, when there were so many who could, and had no chance. But she had been there when he and Mollie came, and her father had come twice a year with her fees, and so she had stayed. There were not many fathers who paid full fees for a daughter.

He entered the hall, and there the father was, a plain brown-faced countryman in a blue cotton gown cut a little too long and too broad for him, but of good stout homewoven stuff. He was not a poor man, it was evident, from his bearing. He rose politely as the white man entered.

"Sit down, please, Mr. Yang. Do not be polite," said Wyn, seating himself also. The girl stood a little to one side, waiting.

"This girl," said the father nodding his head toward her, "I might have left her with you to become a teacher for you out of gratitude for all your efforts, but unfortunately she was early betrothed to the son of a friend whom I do not care to offend, and now the family demand the marriage. Otherwise I would give her to you to help you in your school."

"I thank you certainly," said Wyn. He wondered uncomfortably if in honesty he should tell the father that they could never have used Ru-lan as a teacher because she was too stupid. He thrust an apologetic thought toward God—it was difficult to be honest if it hurt someone else. Mr. Yang was obviously so proud of his daughter. He turned toward Wyn now saying, "She has had, you will remember, sir, eight years of schooling. It is not every man's son who has such a wife. But I have treated her as though she were to be my own daughter-in-law and to remain in my family. I value my friend as myself."

"It is very honorable of you," murmured Wyn. At least he would not tell lies and say he was sorry that Ru-lan must go. He waited in courteous silence until the father rose, briskly dusting cake crumbs from his lap. "There—it is pleasant to sit drinking your tea and eating your cakes, but I have miles of country road to put beneath my beast's feet before night comes. Say good-bye and give your gratitude to your teacher, Ru-lan."

"I thank you, teacher," murmured the girl. "I thank you for all I have learned."

They bowed to him together, father and daughter, and Wyn bowed, waiting at the door while they turned and bowed again.

He watched them while they went out of the compound gate. "I suppose," he thought a little sadly, "that measured by any standard it must be said that we have wasted the church's substance upon that girl. Mollie's hours and mine, too! I wonder why they do not seem so important as dollars in the mission budget? Anyway, all waste! She's not even a church member."

He walked back, a little discouraged. It was so difficult to know what was worth while in the work. One was conscientious, did each day what it seemed should be done, should be taught, and then realized suddenly, as he and Mollie had today, that no fruit was possible. He sighed a little grimly. Well, Ru-lan was gone.

In the village of Long Peace the people were all very well content. They had just finished three days of great feasting entirely at the elder Liu's expense, since he was marrying his eldest son to Ru-lan, the daughter of his brother-friend Yang in the village of The Fighting Cocks. Everybody had eaten. First the tables were set for Mr. Liu's friends among the gentry, and the common people had waited their time, patiently and decently. Then the tables were set again and again, with pork and with fish, broiled with sugar and wine and vinegar, with beef and pork ground and stewed with cabbage and greens, with noodles and with sweet rice. In fact, nothing had been left undone, and everyone had drunk all the wine he could and had eaten far more than he should, and mothers had prudently tied into large blue and white handkerchiefs such tidbits as they could not eat or force their children to eat at table. Servants had been tipped, gifts had been given, and firecrackers exploded in immense volleys. The bride, moreover, had been exhibited and commented upon, and though after all she seemed to be nothing extraordinary, no one liked Elder Liu and Mr. Yang any the less for it.

There had been a great deal of curiosity to see her, because everybody knew Mr. Yang had sent his eldest daughter to a foreign school for eight years, and anything might have happened. She might even

191

have changed the color of her eyes and hair, or the white women might have taught her how to bleach her skin, since it is well known the white people have magic. But she was nothing at all out of the ordinary. She was, in fact, a little more common than otherwise, a large, lumpish girl with very plump round cheeks and small mild eyes. In addition her feet were large. Country wives nudged each other and whispered, "Look at her feet—big feet!" "Yes, but the foreigners do not allow their pupils to bind their feet!" "Ah, indeed! How lucky that the Elder Yang betrothed her in babyhood and to his best friend's son!" Young men glanced at the bride and made jokes concerning the width of her nose and the size of her mouth, and went home in high good humor because they need not be envious of the Elder Liu's son. Indeed, everybody was happy because for once the Elder Liu did not seem to be so very lucky, and one or two fathers whose daughters had been teasing to be allowed to go to a foreign school went home resolute for refusal. What—to waste eight years of fees and then have a daughter at the end who looked exactly as though she had never left the village! So everyone was happy. They went home by moonlight the night of the third day, full of cheerful vilifying talk.

In the house of the Elder Liu, in the court belonging to his eldest son, Ru-lan sat upon the edge of the large nuptial bed, hung with pictures of babies and pomegranates and mandarin ducks and every lucky sign for marriage, and waited for her husband. She had enjoyed everything very much, so much that she often forgot to keep her eyes downcast as she should. But this did not greatly trouble her. She had remembered enough, she thought comfortably, and tonight they had given her a good dinner. The more tedious part of the wedding was over. She had now come to the part which was her own affair.

This was the time, she knew, when maidens should feel shy and uncomfortable and even afraid. She knew because as a very small girl in the women's courts of her father's house she had squatted on her heels listening as all the little girls did to the women's talk. They listened while the women whispered loudly to each other, "I tell you, he was like a tiger—his great eyes—" "I tell you, nothing told is so terrible as—" "I tell you, I was like a chicken before a wolf—"

They all enjoyed telling each other of this hour when their unknown bridegrooms first appeared. She thought now, staring reflectively through the old-fashioned veil of beads that hung over her face, that it was natural they should be afraid of marriage. What they had seen

192

of the thing between men and women was not comfortable. But she had been to school for eight years with the foreigners. There was the difference. Not that the first years she had been there were of any use to her at all. She could not see much use, for instance, in reading books. In the first place books told nothing interesting. If they were about God, there was no understanding them—how could humans understand gods? She had listened politely to Mrs. Burgess and been glad when Mrs. Burgess had been compelled to go to America. For then the dear little Stanley teacher had come, that little pretty round-faced teacher, whose eyes were also brown so that one liked to look at her. The Stanley teacher had worked so hard to teach her that sometimes she almost felt she should try to listen perhaps to what the Stanley teacher was saying, but when she did it had seemed not valuable.

No, she had learned nothing until that day when she had observed the man Stanley place his arms about the woman Stanley. At first she thought with consternation that these were two wicked and unmannered people. But they were not punished if they were. In rapid succession they had two small sons, both healthy, both dark-eyed. Evidently their God was pleased with them. After that she had watched them many times. When they did not know it she had stolen in the night across the school campus, and had gazed steadily between the curtains of the room where they sat after the children were put to bed and, watching them, had come to learn something from them. To this learning she applied her mind. So now she was not at all afraid. She waited peacefully for Yung-en, sitting at ease upon the bed, her hands folded in her red satin lap.

Everywhere through the courts quiet was descending after the noisy days of feasting. Children who had eaten too well ceased their crying and fell asleep, and servants yawned and barred the doors of courtyards and went to their own beds. Her own serving woman was only waiting until the master came in to spread her pallet down across the door to sleep. When everyone was still, when the young men had all gone home, wearied at last with their baiting and teasing of the bridegroom, then through the silent empty courts he would come. She had stolen her glances at him and she was pleased with his looks. He was an honest, sturdy young man, with a square, dark face, not too smiling. He was shy, she could see, not quick to speak. A woman could live with such a man. She was not afraid, having learned so much about a man and a woman.

Then suddenly the door creaked upon its wooden hinges and there he was, still in his bright blue wedding robes. He did not speak, nor did he look at her at once. He came in and sat down beside the table and began to crack watermelon seeds. She rose and poured out a cup of tea for him and he nodded and she sat down again. She was not impatient. He could not go on cracking watermelon seeds all night. Outside the door she heard a loud yawn and soon a muffled snore. Her serving woman was asleep. Now everyone slept except these two.

She waited, smiling a little, watching him through the beads of her veil, but he did not look at her. She waited and at last she caught his eyes, stealing toward her. She answered instantly, frankly, smiling her beam of a smile. He stared at her and coughed and after a second of surprise he grew very red and made haste to return to his watermelon seeds.

She suddenly perceived that he was afraid of her.

"And why are you afraid of me?" she asked, making her voice soft as she had heard the little Stanley teacher's voice soft.

He turned his head from her's. "I am so ignorant," he said at last in a low voice. "You have been away to a foreign school and I have always lived in this village. You will laugh at me."

She watched him. How now would the Stanley teacher speak if the man Stanley had spoken like this? Once the man Stanley had put his head down upon the woman's shoulder and for some trouble had wept as a little boy weeps, and the woman had not laughed. She had taken him into her arms and pressed his head down and murmured to him as a mother murmurs to a suffering child, and soon he was quieted. Ru-lan had not understood the woman Stanley's words, but the sounds she understood, and the way she understood. It had made the man Stanley feel strong again and cease his weeping.

She looked demurely down at her hands and spoke in a small plaintive voice. "I have to confess to you," she said, "although I was so long in that school I have remained ignorant. You cannot be as ignorant as I am. I do believe there are a thousand things you know I do not know. There I remained for eight years shut behind walls, but my brain is too stupid to learn from books. So I am very ignorant. I have everything to learn from you."

He gazed at her now, forgetting that she was his bride and that he was afraid of her. "Did you not learn to read?" he demanded.

"Only a very little," she replied.

194

"Did you read to the end of the Four Books?" he asked again.

"Alas, I never read any of the Four Books," she answered.

"Then what did you do in all that time?" he inquired, astonished.

"I sat on benches in schoolrooms," she replied humbly, "and there were those who talked to me, but I could not understand them, being stupid from birth. They told me of gods and of magic, and of small insects that cause disease if eaten, but then who eats insects? At least we do not. So I learned nothing."

"Nothing at all?" he asked severely.

"Nothing at all," she answered sadly.

He was silent, but now he looked at her quite easily and he had stopped cracking watermelon seeds. She could see the shyness leaving him as he thought over what she had told him.

"I only learned one thing," she said after a long time. Now she leaned forward and looked at him and he looked at her.

"What is that one thing?" he asked.

"There was a white woman who was my teacher," she said, "and she was married to a white man, and they were very lucky, for one after the other they had two strong dark-eyed sons, and this when the other children of white people all have blue or green eyes. I learned from them something."

"What was the thing you learned?" he asked. "Certainly two dark-eyed sons are very lucky."

"I learned," she said considering, choosing some one thing among all she had learned, "that it is lucky when a man and his wife speak together freely and always with kind voices, as though they were friends speaking easily together and not as they do in our houses, where it seems shameful so to speak."

"Do you mean speak together anywhere?"

"Yes, I mean that."

He gazed at her steadily. "What then?"

"And then it is lucky if the husband helps the wife if there is a thing to be done, such as to carry a basket or a bundle, if there is not a servant near."

"What does the wife do?" he asked, astonished.

"She also wishes to carry the things, and so they try mutually to help each other."

"And who wins?" he asked.

"They share the thing," she replied simply.

195

She waited a little, thinking, remembering. . . . Once she had seen the man Stanley lift his wife over a pool of mud in the road, and carry her through and set her down on the other side, one afternoon, when they thought none saw them. But before he set her down he had held her hard and placed his cheek against hers, and then they had gone on hand in hand until they saw her. But she had seen them long since. She had wanted to say, "Do not drop your hands apart. I know it is your pleasure to walk thus." But she had not spoken. . . .

"What else have you learned?" he asked.

"It is lucky," she said slowly, "for a man and his wife to clasp their hands together sometimes—it is not shameful."

He coughed and looked away and she went on quickly. "There are many things not shameful that we have thought shameful—they are lucky between man and wife. But I cannot speak them—they are things to be done rather than to be spoken."

He looked down and did not answer. He did not answer for quite a long time. Then he said a little gruffly, "Then do them—do what you have learned."

She rose slowly and went over to him. She knelt down on the floor before him as often she had seen the woman Stanley do. But she could not go on, although she knew quite well what came next. Next was to put her head down upon his knees and clasp her arms about his waist. But she could not do it. Now it was she who was shy. It had looked so easy when the woman Stanley did it.

"I cannot do it all at once," she faltered. "A little every day. But perhaps—at least take my hands."

He sat quite still and then he lifted her hands in his own. Something rushed between them through their hands, and suddenly her heart began to pound. Did the woman Stanley's heart pound like this also? What was the matter with her?

"What next did you learn?" he asked.

She could not answer. She drew their hands together and laid her head down upon their knotted hands. She should have asked the woman Stanley about this pounding heart.

"Lift up your head," he said. How gentle his voice was, as gentle as the man Stanley's voice was! "Lift up your head and let me take away your veil that I may see you."

She lifted up her head, and he drew his hands away and took off the headdress and the veil and set them on the table and then he looked at her. And then he went on speaking in that same gentle voice, "And did you learn it was lucky for a man to like very well the woman chosen for him?" He had taken her hands again. He was gazing at her, smiling, happy, as the man Stanley gazed at that woman who knelt to him. The man Stanley had also asked something of the woman in that strange tongue of theirs and she had answered. Oh, what was the answer to the gentle question? There must be an answer—she should have learned the answer. Then suddenly it came to her. It came to her, not out of her brain which was so slow and stupid and never quick to speak. It came from her pounding heart. "Yes, it is a lucky thing, I know, and the luck is perfect if the woman likes also very well the man to whom she is given."

She felt his cheek against hers, even as she had learned.

If Ru-lan had been able to write she would long ago have written to her teacher Stanley to ask her why, when she had said she would come to see her, she had not yet come, although it had been now nearly five years since Ru-lan had left the school. In the five years she had grown heavier, as what woman would not who had given birth to three large, strong sons and now a small, pretty daughter, so pretty that the child's father went against all nature and loved her twice as well, apparently, as even he loved his sons.

But then there was of course no man on the earth's surface like Yung-en. The man Stanley was never better to his wife than Yung-en was to Ru-lan. Bit by bit, through the five years, she had told him what she had seen those two white ones do, how they looked at each other, how they spoke, and with the telling new comprehension had come to them of what those looks and words meant. She was now sure that when those two spoke to each other in that strong, soft fashion they said in their own tongue what came welling up from her own heart and Yung-en's. It was wonderful to think how alike were hearts. She knew this because it was so soon an instinct to move freely with Yung-en, walking beside him freely, moving toward him freely and fully when they were alone. She knew that the women in the courts were often disapproving. She knew they said, "It is the boldness she learned in the foreign school—it is the freedom of the modern ways." She smiled, knowing there was truth in what they said.

She pondered a good deal on her own ease. It did not occur to her, for instance, to share the anxiety of the other women lest their husbands take concubines. Did she not know Yung-en's heart? That was what she had learned, how to know his heart. They talked together sometimes about it, and how their life was different from those about them, and Yung-en said gratefully always, "If the man and woman Stanley should ever come to see us, there would not be enough I could do for them to thank them for what you learned from them. If you had not seen and learned, my life would not have been above any other man's. As it is, you have contented me so that all other women in the world might die and I should not know it." She smiled, knowing she had never been beautiful and now was less so than ever, if one should measure her by a beautiful woman. But she feared none of them.

So when suddenly one August morning a letter came from the school she could hardly wait for Yung-en to come home to read it. She had long given up any pretense at reading. The characters she had once known had quite slipped out of her memory. If some woman asked her in curiosity sometimes what a character was on a bit of paper found, she laughed comfortably and said, "If once I knew, that once is long gone. I have so little use for letters these days." Or if her elder son, now beginning to learn, ran to ask her the meaning of a word she would say, always laughing, "You must go ignorant if you ask learning of me, my son!"

She put the letter by until she heard Yung-en come and then she went to him and waited while he opened it, her hand upon his arm. After these five years it was more than ever necessary to her to put her hand upon his arm, and he moved toward her when he felt her touch, understanding.

"It is a letter from the man Stanley," he said after murmuring the letters aloud awhile. "They wish to open a chapel here in our village and preach their religion, and there will be also a school, and he is coming and with him the woman Stanley."

"Of course they would not be separated," she said gently.

"No," he said, folding the letter. He was planning rapidly. "We shall have them here in our own house. There is the south room upon the old peony terrace where I have my few books and where I never go. Prepare it with the best bed and with the blackwood furniture my father gave us from the south. And I shall invite guests—all my friends. I do not care to invite guests for the religion, but it is a way to repay these two if I show myself a friend. Now I can thank them for all they taught you."

198

"Yes," she said. "And we can show them our sons—"

"And we can send our daughter to their school," he cried, smiling. They sat down together in simple pleasure, holding each other's hands, laughing a little. "Everything is lucky in our life," he said.

"Everything," she echoed fervently.

So it was that on a certain morning in August, nearly at the end of summer, she welcomed those two. There they were at the door, standing together, a little thinner than she remembered them, a little gray in their hair. "You are tired," she cried, her heart rushing out to them. "Come in—rest and eat. Oh, how welcome you are!"

Yung-en gave up his work when they came and stayed at home, running hither and thither, himself carrying trays of sweetmeats and keeping plates full and pouring tea and going to see what quilts were rolled upon the bed and if the mosquito net was properly drawn. "I can never do enough for them," he said to her in passing.

Well, there it was. The two Stanleys stayed three days and into the days Yung-en and Ru-lan heaped all that they had, all the years of their happy life together, all their luck in the three sons and the little girl. Ru-lan had meant to dress the children in their best, but then it was so hot that she let it go. It was better that they be comfortable. Besides, they were so beautiful and so healthy it must be a pleasure for anyone to see their little brown bodies bare to the waist. She had meant, too, to clean the house a little more, to wipe the dust from the table legs and from the gilt crevices of the family gods. But the summer days passed so quickly until the guests came, and once they were come there was no time for anything except urging them to eat, to talk, to rest themselves, to enjoy the huge feast and the lanterns hung to welcome them, to see the fireworks Yung-en bought and bade the servants fire for their amusement.

She had planned to try to tell the dear teachers Stanley a little about her own life and how much she owed them. She had planned to say at least that she had been very happy. But there was no time for anything. They were busy about the new school, planning, working hard as they always did.

But they were still happy. She knew that. They still paused as they used to pause, to look at each other deeply. When they went away, so soon, so far too soon, she loved them more than ever. She stood beside Yung-en at the gate waving to them, crying to them to go slowly, to return quickly. And then when Yung-en shouted after them,

"Our daughter shall be your first girl pupil!" her heart overflowed toward them and she cried after them, "Yes—teach her, for you taught me so much!" That was all she had the time to say. But she did not worry—they would understand. She went back into her house with Yung-en. His hand sought hers comfortably, and they sauntered across their courtyard, well content.

Rocking down the road in their rickety mission Ford, Mollie leaned back against Wyn, grateful to be alone again with him. Now, as always, when she sat beside Wyn she began to feel warm, deep peace welling up in her. They were going home, they were together. They were going back to the children. She crept more closely to him, and he put his arm about her. He drove very expertly one-armed.

"Sweetheart!" he said gently. "It was wonderful of you to leave the children and make this trip with me. I shouldn't have blamed you, you know, if you hadn't."

"I can't be away from you, Wyn."

"No, I know." They fell into intimate, peaceful silence.

Over the Chinese landscape twilight was beginning to fall, creeping up in small mists from the ponds and the canals, darkening over the hills from the sky. From the thatched roofs the blue lines of smoke of fires kindled for the evening meal rose straightly into the still air. How strange, how different the scene was from the rough hills of her own home country, from the sharp angular American towns! And yet how little strange, how little different! These were homes, too, and these were people living together in their families. And here was her home. Wherever Wyn was, was her home. She was instantly deeply content, content with everything, with everybody.

Then suddenly she thought of Ru-lan.

"Wyn!" she said. "What did you really think of Ru-lan?"

"Well?" asked Wyn, twinkling at her a little. "What did you really think?"

"It was just exactly as I was afraid it would be," she answered dolefully. "She's lost even the little she had. Wyn, you wouldn't have known, now would you honestly, that Ru-lan had ever been outside that village? Did you see the slightest difference between her house and any other ignorant village woman's house?"

"No," said Wyn thoughtfully. He guided the car skillfully between two deep wheelbarrow ruts.

Mollie stared mournfully over the landscape, the valleys tawny with

200

ripening rice, the hills browning with ending summer, the willow-encircled villages. "No," she continued, "the house was dusty and not very clean, and the children were eating just anything. I saw that little girl chewing on a cucumber, skin and all."

"So did I," he said briefly.

"And Ru-lan is just like an amiable cow. She just sits and smiles and smiles. She doesn't read, she doesn't seem to do anything in the village, she's just an ordinary woman—after all those years away. I don't believe she does one thing different in her home for all the hours I tried to teach her."

"Mollie, did you see those idols?" Wyn said gravely.

"Yes," said Mollie reluctantly.

They rolled along in silence for a moment, remembering the row of gilt figures with the guttered candles before them. They had taught Ru-lan so patiently to say over and over again, "Thou shall have no other gods before Me. . . ." "Ru-lan, what are gods?" she used to ask. Ru-lan had smiled apologetically. "Teacher, tell me, for I do not know."

"They are idols, Ru-lan. You must not worship them, Ru-lan."

"Yes, Teacher, it is what I thought."

And then when Dr. Martin had once asked her in the catechism class what God was, she had said, "Sir, God is an idol." Poor stupid Ru-lan! There was no telling how she would learn a thing. . . .

She thought over the two crowded days, days full of too much food and too much noise and many children and curious neighbors coming in and out to see the newcomers. But Ru-lan had not seemed to mind anything. She had sat tranquil in the midst of the confusion, smiling and smiling. And everybody had seemed fond of her—her children ran to her often, and the neighbors called to her cheerfully, and Yung-en . . . She was struck now, remembering Yung-en.

"Wyn!" she said suddenly, looking up at him.

"Yes, darling?"

He turned and smiled down at her. There she was snuggled down by him like a kitten, looking not a day older . . .

"There was one thing about Ru-lan—her husband really seemed to like her."

"I believe he does," he said slowly. "Yes—I don't know why exactly —she certainly doesn't remember anything we ever taught her!"

The Great Lover

Rupert Brooke

I have been so great a lover: filled my days
So proudly with the splendour of Love's praise,
The pain, the calm, and the astonishment,
Desire illimitable, and still content,
And all dear names men use, to cheat despair,
For the perplexed and viewless streams that bear
Our hearts at random down the dark of life.
Now, ere the unthinking silence on that strife
Steals down, I would cheat drowsy Death so far,
My night shall be remembered for a star
That outshone all the suns of all men's days.
Shall I not crown them with immortal praise
Whom I have loved, who have given me, dared with me
High secrets, and in darkness knelt to see
The inenarrable godhead of delight?
Love is aflame;—we have beaconed the world's night.
A city:—and we have built it, these and I.
An emperor:—we have taught the world to die.
So, for their sakes I loved, ere I go hence,
And the high cause of Love's magnificence,
And to keep loyalties young, I'll write those names
Golden for ever, eagles, crying flames,
And set them as a banner, that men may know,
To dare the generations, burn, and blow
Out on the wind of Time, shining and streaming. . . .

These I have loved:
                    White plates and cups, clean-gleaming,
Ringed with blue lines; and feathery, faery dust;
Wet roofs, beneath the lamp-light; the strong crust
Of friendly bread; and many-tasting food;
Rainbows; and the blue bitter smoke of wood;
And radiant raindrops couching in cool flowers;
And flowers themselves, that sway through sunny hours,
Dreaming of moths that drink them under the moon;
Then, the cool kindliness of sheets, that soon

202

Smooth away trouble; and the rough male kiss
Of blankets; grainy wood; live hair that is
Shining and free; blue-massing clouds; the keen
Unpassioned beauty of a great machine;
The benison of hot water; furs to touch;
The good smell of old clothes; and other such—
The comfortable smell of friendly fingers,
Hair's fragrance, and the musty reek that lingers
About dead leaves and last year's ferns. . . . Dear names,
And thousand other throng to me! Royal flames;
Sweet water's dimpling laugh from tap or spring;
Holes in the ground; and voices that do sing;
Voices in laughter, too; and body's pain,
Soon turned to peace; and the deep-panting train;
Firm sands; the little dulling edge of foam
That browns and dwindles as the wave goes home;
And washen stones, gay for an hour; the cold
Graveness of iron; moist black earthen mould;
Sleep; and high places; footprints in the dew;
And oaks; and brown horse-chestnuts, glossy-new;
And new-peeled sticks; and shining pools on grass;—
All these have been my loves. And these shall pass,
Whatever passes not, in the great hour,
Nor all my passion, all my prayers, have power
To hold them with me through the gate of Death.
They'll play deserter, turn with the traitor breath,
Break the high bond we made, and sell Love's trust
And sacramented covenant to the dust.
——Oh, never a doubt but, somewhere, I shall wake,
And give what's left of love again, and make
New friends, now strangers. . . .
                But the best I've known,
Stays here, and changes, breaks, grows old, is blown
About the winds of the world, and fades from brains
Of living men, and dies. Nothing remains.
O dear my loves, O faithless, once again
This one last gift I give: that after men
Shall know, and later lovers, far-removed,
Praise you, "All these were lovely"; say, "He loved."

203

From Portrait of Jennie

Robert Nathan

The theme of Robert Nathan's exquisite love fantasy about an artist who has made a portrait of Jenny, the girl of his dreams, is expressed here:

"What is it which makes a man and a woman know that they, of all other men and women in the world, belong to each other? Is it no more than chance and meeting? No more than being alive together in the world at the same time? Is it only a curve of the throat, a line of the chin, the way the eyes are set, a way of speaking? Or is it something deeper and stranger, something beyond chance and fortune? Are there others, in other times of the world, whom we would have loved, who would have loved us? Is there, perhaps, one soul among all others—among all who have lived, the endless generations, from world's end to world's end—who must love us or die? And whom we must love, in turn—whom we must seek all our lives long—headlong and homesick —until the end?"

IN THE early morning, in bright spring sunshine, Jennie came back to me. I heard her voice in the hall, and had only time to slip into my coat, before she was up the stairs and in at the door. She had a little suitcase in her hand; she dropped it just inside the doorway, and came flying across the room, and kissed me.

It was the most natural thing in the world. We held each other out at arm's length and looked at each other, smiling, and not saying anything. We couldn't have spoken . . . The whole sunny, sweet-smelling spring morning had come in with her.

204

She was older—I saw that at once; a young lady now, dressed in a travelling suit; she even had gloves on. She was breathless, but only from running up the stairs, or from happiness; her brown eyes never faltered as they searched my face. I took a deep breath. "Jennie," I said; "I've missed you."

"I know," she answered. "I've missed you, too. And it's been longer for me." She drew her hands away from mine with sudden gravity "I'm not in school any more," she said.

"I know," I said. "I can see."

She turned slowly on her heel, and looked around the room with simple joy. "How I've dreamed of this, Eben," she said; "I can't tell you. The nights I've lain awake, thinking of this room . . ."

"I know," I said.

"Do you?" she answered gently. "No, I don't think so."

She stood there, looking around her, and slowly taking off her gloves; and I looked around, too, and wished the room were more in order. I went over to smooth the bed a little, but she stopped me. "No," she said; "don't touch it. Do you remember how I wanted to tidy up for you once, when I was little? Let me do it now. And show me where the coffee is . . . Poor Eben—I did get you up so early. Go and dress yourself, and then we'll have breakfast, and I'll tell you all that's happened."

"But Jennie," I said, "if we have so little time . . ."

"We have a whole long day," she answered breathlessly. "And—and a little more."

I went along down the hall to the washroom, and left Jennie to tidy up, as she wanted. I thought I saw Mrs. Jekes on the landing below, but I didn't pay much attention to her; I was too happy, the day was too lovely . . . a whole long day, and a little more. What did that mean—a little more? I cut myself twice, shaving.

Jennie had learned how to make a bed, and how to make coffee. I hardly knew my room when I got back to it: my work-table was laid with a clean towel, and my two cups, one of them with a broken handle, and the coffeepot, stood side by side, along with a pat of butter I'd had out on the windowsill, and some bread she had toasted on a fork over the gas burner. There was a good smell in the air. We sat down together, hand in hand, to our breakfast.

I told her about the picture; and her fingers tightened on mine. "Oh, but that's grand," she cried. "That's wonderful, Eben. Aren't you happy?"

She was silent for a moment, thinking about something. "Eben," she said at last, "let's do something special—shall we? To celebrate? Because I haven't really very long to stay with you. You see . . . I'm being sent abroad—to France—to a finishing school—for two years."

"Jennie," I cried.

"I know," she said quickly. "I don't want to go; but I guess I have to. And anyhow—it won't seem very long. And then . . ."

"And then?" I asked.

"I'm going to hurry," she said earnestly. "And then some day I'll be as old as you."

"I'm twenty-eight, Jennie," I said gravely. She nodded her head.

"I know it," she replied. "And so will I be . . . then."

"But not when you come back from France," I said.

"No," she agreed. "There'll be a long time still, after that."

She held my hand tight. "I'm going to hurry, though," she said. "I've got to."

For a moment she seemed to be lost in thought, her head bent, her eyes hidden under their long lashes. Then she roused herself, and sat up with a smile. "Let's go on a picnic, Eben," she said. "Somewhere in the country—for a whole day—

"It's something we've never done before."

Something we'd never done before—as though we'd ever done very much of anything. But she didn't have to urge me. A whole day in the country, in the warm spring weather, together . . . "Yes," I said, "yes. That's what we'll do." She could hardly wait for me to finish my coffee; we hurried down the stairs and out into the street, hand in hand; and the bright sunny morning fell on us like an armful of flowers.

Gus was in his cab, at the corner. When he saw me with Jennie, he took his hat off, and looked frightened. I don't believe he had ever thought she was real, or ever expected to see her. I went up to the cab, and opened the door. "Gus," I said, "we're going on a picnic. We're going out into the country for the day . . . somewhere . . . anywhere. I want you to take us. How much will it cost?"

He twisted his hat in his hands, and tried to smile; he seemed to be having some trouble in swallowing. "Now listen, Mack," he said; "now listen . . ."

"It doesn't matter what it costs," I said, and helped Jennie into the cab.

What was the good of being rich, if I couldn't do what I liked?

Gus looked back once or twice, as though to make sure that we were really there. "So it's a fact," he said finally, more to himself than to me; and in a kind of awe. "Well—"

"Where do you want to go, Mack?"

I waved him forward. "Wherever it's green," I said. "Wherever it's country."

I don't know where we went, but it was green and lovely. It was somewhere north of the city—perhaps in Westchester. It took us about an hour to get there. We left the cab by the roadside, and climbed a fence, and ran across a field with a cow in it. The cow didn't notice us. We climbed a little hill, among some trees. Jennie was flushed and breathless, and full of laughter; she and I ran ahead, and Gus came after us.

At noon we sat together on a warm stone wall in the sun at the edge of a meadow, and near a little wood. There were yellow dandelions in the grass, and the air was sweet as honey. We had some sandwiches along—lettuce and bread for Jennie, sausage for Gus and me. We ate our sandwiches, and drank some beer out of cans. It was the first beer Jennie had ever tasted; she didn't like it, she said it tasted bitter.

Gus and Jennie did most of the talking. He told her how he had tried to find her once; and how he had helped me sell the picture; and she told him please to take good care of me, and not to let anything happen. I didn't talk very much; I felt drowsy in the sun, I kept wishing Arne were there, too; I kept thinking about what it would be like some day when we were all together.

Jennie sat on the wall beside me, her head against my shoulder. She had twined a yellow dandelion in her hair; it gave out a fresh, weedy fragrance. The sky was robin's egg blue; I heard a bird singing in the woods. I was happy—happier than I had ever been before, happier than I've ever been since.

Gus left us after lunch, and went back to the cab, to take a nap. Then Jennie too grew silent, resting against me, dreamy and content. After a while, I felt her stir, and draw a long, uneven breath. "What are you thinking, Jennie?" I asked.

She answered slowly and gently, "I'm thinking how beautiful the world is, Eben; and how it keeps on being beautiful—no matter what happens to us. The spring comes year after year, for us, or Egypt; the sun goes down in the same green, lovely sky; the birds sing . . . for us, or for yesterday . . . or for tomorrow. It was never made for

207

anything but beauty, Eben—whether we lived now, or long ago."

"Tomorrow," I said. "But when is tomorrow, Jennie?"

"Does it matter?" she asked. "It's always. This was tomorrow—once. "Promise me you'll never forget."

I quoted softly:

> "Where I come from,
> Nobody knows,
> And where I'm going,
> Everything goes."

She took it up with a little cry of surprise:

> "The wind blows,
> The sea flows—
> And God knows.

"I think He knows, Eben," she said.

And she lifted her lips, trusting and innocent, to mine.

Later we walked in the faint green of the woods, through the shadow of branches, over the ferns and the moss. We found a little brook, and violets hidden among their leaves. Jennie stopped to pick them; she made a tiny bunch, to carry home. "It's to remember today," she said.

The sun began to sink in the west; the shadows fell around us. It grew chilly; we turned, and started home.

Dust

Rupert Brooke

When the white flame in us is gone,
  And we that lost the world's delight
Stiffen in darkness, left alone
  To crumble in our separate night;

When your swift hair is quiet in death,
  And through the lips corruption thrust
Has stilled the labour of my breath—
  When we are dust, when we are dust!—

Not dead, not undesirous yet,
  Still sentient, still unsatisfied,
We'll ride the air, and shine, and flit,
  Around the places where we died,

And dance as dust before the sun,
  And light of foot, and unconfined,
Hurry from road to road, and run
  About the errands of the wind.

And every note, on earth or air,
  Will speed and gleam, down later days,
And like a secret pilgrim fare
  By eager and invisible ways,

Nor ever rest, nor ever lie,
  Till, beyond thinking, out of view,
One mote of all the dust that's I
  Shall meet one atom that was you.

Then in some garden hushed from wind,
  Warm in a sunset's afterglow,
The lovers in the flowers will find
  A sweet and strange unquiet grow

Upon the peace; and, past desiring,
  So high a beauty in the air,
And such a light, and such a quiring,
  And such a radiant ecstasy there,

They'll know not if it's fire, or dew,
  Or out of earth, or in the height,
Singing, or flame, or scent, or hue,
  Or two that pass, in light, to light,

Out of the garden, higher, higher. . . .
  But in that instant they shall learn
The shattering ecstasy of our fire,
  And the weak passionless hearts will burn

And faint in that amazing glow,
  Until the darkness close above;
And they will know—poor fools; they'll know!—
  One moment, what it is to love.

Music I Heard

Conrad Aiken

Music I heard with you was more than music,
And bread I broke with you was more than bread;
Now that I am without you, all is desolate;
All that was once so beautiful is dead.

Your hands once touched this table and this silver,
And I have seen your fingers hold this glass.
These things do not remember you, beloved,—
And yet your touch upon them will not pass.

For it was in my heart you moved among them,
And blessed them with your hands and with your eyes;
And in my heart they will remember always,—
They knew you once, O beautiful and wise.

The Old Lady Shows Her Medals

James M. Barrie

> *Called by many "Barrie's greatest play," the
> Old Lady and her adopted son once met will
> never be forgotten. Some of us also remember
> this old lady in a very great motion picture.*

THREE *nice old ladies and a criminal, who is even nicer, are
discussing the war over a cup of tea. The criminal, who is the hostess,
calls it a dish of tea, which shows that she comes from Caledonia; but
that is not her crime.*

*They are all London charwomen, but three of them, including the
hostess, are what are called professionally 'charwomen and' or simply
'ands.' An 'and' is also a caretaker when required; her name is entered
as such in ink in a registry book, financial transactions take place across
a counter between her and the registrar, and altogether she is of a very
different social status from one who, like Mrs. Haggerty, is a charwoman but nothing else. Mrs. Haggerty, though present, is not at the
party by invitation; having seen Mrs. Dowey buying the winkles, she
followed her downstairs, and so has shuffled into the play and sat down
in it against our wish. We would remove her by force, or at least print
her name in small letters, were it not that she takes offence very readily
and says that nobody respects her. So, as you have slipped in, you can
sit there, Mrs. Haggerty; but keep quiet.*

*There is nothing doing at present in the caretaking way for Mrs.
Dowey, our hostess; but this does not damp her, caretaking being only
to such as she an extra financially and a halo socially. If she had the
honour of being served with an income-tax paper she would probably
fill in one of the nasty little compartments with the words, 'Trade—
charring; Profession (if any)—caretaking.' This home of hers (from
which, to look after your house, she makes occasionally temporary de-
partures in great style, escorting a barrow) is in one of those what-*

care-l streets that you discover only when you have lost your way; on discovering them, your duty is to report them to the authorities, who immediately add them to the map of London. That is why we are now reporting Friday Street. We shall call it, in the rough sketch drawn for tomorrow's press, 'Street in which the criminal resided'; and you will find Mrs. Dowey's home therein marked with a X.

Her abode really consists of one room, but she maintains that there are two; so, rather than argue, let us say that there are two. The other one has no window, and she could not swish her old skirts in it without knocking something over; its grandest display is of tin pans and crockery on top of a dresser which has a lid to it; you have but to whip off the utensils and raise the lid, and, behold, a bath with hot and cold. Mrs. Dowey is very proud of this possession, and when she shows it off, as she does perhaps too frequently, she first signs to you with closed fist (funny old thing that she is) to approach softly. She then tiptoes to the dresser and pops off the lid, as if to take the bath unawares. Then she sucks her lips, and is modest if you have the grace to do the exclamations.

In the real room is a bed, though that is putting the matter too briefly. The fair way to begin, if you love Mrs. Dowey, is to say to her that it is a pity she has no bed. If she is in her best form she will chuckle, and agree that the want of a bed tries her sore; she will keep you on the hooks, so to speak, as long as she can; and then, with that mouse-like movement again, she will suddenly spring the bed on you. You thought it was a wardrobe, but she brings it down from the wall; and lo, a bed. There is nothing else in her abode (which we now see to contain four rooms—kitchen, pantry, bedroom, and bathroom) that is absolutely a surprise; but it is full of 'bits,' every one of which has been paid ready money for, and gloated over and tended until it has become part of its owner. Genuine Doweys, the dealers might call them, though there is probably nothing in the place except the bed that would fetch half-a-crown.

Her home is in the basement, so that the view is restricted to the lower half of persons passing overhead beyond the area stairs. Here at the window Mrs. Dowey sometimes sits of a summer evening gazing, not sentimentally at a flower-pot which contains one poor bulb, nor yearningly at some tiny speck of sky, but with unholy relish at holes in stockings, and the like, which are revealed to her from her point of vantage. You, gentle reader, may flaunt by, thinking that your finery

*awes the street, but Mrs. Dowey can tell (and does) that your soles are
in need of neat repair.*

*Also, lower parts being as expressive as the face to those whose view
is thus limited, she could swear to scores of the passers-by in a court
of law.*

*These four lively old codgers are having a good time at the tea-
table, and wit is flowing free. As you can see by their everyday garments, and by their pails and mops (which are having a little tea-party
by themselves in the corner), it is not a gathering by invitations stretching away into yesterday, it is a purely informal affair; so much more
attractive, don't you think? than banquets elaborately prearranged.
You know how they come about, especially in war-time. Very likely
Mrs. Dowey met Mrs. Twymley and Mrs. Mickleham quite casually
in the street, and meant to do no more than pass the time of day; then,
naturally enough, the word camouflage was mentioned, and they got
heated, but in the end Mrs. Twymley apologised; then, in the odd way
in which one thing leads to another, the winkle man appeared, and
Mrs. Dowey remembered that she had that pot of jam and that Mrs.
Mickleham had stood treat last time; and soon they were all three
descending the area stairs, followed cringingly by the Haggerty
Woman.*

*They have been extremely merry, and never were four hard-worked
old ladies who deserved it better. All a woman can do in war-time
they do daily and cheerfully, just as their men-folk are doing it at the
Front; and now, with the mops and pails laid aside, they sprawl gracefully at ease. There is no intention on their part to consider peace
terms until a decisive victory has been gained in the field (Sarah Ann
Dowey), until the Kaiser is put to the right-about (Emma Mickleham),
and singing very small (Amelia Twymley).*

*At this tea-party the lady who is to play the part of Mrs. Dowey is
sure to want to suggest that our heroine has a secret sorrow, namely,
the crime; but you should see us knocking that idea out of her head!
Mrs. Dowey knows she is a criminal, but, unlike the actress, she does
not know that she is about to be found out; and she is, to put it bluntly
in her own Scotch way, the merriest of the whole clanjamfry. She
presses more tea on her guests, but they wave her away from them in
the pretty manner of ladies who know that they have already had more
than enough.*

MRS. DOWEY. Just one more winkle, Mrs. Mickleham?

213

(Indeed there is only one more. But MRS. MICKLEHAM *indicates politely that if she took this one it would have to swim for it.* THE HAGGERTY WOMAN *takes it long afterwards when she thinks, erroneously, that no one is looking.*

MRS. TWYMLEY *is sulking. Evidently some one has contradicted her. Probably* THE HAGGERTY WOMAN.)

MRS. TWYMLEY. I say it is so.

THE HAGGERTY WOMAN. I say it may be so.

MRS. TWYMLEY. I suppose I ought to know: me that has a son a prisoner in Germany. *(She has so obviously scored that all good feeling seems to call upon her to end here. But she continues rather shabbily.)* Being the only lady present that has that proud misfortune. *(The others are stung.)*

MRS. DOWEY. My son is fighting in France.

MRS. MICKLEHAM. Mine is wounded in two places.

THE HAGGERTY WOMAN. Mine is at Salonaiky.

(The absurd pronunciation of this uneducated person moves the others to mirth.)

MRS. DOWEY. You'll excuse us, Mrs. Haggerty, but the correct pronunciation is Salonikky.

THE HAGGERTY WOMAN *(to cover her confusion)*. I don't think. *(She feels that even this does not prove her case.)* And I speak as one that has War Savings Certificates.

MRS. TWYMLEY. We all have them.

(THE HAGGERTY WOMAN whispers, and the other guests regard her with unfeeling disdain.)

MRS. DOWEY *(to restore cheerfulness)*. Oh, it's a terrible war.

ALL *(brightening)*. It is. You may say so.

MRS. DOWEY *(encouraged)*. What I say is, the men is splendid, but I'm none so easy about the staff. That's your weak point, Mrs. Mickleham.

MRS. MICKLEHAM *(on the defence, but determined to reveal nothing that might be of use to the enemy)*. You may take it from me, the staff's all right.

MRS. DOWEY. And very relieved I am to hear you say it.

(It is here that THE HAGGERTY WOMAN *has the remaining winkle.)*

MRS. MICKLEHAM. You don't understand properly about trench warfare. If I had a map——

MRS. DOWEY *(wetting her finger to draw lines on the table)*. That's

214

the river Sommy. Now, if we had barrages here——

MRS. TWYMLEY. Very soon you would be enfilided. Where's your supports, my lady? (MRS. DOWEY *is damped.*)

MRS. MICKLEHAM. What none of you grasps is that this is a artillery war——

THE HAGGERTY WOMAN (*strengthened by the winkle*). I say that the word is Salonaiky. (*The others purse their lips.*)

MRS. TWYMLEY (*with terrible meaning*). We'll change the subject. Have you seen this week's *Fashion Chat*? (*She has evidently seen and devoured it herself, and even licked up the crumbs.*) The gabardine with accordion pleats has quite gone out.

MRS. DOWEY (*her old face sparkling*). My sakes! You tell me?

MRS. TWYMLEY (*with the touch of haughtiness that comes of great topics*). The plain smock has come in again, with silk lacing, giving that charming chic effect.

MRS. DOWEY. Oho!

MRS. MICKLEHAM. I must say I was always partial to the straight line (*thoughtfully regarding the want of line in* MRS. TWYMLEY'S *person*), though trying to them as is of too friendly a figure.

(*It is here that* THE HAGGERTY WOMAN'S *fingers close unostentatiously upon a piece of sugar.*)

MRS. TWYMLEY (*sailing into the Empyrean*). Lady Dolly Kanister was seen conversing across the railings in a dainty *de jou*.

MRS. DOWEY. Fine would I have liked to see her.

MRS. TWYMLEY. She is equally popular as maid, wife, and munition-worker. Her two children is inset. Lady Pops Babington was married in a tight tulle.

MRS. MICKLEHAM. What was her going-away dress?

MRS. TWYMLEY. A champagny cream velvet with dreamy corsage. She's married to Colonel the Hon. Chingford—'Snubs,' they called him at Eton.

THE HAGGERTY WOMAN (*having disposed of the sugar*). Very likely he'll be sent to Salonaiky.

MRS. MICKLEHAM. Wherever he is sent, she'll have the same tremors as the rest of us. She'll be as keen to get the letters wrote with pencils as you or me.

MRS. TWYMLEY. Them pencil letters!

MRS. DOWEY (*in her sweet Scotch voice, timidly, afraid she may be going too far*). And women in enemy lands gets those pencil letters

215

and then stop getting them, the same as ourselves. Let's occasionally think of that.

(*She has gone too far. Chairs are pushed back.*)

THE HAGGERTY WOMAN. I ask you!

MRS. MICKLEHAM. That's hardly language, Mrs. Dowey.

MRS. DOWEY (*scared*). Kindly excuse. I swear to death I'm none of your pacifists.

MRS. MICKLEHAM. Freely granted.

MRS. TWYMLEY. I've heard of females that have no male relations, and so they have no man-party at the wars. I've heard of them, but I don't mix with them.

MRS. MICKLEHAM. What can the likes of us have to say to them? It's not their war.

MRS. DOWEY (*wistfully*). They are to be pitied.

MRS. MICKLEHAM. But the place for them, Mrs. Dowey, is within doors with the blinds down.

MRS. DOWEY (*hurriedly*). That's the place for them.

MRS. MICKLEHAM. I saw one of them today buying a flag. I thought it was very impudent of her.

MRS. DOWEY (*meekly*). So it was.

MRS. MICKLEHAM (*trying to look modest with indifferent success*). I had a letter from my son, Percy, yesterday.

MRS. TWYMLEY. Alfred sent me his photo.

THE HAGGERTY WOMAN. Letters from Salonaiky is less common.

(*Three bosoms heave, but not, alas,* MRS. DOWEY'S. *Nevertheless she doggedly knits her lips.*)

MRS. DOWEY (*the criminal*). Kenneth writes to me every week. (*There are exclamations. The dauntless old thing holds aloft a packet of letters.*) Look at this. All his.

(THE HAGGERTY WOMAN *frowns.*)

MRS. TWYMLEY. Alfred has little time for writing, being a bombardier.

MRS. DOWEY (*relentlessly*). Do your letters begin 'Dear mother'?

MRS. TWYMLEY. Generally.

MRS. MICKLEHAM. Invariable.

THE HAGGERTY WOMAN. Every time.

MRS. DOWEY (*delivering the knock-out blow*). Kenneth's begin 'Dearest mother.'

(*No one can think of the right reply.*)

216

MRS. TWYMLEY (*doing her best*). A short man, I should say, judging by yourself.

(*She ought to have left it alone.*)

MRS. DOWEY. Six feet two—and a half.

(*The gloom deepens.*)

MRS. MICKLEHAM (*against her better judgment*). A kilty, did you tell me?

MRS. DOWEY. Most certainly. He's in the famous Black Watch.

THE HAGGERTY WOMAN (*producing her handkerchief*). The Surrey Rifles is the famousest.

MRS. MICKLEHAM. There you and the King disagrees, Mrs. Haggerty. His choice is the Buffs, same as my Percy's.

MRS. TWYMLEY (*magnanimously*). Give me the R.H.A. and you can keep all the rest.

MRS. DOWEY. I'm sure I have nothing to say against the Surreys and the R.H.A. and the Buffs; but they are just breeches regiments, I understand.

THE HAGGERTY WOMAN. We can't all be kilties.

MRS. DOWEY (*crushingly*). That's very true.

MRS. TWYMLEY (*it is foolish of her, but she can't help saying it*). Has your Kenneth great hairy legs?

MRS. DOWEY. Tremendous.

(*The wicked woman: but let us also say 'Poor Sarah Ann Dowey.' For at this moment, enter Nemesis. In other words, the less important part of a clergyman appears upon the stair.*)

MRS. MICKLEHAM. It's the reverent gent!

MRS. DOWEY (*little knowing what he is bringing her*). I see he has had his boots heeled.

(*It may be said of* MR. WILLINGS *that his happy smile always walks in front of him. This smile makes music of his life; it means that once again he has been chosen, in his opinion, as the central figure in romance. No one can well have led a more drab existence, but he will never know it; he will always think of himself, humbly though elatedly, as the chosen of the gods. Of him must it have been originally written that adventures are for the adventurous. He meets them at every street corner. For instance, he assists an old lady off the bus, and asks her if he can be of any further help. She tells him that she wants to know the way to Maddox the butcher's. Then comes the kind, triumphant smile; it always comes*)

217

first, followed by its explanation, 'I was there yesterday!' This is the merest sample of the adventures that keep MR. WILLINGS *up to the mark.*

Since the war broke out, his zest for life has become almost terrible. He can scarcely lift a newspaper and read of a hero without remembering that he knows some one of the same name. The Soldiers' Rest he is connected with was once a china emporium, and (mark my words) he had bought his tea service at it. Such is life when you are in the thick of it. Sometimes he feels that he is part of a gigantic spy drama. In the course of his extraordinary comings and goings he meets with Great Personages, of course, and is the confidential recipient of secret news. Before imparting the news he does not, as you might expect, first smile expansively; on the contrary, there comes over his face an awful solemnity, which, however, means the same thing. When divulging the names of the personages, he first looks around to make sure that no suspicious character is about, and then, lowering his voice, tells you, 'I had that from Mr. Farthing himself—he is the secretary of the Bethnal Green Branch,—h'sh!'

There is a commotion about finding a worthy chair for the reverend, and there is also some furtive pulling down of sleeves, but he stands surveying the ladies through his triumphant smile. This amazing man knows that he is about to score again.)

MR. WILLINGS (*waving aside the chairs*). I thank you. But not at all. Friends, I have news.

MRS. MICKLEHAM. News?

THE HAGGERTY WOMAN. From the Front?

MRS. TWYMLEY. My Alfred, sir?

(*They are all grown suddenly anxious—all except the hostess, who knows that there can never be any news from the Front for her.*)

MR. WILLINGS. I tell you at once that all is well. The news is for Mrs. Dowey.

(*She stares.*)

MRS. DOWEY. News for me?

MR. WILLINGS. Your son, Mrs. Dowey—he has got five days' leave. (*She shakes her head slightly, or perhaps it only trembles a little on its stem.*) Now, now, good news doesn't kill.

MRS. TWYMLEY. We're glad, Mrs. Dowey.

MRS. DOWEY. You're sure?

MR. WILLINGS. Quite sure. He has arrived.

MRS. DOWEY. He is in London?

MR. WILLINGS. He is. I have spoken to him.

MRS. MICKLEHAM. You lucky woman.

(*They might see that she is not looking lucky, but experience has told them how differently these things take people.*)

MR. WILLINGS (*marvelling more and more as he unfolds his tale*). Ladies, it is quite a romance. I was in the—(*he looks around cautiously, but he knows that they are all to be trusted*)—in the Church Army quarters in Central Street, trying to get on the track of one or two of our missing men. Suddenly my eyes—I can't account for it—but suddenly my eyes alighted on a Highlander seated rather drearily on a bench, with his kit at his feet.

THE HAGGERTY WOMAN. A big man?

MR. WILLINGS. A great brawny fellow. (THE HAGGERTY WOMAN *groans.*) 'My friend,' I said at once, 'welcome back to Blighty.' I make a point of calling it Blighty. 'I wonder,' I said, 'if there is anything I can do for you?' He shook his head. 'What regiment?' I asked. (*Here he very properly lowers his voice to a whisper.*) 'Black Watch, 5th Battalion,' he said. 'Name?' I asked. 'Dowey,' he said.

MRS. MICKLEHAM. I declare! I do declare!

MR. WILLINGS (*showing how the thing was done, with the help of a chair*). I put my hand on his shoulder as it might be thus. 'Kenneth Dowey,' I said, 'I know your mother.'

MRS. DOWEY (*wetting her lips*). What did he say to that?

MR. WILLINGS. He was incredulous. Indeed, he seemed to think I was balmy. But I offered to bring him straight to you. I told him how much you had talked to me about him.

MRS. DOWEY. Bring him here!

MRS. MICKLEHAM. I wonder he needed to be brought.

MR. WILLINGS. He had just arrived, and was bewildered by the great city. He listened to me in the taciturn Scotch way, and then he gave a curious laugh.

MRS. TWYMLEY. Laugh?

MR. WILLINGS (*whose wild life has brought him into contact with the strangest people*). The Scotch, Mrs. Twymley, express their emotions differently from us. With them tears signify a rollicking mood, while merriment denotes that they are plunged in gloom. When I had finished he said at once, 'Let us go and see the old lady.'

219

MRS. DOWEY (*backing, which is the first movement she has made since he began his tale*). Is he—coming?

MR. WILLINGS (*gloriously*). He has come. He is up there. I told him I thought I had better break the joyful news to you.

(*Three women rush to the window.* MRS. DOWEY *looks at her pantry door, but perhaps she remembers that it does not lock on the inside. She stands rigid, though her face has gone very gray.*)

MRS. DOWEY. Kindly get them to go away.

MR. WILLINGS. Ladies, I think this happy occasion scarcely requires you. (*He is not the man to ask of woman a sacrifice that he is not prepared to make himself.*) I also am going instantly.

(*They all survey* MRS. DOWEY, *and understand—or think they understand.*)

MRS. TWYMLEY (*pail and mop in hand*). I would thank none for their company if my Alfred was at the door.

MRS. MICKLEHAM (*similarly burdened*). The same from me. Shall I send him down, Mrs. Dowey? (*The old lady does not hear her. She is listening, terrified, for a step on the stair.*) Look at the poor, joyous thing, sir. She has his letters in her hand.

(*The three women go.* MR. WILLINGS *puts a kind hand on* MRS. DOWEY'S *shoulder. He thinks he so thoroughly understands the situation.*)

MR. WILLINGS. A good son, Mrs. Dowey, to have written to you so often.

(*Our old criminal quakes, but she grips the letters more tightly.* PRIVATE DOWEY *descends.*)

Dowey, my friend, there she is, waiting for you, with your letters in her hand.

DOWEY (*grimly*). That's great.

(MR. WILLINGS *ascends the stair without one backward glance, like the good gentleman he is; and the* DOWEYS *are left together, with nearly the whole room between them. He is a great rough chunk of Scotland, howked out of her not so much neatly as liberally; and in his Black Watch uniform, all caked with mud, his kit and nearly all his worldly possessions on his back, he is an apparition scarcely less fearsome (but so much less ragged) than those ancestors of his who trotted with Prince Charlie to Derby. He stands silent, scowling at the old lady, daring her to raise her head; and she would like very much to do it, for she longs to have a first*

220

glimpse of her son. When he does speak, it is to jeer at her.)

Do you recognise your loving son, missis? (*'Oh, the fine Scotch tang of him,' she thinks.*)

MRS. DOWEY (*trembling*). I'm pleased I wrote so often. (*'Oh, but he's raised,' she thinks.*)

(*He strides toward her, and seizes the letters roughly.*)

DOWEY. Let's see them.

(*There is a string round the package, and he unties it, and examines the letters at his leisure with much curiosity. The envelopes are in order, all addressed in pencil to* MRS. DOWEY, *with the proud words 'Opened by Censor' on them. But the letter paper inside contains not a word of writing.*)

DOWEY. Nothing but blank paper! Is this your writing in pencil on the envelope?

(*She nods, and he gives the matter further consideration.*)

The covey told me you were a charwoman; so I suppose you picked the envelopes out of waste-paper baskets, or such like, and then changed the addresses?

(*She nods, and he gives the matter further consideration.*)

legs. When, however, he would cast the letters into the fire, she flames up with sudden spirit. She clutches them.)

MRS. DOWEY. Don't you burn them letters, mister.

DOWEY. They're not real letters.

MRS. DOWEY. They're all I have.

DOWEY (*returning to irony*). I thought you had a son?

MRS. DOWEY. I never had a man nor a son nor anything. I just call myself Missis to give me a standing.

DOWEY. Well, it's past my seeing through.

(*He turns to look for some explanation from the walls. She gets a peep at him at last. Oh, what a grandly set-up man! Oh, the stride of him. Oh, the noble rage of him. Oh, Samson had been like this before that woman took him in hand.*)

DOWEY (*whirling round on her*). What made you do it?

MRS. DOWEY. It was everybody's war, mister, except mine. (*She beats her arms.*) I wanted it to be my war too.

DOWEY. You'll need to be plainer. And yet I'm d—d if I care to hear you, you lying old trickster.

(*The words are merely what were to be expected, and so are endurable; but he has moved towards the door.*)

221

MRS. DOWEY. You're not going already, mister?

DOWEY. Yes, I just came to give you an ugly piece of my mind.

MRS. DOWEY (*holding out her arms longingly*). You haven't gave it to me yet.

DOWEY. You have a cheek!

MRS. DOWEY (*giving further proof of it*). You wouldn't drink some tea?

DOWEY. Me! I tell you I came here for the one purpose of blazing away at you.

(*It is such a roaring negative that it blows her into a chair. But she is up again in a moment, is this spirited old lady.*)

MRS. DOWEY. You could drink the tea while you was blazing away. There's winkles.

DOWEY. Is there?

(*He turns interestedly toward the table, but his proud Scots character checks him, which is just as well, for what she should have said was that there had been winkles.*)

Not me. You're just a common rogue. (*He seats himself far from the table.*) Now, then, out with it. Sit down! (*She sits meekly; there is nothing she would not do for him.*) As you char, I suppose you are on your feet all day.

MRS. DOWEY. I'm more on my knees.

DOWEY. That's where you should be to me.

MRS. DOWEY. Oh, mister, I'm willing.

DOWEY. Stop it. Go on, you accomplished liar.

MRS. DOWEY. It's true that my name is Dowey.

DOWEY. It's enough to make me change mine.

MRS. DOWEY. I've been charring and charring and charring as far back as I mind. I've been in London this twenty years.

DOWEY. We'll skip your early days. I have an appointment.

MRS. DOWEY. And then when I was old the war broke out.

DOWEY. How could it affect you?

MRS. DOWEY. Oh, mister, that's the thing. It didn't affect me. It affected everybody but me. The neighbours looked down on me. Even the posters, on the walls, of the woman saying, 'Go, my boy,' leered at me. I sometimes cried by myself in the dark. You won't have a cup of tea?

DOWEY. No.

MRS. DOWEY. Sudden-like the idea came to me to pretend I had a son.

DOWEY. You depraved old limmer! But what in the name of Old Nick made you choose me out of the whole British Army?

MRS. DOWEY (*giggling*). Maybe, mister, it was because I liked you best.

DOWEY. Now, now, woman.

MRS. DOWEY. I read one day in the papers, 'In which he was assisted by Private K. Dowey, 5th Battalion, Black Watch.'

DOWEY (*flattered*). Did you, now! Well, I expect that's the only time I was ever in the papers.

MRS. DOWEY (*trying it on again*). I didn't choose you for that alone. I read a history of the Black Watch first, to make sure it was the best regiment in the world.

DOWEY. Anybody could have told you that.

(*He is moving about now in better humour, and, meeting the loaf in his stride, he cuts a slice from it. He is hardly aware of this, but* MRS. DOWEY *knows.*)

I like the Scotch voice of you, woman. It drummles on like a hill burn.

MRS. DOWEY. Prosen Water runs by where I was born. Maybe it teached me to speak, mister.

DOWEY. Canny, woman, canny.

MRS. DOWEY. I read about the Black Watch's ghostly piper that plays proudly when the men of the Black Watch do well, and prouder when they fall.

DOWEY. There's some foolish story of that kind.

(*He has another careless slice off the loaf.*)

But you couldn't have been living here at that time, or they would have guessed. I suppose you flitted?

MRS. DOWEY. Yes, it cost me eleven and sixpence.

DOWEY. How did you guess the *K* in my name stood for Kenneth?

MRS. DOWEY. Does it?

DOWEY. Umpha!

MRS. DOWEY. An angel whispered it to me in my sleep.

DOWEY. Well, that's the only angel in the whole black business.

(*He chuckles.*)

You little thought I would turn up! (*Wheeling suddenly on her*) Or did you?

MRS. DOWEY. I was beginning to weary for a sight of you, Kenneth.

DOWEY. What word was that?

MRS. DOWEY. Mister.

(*He helps himself to butter, and she holds out the jam pot to him, but he haughtily rejects it. Do you think she gives in now? Not a bit of it.*)

DOWEY (*sarcastic again*). I hope you're pleased with me now you see me.

MRS. DOWEY. I'm very pleased. Does your folk live in Scotland?

DOWEY. Glasgow.

MRS. DOWEY. Both living?

DOWEY. Ay.

MRS. DOWEY. Is your mother terrible proud of you?

DOWEY. Naturally.

MRS. DOWEY. You'll be going to them?

DOWEY. After I've had a skite in London first.

MRS. DOWEY (*sniffing*). So she is in London!

DOWEY. Who?

MRS. DOWEY. Your young lady.

DOWEY. Are you jealyous?

MRS. DOWEY. Not me.

DOWEY. You needna be. She's a young thing.

MRS. DOWEY. You surprises me. A beauty, no doubt?

DOWEY. You may be sure. (*He tries the jam.*) She's a titled person. She is equally popular as maid, wife and munition-worker.

(MRS. DOWEY *remembers Lady Dolly Kanister, so familiar to readers of fashionable gossip, and a very leery expression indeed comes into her face.*)

MRS. DOWEY. Tell me more about her, man.

DOWEY. She has sent me a lot of things, especially cakes, and a worsted waistcoat, with a loving message on the enclosed card.

(*The old lady is now in a quiver of excitement. She loses control of her arms, which jump excitedly this way and that.*)

MRS. DOWEY. You'll try one of my cakes, mister?

DOWEY. Not me.

MRS. DOWEY. They're of my own making.

DOWEY. No, I thank you.

(*But with a funny little run she is in the pantry and back again. She pushes a cake before him, at sight of which he gapes.*)

MRS. DOWEY. What's the matter? Tell me, oh, tell me, mister!

DOWEY. That's exactly the kind of cake that her ladyship sends me.

(MRS. DOWEY *is now a very glorious old character indeed.*)

MRS. DOWEY. Is the waistcoat right, mister? I hope the Black Watch colours pleased you.

DOWEY. Wha—at! Was it you?

MRS. DOWEY. I daredna give my own name, you see, and I was always reading hers in the papers.

(*The badgered man looms over her, terrible for the last time.*)

DOWEY. Woman, is there no getting rid of you!

MRS. DOWEY. Are you angry?

(*He sits down with a groan.*)

DOWEY. Oh, hell! Give me some tea.

(*She rushes about preparing a meal for him, every bit of her wanting to cry out to every other bit, 'Oh, glory, glory, glory!' For a moment she hovers behind his chair. 'Kenneth!' she murmurs. 'What?' he asks, no longer aware that she is taking a liberty. 'Nothing,' she says, 'just Kenneth,' and is off gleefully for the tea-caddy. But when his tea is poured out, and he has drunk a saucerful, the instinct of self-preservation returns to him between two bites.*)

DOWEY. Don't you be thinking, missis, for one minute that you have got me.

MRS. DOWEY. No, no.

(*On that understanding he unbends.*)

DOWEY. I have a theatre tonight, followed by a randy-dandy.

MRS. DOWEY. Oho! Kenneth, this is a queer first meeting!

DOWEY. It is, woman, oh, it is. (*Guardedly*) And it's also a last meeting.

MRS. DOWEY. Yes, yes.

DOWEY. So here's to you—you old mop and pail. *Ave atque vale.*

MRS. DOWEY. What's that?

DOWEY. That means Hail and Farewell.

MRS. DOWEY. Are you a scholar?

DOWEY. Being Scotch, there's almost nothing I don't know.

MRS. DOWEY. What was you to trade?

DOWEY. Carter, glazier, orraman, any rough jobs.

MRS. DOWEY. You're a proper man to look at.

DOWEY. I'm generally admired.

MRS. DOWEY. She's an enviable woman.

DOWEY. Who?

MRS. DOWEY. Your mother.

DOWEY. Eh? Oh, that was just protecting myself from you. I have

225

neither father nor mother nor wife nor grandmama. (*Bitterly*) This party never even knew who his proud parents were.

MRS. DOWEY. Is that—(*gleaming*)—is that true?

DOWEY. It's gospel.

MRS. DOWEY. Heaven be praised!

DOWEY. Eh? None of that! I was a fool to tell you. But don't think you can take advantage of it. Pass the cake.

MRS. DOWEY. I dare say it's true we'll never meet again, Kenneth, but—but if we do, I wonder where it will be?

DOWEY. Not in this world.

MRS. DOWEY. There's no telling. (*Leering ingratiatingly*) It might be at Berlin.

DOWEY. Tod, if I ever get to Berlin, I believe I'll find you there waiting for me!

MRS. DOWEY. With a cup of tea for you in my hand.

DOWEY. Yes, and (*heartily*) very good tea too.

(*He has partaken heavily, he is now in high good humour.*)

MRS. DOWEY. Kenneth, we could come back by Paris!

DOWEY. All the ladies likes to go to Paris.

MRS. DOWEY. Oh, Kenneth, Kenneth, if just once before I die I could be fitted for a Paris gown with dreamy corsage!

DOWEY. You're all alike, old covey. We have a song about it. (*He sings:*)

> 'Mrs. Gill is very ill,
> Nothing can improve her
> But to see the Tuileries
> And waddle through the Louvre.'

(*No song ever had a greater success.* MRS. DOWEY *is doubled up with mirth. When she comes to, when they both come to, for there are a pair of them, she cries:*)

MRS. DOWEY. You must learn me that (*and off she goes in song also:*)

> 'Mrs. Dowey's very ill,
> Nothing can improve her.'

DOWEY.

> 'But dressed up in a Paris gown
> To waddle through the Louvre.'

(*They fling back their heads, she points at him, he points at her.*)

226

MRS. DOWEY (*ecstatically*). Hairy legs!

(*A mad remark, which brings him to his senses; he remembers who and what she is.*)

DOWEY. Mind your manners! (*Rising*) Well, thank you for my tea. I must be stepping.

(*Poor* MRS. DOWEY, *he is putting on his kit.*)

MRS. DOWEY. Where are you living?

(*He sighs.*)

DOWEY. That's the question. But there's a place called The Hut, where some of the 2nd Battalion are. They'll take me in. Beggars (*bitterly*) can't be choosers.

MRS. DOWEY. Beggars?

DOWEY. I've never been here before. If you knew (*a shadow comes over him*) what it is to be in such a place without a friend. I was crazy with glee, when I got my leave, at the thought of seeing London at last, but after wandering its streets for four hours, I would almost have been glad to be back in the trenches.

(*'If you knew,' he has said, but indeed the old lady knows.*)

MRS. DOWEY. That's my quandorum too, Kenneth.

(*He nods sympathetically.*)

DOWEY. I'm sorry for you, you poor old body. (*Shouldering his kit.*) But I see no way out for either of us.

MRS. DOWEY (*cooing*). Do you not?

DOWEY. Are you at it again!

(*She knows that it must be now or never. She has left her biggest guns for the end. In her excitement she is rising up and down on her toes.*)

MRS. DOWEY. Kenneth, I've heard that the thing a man on leave longs for more than anything else is a bed with sheets, and a bath.

DOWEY. You never heard anything truer.

MRS. DOWEY. Go into that pantry, Kenneth Dowey, and lift the dresser-top, and tell me what you see.

(*He goes. There is an awful stillness. He returns, impressed.*)

DOWEY. It's a kind of a bath!

MRS. DOWEY. You could do yourself there pretty, half at a time.

DOWEY. Me?

MRS. DOWEY. There's a woman through the wall that would be very willing to give me a shake-down till your leave is up.

(*He snorts.*)

227

DOWEY. Oh, is there!

(*She has not got him yet, but there is still one more gun.*)

MRS. DOWEY. Kenneth, look!

(*With these simple words she lets down the bed. She says no more; an effect like this would be spoilt by language. Fortunately he is not made of stone. He thrills.*)

DOWEY. Gosh! That's the dodge we need in the trenches.

MRS. DOWEY. That's your bed, Kenneth.

DOWEY. Mine? (*He grins at her.*) You queer old divert. What can make you so keen to be burdened by a lump like me?

MRS. DOWEY. He! he! he! he!

DOWEY. I tell you, I'm the commonest kind of man.

MRS. DOWEY. I'm just the commonest kind of old wifie myself.

DOWEY. I've been a kick-about all my life, and I'm no great shakes at the war.

MRS. DOWEY. Yes, you are. How many Germans have you killed?

DOWEY. Just two for certain, and there was no glory in it. It was just because they wanted my shirt.

MRS. DOWEY. Your shirt?

DOWEY. Well, they said it was their shirt.

MRS. DOWEY. Have you took prisoners?

DOWEY. I once took half a dozen, but that was a poor affair too.

MRS. DOWEY. How could one man take half a dozen?

DOWEY. Just in the usual way. I surrounded them.

MRS. DOWEY. Kenneth, you're just my ideal.

DOWEY. You're easily pleased.

(*He turns again to the bed.*)

Let's see how the thing works.

(*He kneads the mattress with his fist, and the result is so satisfactory that he puts down his kit.*)

Old lady, if you really want me, I'll bide.

MRS. DOWEY. Oh! oh! oh! oh!

(*Her joy is so demonstrative that he has to drop a word of warning.*)

DOWEY. But, mind you, I don't accept you as a relation. For your personal glory, you can go on pretending to the neighbours; but the best I can say for you is that you're on your probation. I'm a cautious character, and we must see how you'll turn out.

MRS. DOWEY. Yes, Kenneth.

DOWEY. And now, I think, for that bath. My theatre begins at six-thirty. A cove I met on a bus is going with me.

(*She is a little alarmed.*)

MRS. DOWEY. You're sure you'll come back?

DOWEY. Yes, yes. (*Handsomely*) I leave my kit in pledge.

MRS. DOWEY. You won't liquor up too freely, Kenneth?

DOWEY. You're the first (*chuckling*) to care whether I do or not. (*Nothing she has said has pleased the lonely man so much as this.*) I promise. Tod, I'm beginning to look forward to being wakened in the morning by hearing you cry, 'Get up, you lazy swine.' I've kind of envied men that had womenfolk with the right to say that.

(*He is passing to the bathroom when a diverting notion strikes him.*)

MRS. DOWEY. What is it, Kenneth?

DOWEY. The theatre. It would be showier if I took a lady.

(MRS. DOWEY *feels a thumping at her breast.*)

MRS. DOWEY. Kenneth, tell me this instant what you mean. Don't keep me on the jumps.

(*He turns her round.*)

DOWEY. No, it couldn't be done.

MRS. DOWEY. Was it me you were thinking of?

DOWEY. Just for the moment (*regretfully*), but you have no style.

(*She catches hold of him by the sleeve.*)

MRS. DOWEY. Not in this, of course. But, oh, Kenneth, if you saw me in my merino! It's laced up the back in the very latest.

DOWEY. Hum (*doubtfully*); but let's see it.

(*It is produced from a drawer, to which the old lady runs with almost indecent haste. The connoisseur examines it critically.*)

DOWEY. Looks none so bad. Have you a bit of chiffon for the neck? It's not bombs nor Kaisers nor Tipperary that men in the trenches think of, it's chiffon.

MRS. DOWEY. I swear I have, Kenneth. And I have a bangle, and a muff, and gloves.

DOWEY. Ay, ay. (*He considers.*) Do you think you could give your face less of a homely look?

MRS. DOWEY. I'm sure I could.

DOWEY. Then you can have a try. But, mind you, I promise nothing. All will depend on the effect.

(*He goes into the pantry, and the old lady is left alone. Not alone,*

229

for she is ringed round by entrancing hopes and dreadful fears. They beam on her and jeer at her, they pull her this way and that; with difficulty she breaks through them and rushes to her pail, hot water, soap, and a looking-glass. Our last glimpse of her for this evening shows her staring (not discontentedly) at her soft old face, licking her palm, and pressing it to her hair. Her eyes are sparkling.

One evening a few days later MRS. TWYMLEY *and* MRS. MICKLE-HAM *are in* MRS. DOWEY'S *house, awaiting that lady's return from some fashionable dissipation. They have undoubtedly been discussing the war, for the first words we catch are:)*

MRS. MICKLEHAM. I tell you flat, Amelia, I bows no knee to junkerdom.

MRS. TWYMLEY. Sitting here by the fire, you and me, as one to another, what do you think will happen after the war? Are we to go back to being as we were?

MRS. MICKLEHAM. Speaking for myself, Amelia, not me. The war has wakened me up to a understanding of my own importance that is really astonishing.

MRS. TWYMLEY. Same here. Instead of being the poor worms the like of you and me thought we was, we turns out to be visible departments of a great and haughty empire.

(They are well under way, and with a little luck we might now hear their views on various passing problems of the day, such as the neglect of science in our public schools. But in comes THE HAGGERTY WOMAN *and spoils everything. She is attired, like them, in her best, but the effect of her is that her clothes have gone out for a walk, leaving her at home.)*

MRS. MICKLEHAM *(with deep distaste)*. Here's that submarine again.

*(*THE HAGGERTY WOMAN *cringes to them, but gets no encouragement.)*

THE HAGGERTY WOMAN. It's a terrible war.

MRS. TWYMLEY. Is that so?

THE HAGGERTY WOMAN. I wonder what will happen when it ends?

MRS. MICKLEHAM. I have no idea.

(The intruder produces her handkerchief, but does not use it. After all, she is in her best.)

THE HAGGERTY WOMAN. Are they not back yet?

(Perfect ladies must reply to a direct question.)

230

MRS. MICKLEHAM. No (*icily*). We have been waiting this half hour. They are at the theatre again.

THE HAGGERTY WOMAN. You tell me! I just popped in with an insignificant present for him, as his leave is up.

MRS. TWYMLEY. The same errand brought us.

THE HAGGERTY WOMAN. My present is cigarettes.

(*They have no intention of telling her what their presents are, but the secret leaps from them.*)

MRS. MICKLEHAM. So is mine.

MRS. TWYMLEY. Mine too.

(*Triumph of* THE HAGGERTY WOMAN. *But it is short-lived.*)

MRS. MICKLEHAM. Mine has gold tips.

MRS. TWYMLEY. So has mine.

(THE HAGGERTY WOMAN *need not say a word. You have only to look at her to know that her cigarettes are not gold-tipped. She tries to brazen it out, which is so often a mistake.*)

THE HAGGERTY WOMAN. What care I? Mine is Exquisytos.

(*No wonder they titter.*)

MRS. MICKLEHAM. Excuse us, Mrs. Haggerty (if that's your name), but the word is Exquiseetos.

THE HAGGERTY WOMAN. Much obliged. (*She weeps.*)

MRS. MICKLEHAM. I think I heard a taxi.

MRS. TWYMLEY. It will be her third this week.

(*They peer through the blind. They are so excited that rank is forgotten.*)

THE HAGGERTY WOMAN. What is she in?

MRS. MICKLEHAM. A new astrakhan jacket he gave her, with Venus sleeves.

THE HAGGERTY WOMAN. Has she sold her gabardine coat?

MRS. MICKLEHAM. Not her! She has them both at the theatre, warm night though it is. She's wearing the astrakhan, and carrying the gabardine, flung careless-like over her arm.

THE HAGGERTY WOMAN. I saw her strutting about with him yesterday, looking as if she thought the two of them made a procession.

MRS. TWYMLEY. H'sh! (*peeping*). Strike me dead, if she's not coming mincing down the stair, hooked on his arm!

(*Indeed it is thus that* MRS. DOWEY *enters. Perhaps she had seen shadows lurking on the blind, and at once hooked on to* KENNETH *to impress the visitors. She is quite capable of it.*

231

Now we see what KENNETH *saw that afternoon five days ago when he emerged from the bathroom and found the old trembler awaiting his inspection. Here are the muff and the gloves and the chiffon, and such a kind old bonnet that it makes you laugh at once; I don't know how to describe it, but it is trimmed with a kiss, as bonnets should be when the wearer is old and frail. We must take the merino for granted until she steps out of the astrakhan. She is dressed up to the nines, there is no doubt about it. Yes, but is her face less homely? Above all, has she style? The answer is in a stout affirmative. Ask* KENNETH. *He knows. Many a time he has had to go behind a door to roar hilariously at the old lady. He has thought of her as a lark to tell his mates about by and by; but for some reason that he cannot fathom, he knows now that he will never do that.)*

MRS. DOWEY (*affecting surprise*). Kenneth, we have visitors!

DOWEY. Your servant, ladies.

(*He is no longer mud-caked and dour. A very smart figure is this* PRIVATE DOWEY, *and he winks engagingly at the visitors, like one who knows that for jolly company you cannot easily beat charwomen. The pleasantries that he and they have exchanged this week! The sauce he has given them. The wit of* MRS. MICKLEHAM'S *retorts. The badinage of* MRS. TWYMLEY. *The neat giggles of* THE HAGGERTY WOMAN. *There has been nothing like it since you took the countess in to dinner.*)

MRS. TWYMLEY. We should apologise. We're not meaning to stay.

MRS. DOWEY. You are very welcome. Just wait (*the ostentation of this!*) till I get out of my astrakhan—and my muff—and my gloves—and (*it is the bonnet's turn now*) my Excelsior.

(*At last we see her in the merino* (*a triumph*).)

MRS. MICKLEHAM. You've given her a glory time, Mr. Dowey.

DOWEY. It's her that has given it to me, missis.

MRS. DOWEY. Hey! hey! hey! hey! He just pampers me (*waggling her fists*). The Lord forgive us, but this being the last night, we had a sit-down supper at a restaurant! (*Vehemently*) I swear by God that we had champagny wine. (*There is a dead stillness, and she knows very well what it means, she has even prepared for it.*) And to them as doubts my words—here's the cork.

(*She places the cork, in its lovely gold drapery, upon the table.*)

MRS. MICKLEHAM. I'm sure!

232

MRS. TWYMLEY. I would thank you, Mrs. Dowey, not to say a word against my Alfred.

MRS. DOWEY. Me!

DOWEY. Come, come, ladies (*in the masterful way that is so hard for women to resist*); if you say another word, I'll kiss the lot of you.

(*There is a moment of pleased confusion.*)

MRS. MICKLEHAM. Really, them sodgers!

THE HAGGERTY WOMAN. The kilties is the worst!

MRS. TWYMLEY (*heartily*). I'm sure we don't grudge you your treats, Mrs. Dowey; and sorry we are that this is the end.

DOWEY. Yes, it's the end (*with a troubled look at his old lady*); I must be off in ten minutes.

(*The little soul is too gallant to break down in company. She hurries into the pantry and shuts the door.*)

MRS. MICKLEHAM. Poor thing! But we must run, for you'll be having some last words to say to her.

DOWEY. I kept her out long on purpose so as to have less time to say them in.

(*He more than half wishes that he could make a bolt to a public-house.*)

MRS. TWYMLEY. It's the best way. (*In the important affairs of life there is not much that any one can teach a charwoman.*) Just a mere nothing, to wish you well, Mr. Dowey.

(*All three present him with the cigarettes.*)

MRS. MICKLEHAM. A scraping, as one might say.

THE HAGGERTY WOMAN (*enigmatically*). The heart is warm though it may not be gold-tipped.

DOWEY. You bricks!

THE LADIES. Good luck, cocky.

DOWEY. The same to you. And if you see a sodger man up there in a kilt, he is one that is going back with me. Tell him not to come down, but—but to give me till the last minute, and then to whistle.

(*It is quite a grave man who is left alone, thinking what to do next. He tries a horse laugh, but that proves of no help. He says 'Hell!' to himself, but it is equally ineffective. Then he opens the pantry door and calls.*)

DOWEY. Old lady.

(*She comes timidly to the door, her hand up as if to ward off a blow.*)

233

MRS. DOWEY. Is it time?

(*An encouraging voice answers her.*)

DOWEY. No, no, not yet. I've left word for Dixon to whistle when go I must.

MRS. DOWEY. All is ended.

DOWEY. Now, then, you promised to be gay. We were to help one another.

MRS. DOWEY. Yes, Kenneth.

DOWEY. It's bad for me, but it's worse for you.

MRS. DOWEY. The men have medals to win, you see.

DOWEY. The women have their medals too.

(*He knows she likes him to order her about, so he tries it again.*)

DOWEY. Come here. No, I'll come to you. (*He stands gaping at her wonderingly. He has no power of words, nor does he quite know what he would like to say.*) God!

MRS. DOWEY. What is it, Kenneth?

DOWEY. You're a woman.

MRS. DOWEY. I had near forgot it.

(*He wishes he was at the station with* DIXON. DIXON *is sure to have a bottle in his pocket. They will be roaring a song presently. But in the meantime—there is that son business. Blethers, the whole thing, of course—or mostly blethers. But it's the way to please her.*)

DOWEY. Have you noticed you have never called me son?

MRS. DOWEY. Have I noticed it! I was feared, Kenneth. You said I was on probation.

DOWEY. And so you were. Well, the probation's ended. (*He laughs uncomfortably.*) The like of me! But if you want me you can have me.

MRS. DOWEY. Kenneth, will I do?

DOWEY (*artfully gay*). Woman, don't be so forward. Wait till I have proposed.

MRS. DOWEY. Propose for a mother?

DOWEY. What for no? (*In the grand style*) Mrs. Dowey, you queer carl, you spunky tiddy, have I your permission to ask you the most important question a neglected orphan can ask of an old lady?

(*She bubbles with mirth. Who could help it, the man has such a way with him.*)

MRS. DOWEY. None of your sauce, Kenneth.

DOWEY. For a long time, Mrs. Dowey, you **cannot have been un**aware of my sonnish feelings for you.

234

MRS. DOWEY. Wait till I get my mop to you!

DOWEY. And if you're not willing to be my mother, I swear I'll never ask another.

(*The old divert pulls him down to her and strokes his hair.*) Was I a well-behaved infant, mother?

MRS. DOWEY. Not you, sonny, you were a rampaging rogue.

DOWEY. Was I slow in learning to walk?

MRS. DOWEY. The quickest in our street. He! he! he! (*She starts up.*) Was that the whistle?

DOWEY. No, no. See here. In taking me over you have, in a manner of speaking, joined the Black Watch.

MRS. DOWEY. I like to think that, Kenneth.

DOWEY. Then you must behave so that the ghost piper can be proud of you. 'Tion! (*She stands bravely at attention.*) That's the style. Now listen. I've sent in your name as being my nearest of kin, and your allowance will be coming to you weekly in the usual way.

MRS. DOWEY. Hey! hey! hey! Is it wicked, Kenneth?

DOWEY. I'll take the responsibility for it in both worlds. You see, I want you to be safeguarded in case anything hap——

MRS. DOWEY. Kenneth!

DOWEY. 'Tion! Have no fear. I'll come back, covered with mud and medals. Mind you have that cup of tea waiting for me. (*He is listening for the whistle. He pulls her on to his knee.*)

MRS. DOWEY. Hey! hey! hey! hey!

DOWEY. What fun we'll have writing to one another! Real letters this time.

MRS. DOWEY. Yes.

DOWEY. It would be a good plan if you began the first letter as soon as I've gone.

MRS. DOWEY. I will.

DOWEY. I hope Lady Dolly will go on sending me cakes.

MRS. DOWEY. You may be sure.

(*He ties his scarf round her neck.*)

DOWEY. You must have been a bonny thing when you were young.

MRS. DOWEY. Away with you!

DOWEY. That scarf sets you fine.

MRS. DOWEY. Blue was always my colour.

(*The whistle sounds.*)

DOWEY. Old lady, you are what Blighty means to me now.

(She hides in the pantry again. She is out of sight to us, but she does something that makes PRIVATE DOWEY *take off his bonnet. Then he shoulders his equipment and departs. That is he laughing coarsely with* DIXON.

We have one last glimpse of the old lady—a month or two after KENNETH'S *death in action. It would be rosemary to us to see her in her black dress, of which she is very proud; but let us rather peep at her in the familiar garments that make a third to her mop and pail. It is early morning, and she is having a look at her medals before setting off on the daily round. They are in a drawer, with the scarf covering them, and on the scarf a piece of lavender. First, the black frock, which she carries in her arms like a baby. Then her War Savings Certificates,* KENNETH'S *bonnet, a thin packet of real letters, and the famous champagne cork. She kisses the letters, but she does not blub over them. She strokes the dress, and waggles her head over the certificates and presses the bonnet to her cheeks, and rubs the tinsel of the cork carefully with her apron. She is a tremulous old 'un; yet she exults, for she owns all these things, and also the penny flag on her breast. She puts them away in the drawer, the scarf over them, the lavender on the scarf. Her air of triumph well becomes her. She lifts the pail and the mop, and slouches off gamely to the day's toil.)*

From The Prophet

Kahlil Gibran

ON LOVE

Love gives naught but itself
and takes naught but from itself.
Love possesses not nor would
it be possessed;
For love is sufficient unto love.

From The Prophet

Kahlil Gibran

On Marriage

... But let there be spaces in your
togetherness,
And let the winds of the
heavens dance between you.

Love one another, but make
not a bond of love:
Let it rather be a moving sea
between the shores of your souls.
Fill each other's cup but drink
not from one cup.
Give one another of your bread
but eat not from the same loaf.
Sing and dance together and
be joyous, but let each one of
you be alone,
Even as the strings of a lute
are alone though they quiver
with the same music.

On Children

Your children are not your
children.
They are the sons and daughters of Life's longing for itself.
They come through you but
not from you,
And though they are with you

yet they belong not to you.
You may give them your love
but not your thoughts.
For they have their own
thoughts.
You may house their bodies
but not their souls,
For their souls dwell in the
house of tomorrow, which you
cannot visit, even in your dreams.
You may strive to be like them,
but seek not to make them like you.
For life goes not backward
nor tarries with yesterday.

Appraisal

Sara Teasdale

Never think she loves him wholly,
Never believe her love is blind,
All his faults are locked securely
In a closet of her mind;
All his indecisions folded
Like old flags that time has faded,
Limp and streaked with rain,
And his cautiousness like garments
Frayed and thin, with many a stain—
Let them be, oh, let them be,
There is treasure to outweigh them,
His proud will that sharply stirred,
Climbs as surely as the tide,
Senses strained too taut to sleep,
Gentleness to beast and bird,
Humor flickering hushed and wide
As the moon on moving water,
And a tenderness too deep
To be gathered in a word.

"I Love You"

Sara Teasdale

When April bends above me
  And finds me fast asleep,
Dust need not keep the secret
  A live heart died to keep.

When April tells the thrushes,
  The meadow-larks will know,
And pipe the three words lightly
  To all the winds that blow.

Above his roof the swallows,
  In notes like far-blown rain,
Will tell the chirping sparrow
  Beside his window-pane.

O sparrow, little sparrow,
  When I am fast asleep,
Then tell my love the secret
  That I have died to keep.

For a Young Friend

Adelaide Love

Since now the tides of love have swept the shore
Of your young heart, I pray it be high tide
Forever and a day, that nevermore
The beautiful, proud waters will subside.

Yet, should they ebb, they will leave scattered shells
Of lovely architecture, memories
That mark where lately rose the shining swells
And mighty music of imperial seas.

For the Beloved

Adelaide Love

Let there be you beside me in the twilight
After the color and vehemence of the day,
When the silence holds, as a shell holds a pearl in its hollow,
The word that we need not say.

Let there be you beside me in the twilight
After the splendor and turbulence of the years,
When the silence shall hold remembrance of laughter and
    heartache,
Of peace and passion, of hope and desperate tears.

Let there be you beside me in the twilight,
As my lips assume the silence no lips have broken,
And death shall find that for two so long accustomed
To dusk without need of words, he has no token.

240

Good-bye, Mr. Chips!

James Hilton

> *A modern classic about the most famous schoolmaster of all time.*

I

WHEN you are getting on in years (but not ill, of course), you get very sleepy at times, and the hours seem to pass like lazy cattle moving across a landscape. It was like that for Chips as the autumn term progressed and the days shortened till it was actually dark enough to light the gas before call-over. For Chips, like some old sea captain, still measured time by the signals of the past; and well he might, for he lived at Mrs. Wickett's, just across the road from the School. He had been there more than a decade, ever since he finally gave up his mastership; and it was Brookfield far more than Greenwich time that both he and his landlady kept. 'Mrs. Wickett,' Chips would sing out, in that jerky, high-pitched voice that had still a good deal of sprightliness in it, 'you might bring me a cup of tea before prep, will you?'

When you are getting on in years it is nice to sit by the fire and drink a cup of tea and listen to the school bell sounding dinner, call-over, prep, and lights-out. Chips always wound up the clock after that last bell; then he put the wire guard in front of the fire, turned out the gas, and carried a detective novel to bed. Rarely did he read more than a page of it before sleep came swiftly and peacefully, more like a mystic intensifying of perception than any changeful entrance into another world. For his days and nights were equally full of dreaming.

He was getting on in years (but not ill, of course); indeed, as Doctor Merivale said, there was really nothing the matter with him. 'My dear fellow, you're fitter than I am,' Merivale would say, sipping a glass of sherry when he called every fortnight or so. 'You're past the age when people get these horrible diseases; you're one of the few lucky ones who're going to die a really natural death. That is, of course, if you die at all. You're such a remarkable old boy that one never knows.'

241

But when Chips had a cold or when east winds roared over the fen-lands, Merivale would sometimes take Mrs. Wickett aside in the lobby and whisper: 'Look after him, you know. His chest . . . it puts a strain on his heart. Nothing really wrong with him—only anno domini, but that's the most fatal complaint of all, in the end.'

Anno domini . . . by Jove, yes. Born in 1848, and taken to the Great Exhibition as a toddling child—not many people still alive could boast a thing like that. Besides, Chips could even remember Brookfield in Wetherby's time. A phenomenon, that was. Wetherby had been an old man in those days—1870—easy to remember because of the Franco-Prussian War. Chips had put in for Brookfield after a year at Melbury, which he hadn't liked, because he had been ragged there a good deal. But Brookfield he *had* liked, almost from the beginning. He remem-bered that day of his preliminary interview—sunny June, with the air full of flower scents and the plick-plock of cricket on the pitch. Brook-field was playing Barnhurst, and one of the Barnhurst boys, a chubby little fellow, made a brilliant century. Queer that a thing like that should stay in the memory so clearly. Wetherby himself was very fatherly and courteous; he must have been ill then, poor chap, for he died during the summer vacation, before Chips began his first term. But the two had seen and spoken to each other, anyway.

Chips often thought, as he sat by the fire at Mrs. Wickett's: I am probably the only man in the world who has a vivid recollection of old Wetherby. . . . Vivid, yes; it was a frequent picture in his mind, that summer day with the sunlight filtering through the dust in Wetherby's study. 'You are a young man, Mr. Chipping, and Brookfield is an old foundation. Youth and age often combine well. Give your enthusiasm to Brookfield, and Brookfield will give you something in return. And don't let anyone play tricks with you. I—er—gather that discipline was not always your strong point at Melbury?'

'Well, no, perhaps not, sir.'

'Never mind; you're full young; it's largely a matter of experience. You have another chance here. Take up a firm attitude from the be-ginning—that's the secret of it.'

Perhaps it was. He remembered that first tremendous ordeal of taking prep; a September sunset more than half a century ago; Big Hall full of lusty barbarians ready to pounce on him as their legitimate prey. His youth, fresh-complexioned, high-collared, and side-whisk-ered (odd fashions people followed in those days), at the mercy of five hundred unprincipled ruffians to whom the baiting of new masters was a fine art, an exciting sport, and something of a tradition. Decent little beggars individually, but, as a mob, just pitiless and implacable. The sudden hush as he took his place at the desk on the dais; the scowl he assumed to cover his inward nervousness; the tall clock ticking behind him, and the smells of ink and varnish; the last blood-red rays slanting in slabs through the stained-glass windows. Someone dropped a desk lid. Quickly, he must take everyone by surprise; he must show that there was no nonsense about him. 'You there in the fifth row—you with the red hair—what's your name?' 'Colley, sir.' 'Very well, Colley, you have a hundred lines.' No trouble at all after that. He had won his first round.

And years later, when Colley was an alderman of the City of London and a baronet and various other things, he sent his son (also red-haired) to Brookfield, and Chips would say: 'Colley, your father was the first boy I ever punished when I came here twenty-five years ago. He deserved it then, and you deserve it now.' How they all laughed; and how Sir Richard laughed when his son wrote home the story in next Sunday's letter!

And again, years after that, many years after that, there was an even better joke. For another Colley had just arrived—son of the Colley who was a son of the first Colley. And Chips would say, punctuating his remarks with that little 'umph-um' that had by then become a habit with him: 'Colley, you are—umph—a splendid example of—umph—inherited traditions. I remember your grandfather—umph—he could never grasp the Ablative Absolute. A stupid fellow, your grandfather. And your father, too—umph—I remember him—he used to sit at that far desk by the wall—he wasn't much better, either. But I do believe—my dear Colley—that you are—umph—the biggest fool of the lot!' Roars of laughter.

A great joke, this growing old—but a sad joke, too, in a way. And as Chips sat by his fire with autumn gales rattling the windows, the waves of humor and sadness swept over him very often until tears fell, so that when Mrs. Wickett came in with his cup of tea she did not know whether he had been laughing or crying. And neither did Chips himself.

II

Across the road behind a rampart of ancient elms lay Brookfield,

243

russet under its autumn mantle of creeper. A group of eighteenth-century buildings centred upon a quadrangle, and there were acres of playing fields beyond; then came the small dependent village and the open fen country. Brookfield, as Wetherby had said, was an old foundation; established in the reign of Elizabeth, as a grammar school. It might, with better luck, have become as famous as Harrow. Its luck, however, had been not so good; the School went up and down, dwindling almost to nonexistence at one time, becoming almost illustrious at another. It was during one of these latter periods, in the reign of the first George, that the main structure had been rebuilt and large additions made. Later, after the Napoleonic Wars and until mid-Victorian days, the School declined again, both in numbers and in repute. Wetherby, who came in 1840, restored its fortunes somewhat; but its subsequent history never raised it to front-rank status. It was, nevertheless, a good school of the second rank. Several notable families supported it; it supplied fair samples of the history-making men of the age—judges, members of parliament, colonial administrators, a few peers and bishops. Mostly, however, it turned out merchants, manufacturers, and professional men, with a good sprinkling of country squires and parsons. It was the sort of school which, when mentioned, would sometimes make snobbish people confess that they rather thought they had heard of it.

But if it had not been this sort of school it would probably not have taken Chips. For Chips, in any social or academic sense, was just as respectable, but no more brilliant, than Brookfield itself.

It had taken him some time to realize this, at the beginning. Not that he was boastful or conceited, but he had been, in his early twenties, as ambitious as most other young men at such an age. His dream had been to get a headship eventually, or at any rate a senior mastership in a really first-class school; it was only gradually, after repeated trials and failures, that he realized the inadequacy of his qualifications. His degree, for instance, was not particularly good, and his discipline, though good enough and improving, was not absolutely reliable under all conditions. He had no private means and no family connections of any importance. About 1880, after he had been at Brookfield a decade, he began to recognize that the odds were heavily against his being able to better himself by moving elsewhere; but about that time, also, the possibility of staying where he was began to fill a comfortable niche in his mind. At forty, he was rooted, settled, and quite happy. At fifty, he was the doyen of the staff. At sixty, under a new and youthful Head, he *was* Brookfield—the guest of honor at Old Brookfeldian dinners, the court of appeal in all matters affecting Brookfield history and traditions. And in 1913, when he turned sixty-five, he retired, was presented with a check and a writing desk and a clock, and went across the road to live at Mrs. Wickett's. A decent career, decently closed; three cheers for old Chips, they all shouted, at that uproarious end-of-term dinner.

Three cheers, indeed; but there was more to come, an unguessed epilogue, an encore played to a tragic audience.

III

It was a small but very comfortable and sunny room that Mrs. Wickett let to him. The house itself was ugly and pretentious; but that didn't matter. It was convenient—that was the main thing. For he liked, if the weather were mild enough, to stroll across to the playing fields in an afternoon and watch the games. He liked to smile and exchange a few words with the boys when they touched their caps to him. He made a special point of getting to know all the new boys and having them to tea with him during their first term. He always ordered a walnut cake with pink icing from Reddaway's, in the village, and during the winter term there were crumpets, too—a little pile of them in front of the fire, soaked in butter so that the bottom one lay in a little shallow pool. His guests found it fun to watch him make tea—mixing careful spoonfuls from different caddies. And he would ask the new boys where they lived, and if they had family connections at Brookfield. He kept watch to see that their plates were never empty, and punctually at five, after the session had lasted an hour, he would glance at the clock and say: 'Well—umph—it's been very delightful— umph—meeting you like this—I'm sorry—umph—you can't stay. . . .' And he would smile and shake hands with them in the porch, leaving them to race across the road to the School with their comments. 'Decent old boy, Chips. Gives you a jolly good tea, anyhow, and you *do* know when he wants you to push off. . . .'

And Chips also would be making his comments—to Mrs. Wickett when she entered his room to clear away the remains of the party. 'A most—umph—interesting time, Mrs. Wickett. Young Branksome tells me—umph—that his uncle was Major Collingwood—the Collingwood we had here in—umph—nought-two, I think it was. Dear me, I remember Collingwood very well. I once thrashed him—umph—for climbing on to the gymnasium roof—to get a ball out of the gutter. Might have—umph—broken his neck, the young fool. Do you remember him, Mrs. Wickett? He must have been in your time.'

Mrs. Wickett, before she saved money, had been in charge of the linen room at the School.

'Yes, I knew 'im, sir. Cheeky, 'e was to me, gener'ly. But we never 'ad no bad words between us. Just cheeky-like. 'E never meant no harm. That kind never does, sir. Wasn't it 'im that got the medal, sir?'

'Yes, a D.S.O.'

'Will you be wanting anything else, sir?'

'Nothing more now—umph—till chapel time. He was killed—in Egypt, I think. . . . Yes—umph—you can bring my supper about then.'

'Very good, sir.'

A pleasant, placid life, at Mrs. Wickett's. He had no worries; his pension was adequate, and there was a little money saved up besides. He could afford everything and anything he wanted. His room was furnished simply and with schoolmasterly taste: a few bookshelves and sporting trophies; a mantelpiece crowded with fixture cards and signed photographs of boys and men; a worn Turkey carpet; big easy-chairs; pictures on the wall of the Acropolis and the Forum. Nearly everything had come out of his old housemaster's room in School House. The books were chiefly classical, the classics having been his subject; there was, however, a seasoning of history and belles-lettres. There was also a bottom shelf piled up with cheap editions of detective novels. Chips enjoyed these. Sometimes he took down Vergil or Xenophon and read for a few moments, but he was soon back again with Doctor Thorndyke or Inspector French. He was not, despite his long years of assiduous teaching, a very profound classical scholar; indeed, he thought of Latin and Greek far more as dead languages from which English gentlemen ought to know a few quotations than as living tongues that had ever been spoken by living people. He liked those short leading articles in the *Times* that introduced a few tags that he recognized. To be among the dwindling number of people who understood such things was to him a kind of secret and valued freemasonry; it represented, he felt, one of the chief benefits to be derived from a classical education.

So there he lived, at Mrs. Wickett's, with his quiet enjoyments of reading and talking and remembering; an old man, white-haired and only a little bald, still fairly active for his years, drinking tea, receiving callers, busying himself with corrections for the next edition of the Brookfeldian Directory, writing his occasional letters in thin, spidery, but very legible script. He had new masters to tea, as well as new boys. There were two of them that autumn term, and as they were leaving after their visit one of them commented: 'Quite a character, the old boy, isn't he? All that fuss about mixing the tea—a typical bachelor, if ever there was one.'

Which was oddly incorrect; because Chips was not a bachelor at all. He had married; though it was so long ago that none of the staff at Brookfield could remember his wife.

IV

There came to him, stirred by the warmth of the fire and the gentle aroma of tea, a thousand tangled recollections of old times. Spring— the spring of 1896. He was forty-eight—an age at which a permanence of habits begins to be predictable. He had just been appointed house-master; with this and his classical forms, he had made for himself a warm and busy corner of life. During the summer vacation he went up to the Lake District with Rowden, a colleague; they walked and climbed for a week, until Rowden had to leave suddenly on some family business. Chips stayed on alone at Wasdale Head, where he boarded in a small farmhouse.

One day, climbing on Great Gable, he noticed a girl waving excit-edly from a dangerous-looking ledge. Thinking she was in difficulties, he hastened toward her, but in doing so slipped himself and wrenched his ankle. As it turned out, she was not in difficulties at all, but was merely signaling to a friend farther down the mountain; she was an expert climber, better even than Chips, who was pretty good. Thus he found himself the rescued instead of the rescuer; and neither rôle was one for which he had much relish. For he did not, he would have said, care for women; he never felt at home or at ease with them; and that monstrous creature beginning to be talked about, the New Woman of the nineties, filled him with horror. He was a quiet, conventional per-son, and the world, viewed from the haven of Brookfield, seemed to him full of distasteful innovations; there was a fellow named Bernard Shaw who had the strangest and most reprehensible opinions; there was Ibsen, too, with his disturbing plays; and there was this new craze for bicycling which was being taken up by women equally with men.

Chips did not hold with all this modern newness and freedom. He had a vague notion, if he ever formulated it, that nice women were weak, timid, and delicate, and that nice men treated them with a polite but rather distant chivalry. He had not, therefore, expected to find a woman on Great Gable; but, having encountered one who seemed to need masculine help, it was even more terrifying that she should turn the tables by helping him. For she did. She and her friend had to. He could scarcely walk, and it was a hard job getting him down the steep track to Wasdale.

Her name was Katherine Bridges; she was twenty-five—young enough to be Chips's daughter. She had blue, flashing eyes and freckled cheeks and smooth straw-colored hair. She too was staying at a farm, on holiday with a girl friend, and as she considered herself responsible for Chips's accident, she used to bicycle along the side of the lake to the house in which the quiet, middle-aged, serious-looking man lay resting.

That was how she thought of him at first. And he, because she rode a bicycle and was unafraid to visit a man alone in a farmhouse sitting room, wondered vaguely what the world was coming to. His sprain put him at her mercy, and it was soon revealed to him how much he might need that mercy. She was a governess out of a job, with a little money saved up; she read and admired Ibsen; she believed that women ought to be admitted to the universities; she even thought they ought to have a vote. In politics she was a radical, with leanings toward the views of people like Bernard Shaw and William Morris. All her ideas and opinions she poured out to Chips during those summer afternoons at Wasdale Head; and he, because he was not very articulate, did not at first think it worth while to contradict them. Her friend went away, but she stayed; what *could* you do with such a person, Chips thought. He used to hobble with sticks along a footpath leading to the tiny church; there was a stone slab on the wall, and it was comfortable to sit down, facing the sunlight and the green-brown majesty of the Gable, and listening to the chatter of—well, yes, Chips had to admit it—a very beautiful girl.

He had never met anyone like her. He had always thought that the modern type, this 'new woman' business, would repel him; and here she was, making him positively look forward to the glimpse of her safety bicycle careering along the lakeside road. And she, too, had never met anyone like *him*. She had always thought that middle-aged men who read the *Times* and disapproved of modernity were terrible bores; yet here he was, claiming her interest and attention far more than youths of her own age. She liked him, initially, because he was so hard to get to know, because he had gentle and quiet manners, because his opinions dated from those utterly impossible seventies and eighties and even earlier—yet were, for all that, so thoroughly honest; and because—because his eyes were brown and he looked charming when he smiled. 'Of course, *I* shall call you Chips, too,' she said, when she learned that that was his nickname at school.

Within a week they were head over heels in love; before Chips could walk without a stick, they considered themselves engaged; and they were married in London a week before the beginning of the autumn term.

V

When Chips, dreaming through the hours at Mrs. Wickett's, recollected those days, he used to look down at his feet and wonder which one it was that had performed so signal a service. That, the trivial cause of so many momentous happenings, was the one thing of which details evaded him. But he resaw the glorious hump of the Gable (he had never visited the Lake District since), and the mouse-gray depths of Wastwater under the Screes; he could resmell the washed air after heavy rain, and refollow the ribbon of the pass across to Sty Head. So clearly it lingered, that time of dizzy happiness, those evening strolls by the waterside, her cool voice and her gay laughter. She had been a very happy person, always.

They had both been so eager, planning a future together; but he had been rather serious about it, even a little awed. It would be all right, of course, her coming to Brookfield; other housemasters were married. And she liked boys, she told him, and would enjoy living among them. 'Oh, Chips, I'm so glad you are what you are. I was afraid you were a solicitor or a stockbroker or a dentist or a man with a big cotton business in Manchester. When I first met you, I mean. Schoolmastering's so different, so important, don't you think? To be influencing those who are going to grow up and matter to the world . . .'

Chips said he hadn't thought of it like that—or, at least, not often. He did his best; that was all anyone could do in any job.

'Yes, of course, Chips. I do love you for saying simple things like that.'

And one morning—another memory gem-clear when he turned to

it—he had for some reason been afflicted with an acute desire to depreciate himself and all his attainments. He had told her of his only mediocre degree, of his occasional difficulties of discipline, of the certainty that he would never get a promotion, and of his complete ineligibility to marry a young and ambitious girl. And at the end of it all she had laughed in answer.

She had no parents and was married from the house of an aunt in Ealing. On the night before the wedding, when Chips left the house to return to his hotel, she said, with mock gravity: 'This is an occasion, you know—this last farewell of ours. I feel rather like a new boy beginning his first term with you. Not scared, mind you—but just, for once, in a thoroughly respectful mood. Shall I call you "sir"—or would "Mr. Chips" be the right thing? "Mr. Chips," I think. Good-bye, then—good-bye, Mr. Chips. . . .'

(A hansom clop-clopping in the roadway; green-pale gas lamps flickering on a wet pavement; newsboys shouting something about South Africa; Sherlock Holmes in Baker Street.)

'Good-bye, Mr. Chips. . . .'

VI

There had followed then a time of such happiness that Chips, remembering it long afterward, hardly believed it could ever have happened before or since in the world. For his marriage was a triumphant success. Katherine conquered Brookfield as she had conquered Chips; she was immensely popular with boys and masters alike. Even the wives of the masters, tempted at first to be jealous of one so young and lovely, could not long resist her charms.

But most remarkable of all was the change she made in Chips. Till his marriage he had been a dry and rather neutral sort of person; liked and thought well of by Brookfield in general, but not of the stuff that makes for great popularity or that stirs great affection. He had been at Brookfield for over a quarter of a century, long enough to have established himself as a decent fellow and a hard worker; but just too long for anyone to believe him capable of ever being much more. He had, in fact, already begun to sink into that creeping dry rot of pedagogy which is the worst and ultimate pitfall of the profession; giving the same lessons year after year had formed a groove into which the other affairs of his life adjusted themselves with insidious ease. He worked well; he was conscientious; he was a fixture that gave service, satisfaction, confidence, everything except inspiration.

And then came this astonishing girl-wife whom nobody had expected—least of all Chips himself. She made him, to all appearances, a new man; though most of the newness was really a warming to life of things that were old, imprisoned, and unguessed. His eyes gained sparkle; his mind, which was adequately if not brilliantly equipped, began to move more adventurously. The one thing he had always had, a sense of humor, blossomed into a sudden richness to which his years lent maturity. He began to feel a greater sureness; his discipline improved to a point at which it could become, in a sense, less rigid; he became more popular. When he had first come to Brookfield he had aimed to be loved, honored, and obeyed—but obeyed, at any rate. Obedience he had secured, and honor had been granted him; but only now came love, the sudden love of boys for a man who was kind without being soft, who understood them well enough, but not too much, and whose private happiness linked them with their own. He began to make little jokes, the sort that schoolboys like—mnemonics and puns that raised laughs and at the same time imprinted something in the mind. There was one that never failed to please, though it was only a sample of many others. Whenever his Roman History forms came to deal with the Lex Canuleia, the law that permitted patricians to marry plebeians, Chips used to add: 'So that, you see, if Miss Plebs wanted Mr. Patrician to marry her, and he said he couldn't, she probably replied: "Oh yes, you can, you liar!" ' Roars of laughter.

And Kathie broadened his views and opinions, also, giving him an outlook far beyond the roofs and turrets of Brookfield, so that he saw his country as something deep and gracious to which Brookfield was but one of many feeding streams. She had a cleverer brain than his, and he could not confute her ideas even if and when he disagreed with them; he remained, for instance, a Conservative in politics, despite all her radical-socialist talk. But even where he did not accept, he absorbed; her young idealism worked upon his maturity to produce an amalgam very gentle and wise.

Sometimes she persuaded him completely. Brookfield, for example, ran a mission in East London, to which boys and parents contributed generously with money but rarely with personal contact. It was Katherine who suggested that a team from the mission should come up to Brookfield and play one of the School's elevens at soccer. The idea was so revolutionary that from anyone but Katherine it could not have

251

survived its first frosty reception. To introduce a group of slum boys to the serene pleasaunces of better-class youngsters seemed at first a wanton stirring of all kinds of things that had better be left untouched. The whole staff was against it, and the School, if its opinion could have been taken, was probably against it too. Everyone was certain that the East End lads would be hooligans, or else that they would be made to feel uncomfortable; anyhow, there would be 'incidents,' and everyone would be confused and upset. Yet Katherine persisted.

'Chips,' she said, 'they're wrong, you know, and I'm right. I'm looking ahead to the future, they and you are looking back to the past. England isn't always going to be divided into officers and "other ranks." And those Poplar boys are just as important—to England—as Brookfield is. You've got to have them here, Chips. You can't satisfy your conscience by writing a check for a few guineas and keeping them at arm's length. Besides, they're proud of Brookfield—just as you are. Years hence, maybe, boys of that sort will be coming here—a few of them, at any rate. Why not? Why ever not? Chips, dear, remember this is eighteen-ninety-seven—not sixty-seven, when you were up at Cambridge. You got your ideas well stuck in those days, and good ideas they were too, a lot of them. But a few—just a few, Chips—want unsticking. . . .'

Rather to her surprise, he gave way and suddenly became a keen advocate of the proposal, and the *volte-face* was so complete that the authorities were taken unawares and found themselves consenting to the dangerous experiment. The boys from Poplar arrived at Brookfield one Saturday afternoon, played soccer with the School's second team, were honorably defeated by seven goals to five, and later had high tea with the School team in the Dining Hall. They then met the Head and were shown over the School, and Chips saw them off at the railway station in the evening. Everything had passed without the slightest hitch of any kind, and it was clear that the visitors were taking away with them as fine an impression as they had left behind.

They took back with them also the memory of a charming woman who had met them and talked to them; for once, years later, during the War, a private stationed at a big military camp near Brookfield called on Chips and said he had been one of that first visiting team. Chips gave him tea and chatted with him, till at length, shaking hands, the man said: 'And 'ow's the missus, sir? I remember her very well.'

'Do you?' Chips answered, eagerly. 'Do you remember her?'

'Rather. I should think anyone would.'

And Chips replied: 'They don't, you know. At least, not here. Boys come and go; new faces all the time; memories don't last. Even masters don't stay forever. Since last year—when old Gribble retired—he's—um—the School butler—there hasn't been anyone here who ever saw my wife. She died, you know, less than a year after your visit. In ninety-eight.'

'I'm real sorry to 'ear that, sir. There's two or three o' my pals, any-how, who remember 'er clear as anything, though we did only see 'er that wunst. Yes, we remember 'er, all right.'

'I'm very glad. . . . That was a grand day we all had—and a fine game, too.'

'One o' the best days aht I ever 'ad in me life. Wish it was then and not nah—straight, I do. I'm off to Frawnce tomorrer.'

A month or so later Chips heard that he had been killed at Pass-chendaele.

VII

And so it stood, a warm and vivid patch in his life, casting a radiance that glowed in a thousand recollections. Twilight at Mrs. Wickett's, when the School bell clanged for call-over, brought them back to him in a cloud—Katherine scampering along the stone corridors, laughing beside him at some 'howler' in an essay he was marking, taking the cello part in a Mozart trio for the School concert, her creamy arm sweeping over the brown sheen of the instrument. She had been a good player and a fine musician. And Katherine furred and muffed for the December house matches, Katherine at the Garden Party that followed Speech Day Prize-giving, Katherine tendering her advice in any little problem that arose. Good advice, too—which he did not always take, but which always influenced him. 'Chips, dear, I'd let them off if I were you. After all, it's nothing very serious.'

'I know. I'd like to let them off, but if I do I'm afraid they'll do it again.'

'Try telling them that, frankly, and give them the chance.'

'I might.'

And there were other things, occasionally, that *were* serious.

'You know, Chips, having all these hundreds of boys cooped up here is really an unnatural arrangement, when you come to think about it. So that when anything does occur that oughtn't to, don't you think it's

253

a bit unfair to come down on them as if it were their own fault for being here?'

'Don't know about that, Kathie, but I do know that for everybody's sake we have to be pretty strict about this sort of thing. One black sheep can contaminate others.'

'After he himself has been contaminated to begin with. After all, that's what probably *did* happen, isn't it?'

'Maybe. We can't help it. Anyhow, I believe Brookfield is better than a lot of other schools. All the more reason to keep it so.'

'But this boy, Chips . . . you're going to sack him?'

'The Head probably will, when I tell him.'

'And you're going to tell the Head?'

'It's a duty, I'm afraid.'

'Couldn't you think about it a bit . . . talk to the boy again . . . find out how it began. . . . After all—apart from this business—isn't he rather a nice boy?'

'Oh, he's all right.'

'Then, Chips dear, don't you think there *ought* to be some other way . . .'

And so on. About once in ten times he was adamant and wouldn't be persuaded. In about half of these exceptional cases he afterward rather wished he had taken her advice. And years later, whenever he had trouble with a boy, he was always at the mercy of a softening wave of reminiscence; the boy would stand there, waiting to be told his punishment, and would see, if he were observant, the brown eyes twinkle into a shine that told him all was well. But he did not guess that at such a moment Chips was remembering something that had happened long before he was born; that Chips was thinking: Young ruffian, I'm hanged if *I* can think of any reason to let him off, but I'll bet *she* would have done!

But she had not always pleaded for leniency. On rather rare occasions she urged severity where Chips was inclined to be forgiving. 'I don't like his type, Chips. He's too cocksure of himself. If he's looking for trouble I should certainly let him have it.'

What a host of little incidents, all deep-buried in the past—problems that had once been urgent, arguments that had once been keen, anecdotes that were funny only because one remembered the fun. Did any emotion really matter when the last trace of it had vanished from human memory; and if that were so, what a crowd of emotions clung to him as to their last home before annihilation! He must be kind to them, must treasure them in his mind before their long sleep. That affair of Archer's resignation, for instance—a queer business, that was. And that affair about the rat that Dunster put in the organ loft while old Ogilvie was taking choir practice. Ogilvie was dead and Dunster drowned at Jutland; of others who had witnessed or heard of the incident, probably most had forgotten. And it had been like that, with other incidents, for centuries. He had a sudden vision of thousands and thousands of boys, from the age of Elizabeth onward; dynasty upon dynasty of masters; long epochs of Brookfield history that had left not even a ghostly record. Who knew why the old fifth-form room was called 'the Pit'? There was probably a reason, to begin with; but it had since been lost—lost like the lost books of Livy. And what happened at Brookfield when Cromwell fought at Naseby, near by? How did Brookfield react to the great scare of the 'Forty-Five'? Was there a whole holiday when news came of Waterloo? And so on, up to the earliest time that he himself could remember—1870, and Wetherby saying, by way of small talk after their first and only interview: 'Looks as if we shall have to settle with the Prussians ourselves one of these fine days, eh?'

When Chips remembered things like this he often felt that he would write them down and make a book of them; and during his years at Mrs. Wickett's he sometimes went even so far as to make desultory notes in an exercise book. But he was soon brought up against difficulties—the chief one being that writing tired him, both mentally and physically. Somehow, too, his recollections lost much of their flavor when they were written down; that story about Rushton and the sack of potatoes, for instance—it would seem quite tame in print, but Lord, how funny it had been at the time! It was funny, too, to remember it; though perhaps if you didn't remember Rushton . . . and who would, anyway, after all those years? It was such a long time ago. . . . Mrs. Wickett, did you ever know a fellow named Rushton? Before your time, I dare say . . . went to Burma in some government job . . . or was it Borneo? . . . Very funny fellow, Rushton. . . .

And there he was, dreaming again before the fire, dreaming of times and incidents in which he alone could take secret interest. Funny and sad, comic and tragic, they all mixed up in his mind, and some day, however hard it proved, he *would* sort them out and make a book of them. . . .

VIII

And there was always in his mind that spring day in ninety-eight when he had paced through Brookfield village as in some horrifying nightmare, half struggling to escape into an outside world where the sun still shone and where everything had happened differently. Young Faulkner had met him there in the lane outside the School. 'Please, sir, may I have the afternoon off? My people are coming up.'

'Eh? What's that? Oh yes, yes. . . .'

'Can I miss Chapel, too, sir?'

'Yes . . . yes . . .'

'And may I go to the station to meet them?'

He nearly answered: 'You can go to blazes for all I care. My wife is dead and my child is dead, and I wish I were dead myself.'

Actually he nodded and stumbled on. He did not want to talk to anybody or to receive condolences; he wanted to get used to things, if he could, before facing the kind words of others. He took his fourth form as usual after call-over, setting them grammar to learn by heart while he himself stayed at his desk in a cold, continuing trance. Suddenly someone said: 'Please, sir, there are a lot of letters for you.'

So there were; he had been leaning his elbows on them; they were all addressed to him by name. He tore them open one after the other, but each contained nothing but a blank sheet of paper. He thought in a distant way that it was rather peculiar, but he made no comment; the incident gave hardly an impact upon his vastly greater preoccupations. Not till days afterward did he realize that it had been a piece of April foolery.

They had died on the same day, the mother and the child just born; on April 1, 1898.

IX

Chips changed his more commodious apartments in School House for his old original bachelor quarters. He thought at first he would give up his housemastership, but the Head persuaded him otherwise; and later he was glad. The work gave him something to do, filled up an emptiness in his mind and heart. He was different; everyone noticed it. Just as marriage had added something, so did bereavement; after the first stupor of grief he became suddenly the kind of man whom boys, at any rate, unhesitatingly classed as 'old.' It was not that he was less active; he could still knock up a half century on the cricket field; nor was it that he had lost any interest or keenness in his work. Actually, too, his hair had been graying for years; yet now, for the first time, people seemed to notice it. He was fifty. Once, after some energetic fives, during which he had played as well as many a fellow half his age, he overheard a boy saying: 'Not half bad for an old chap like him.'

Chips, when he was over eighty, used to recount that incident with many chuckles. 'Old at fifty, eh? Umph—it was Naylor who said that, and Naylor can't be far short of fifty himself by now! I wonder if he still thinks that fifty's such an age? Last I heard of him, he was lawyering, and lawyers live long—look at Halsbury—umph—Chancellor at eighty-two, and died at ninety-nine. There's an—umph—age for you! Too old at fifty—why, fellows like that are too *young* at fifty. . . . I was myself . . . a mere infant. . . .'

And there was a sense in which it was true. For with the new century there settled upon Chips a mellowness that gathered all his developing mannerisms and his oft-repeated jokes into a single harmony. No longer did he have those slight and occasional disciplinary troubles, or feel diffident about his own work and worth. He found that his pride in Brookfield reflected back, giving him cause for pride in himself and his position. It was a service that gave him freedom to be supremely and completely himself. He had won, by seniority and ripeness, an uncharted no-man's-land of privilege; he had acquired the right to those gentle eccentricities that so often attack schoolmasters and parsons. He wore his gown till it was almost too tattered to hold together; and when he stood on the wooden bench by Big Hall steps to take call-over, it was with an air of mystic abandonment to ritual. He held the School List, a long sheet curling over a board; and each boy, as he passed, spoke his own name for Chips to verify and then tick off on the list. That verifying glance was an easy and favorite subject of mimicry throughout the School—steel-rimmed spectacles slipping down the nose, eyebrows lifted, one a little higher than the other, a gaze half rapt, half quizzical. And on windy days, with gown and white hair and School List fluttering in uproarious confusion, the whole thing became a comic turn sandwiched between afternoon games and the return to classes.

Some of those names, in little snatches of a chorus, recurred to him ever afterward without any effort of memory. . . . Ainsworth, Attwood, Avonmore, Babcock, Baggs, Barnard, Bassenthwaite, Battersby, Beccles, Bedford-Marshall, Bentley, Best . . .

Another one: —

. . . Unsley, Vailes, Wadham, Wagstaff, Wallington, Waters Primus, Waters Secundus, Watling, Waveney, Webb . . .

And yet another that comprised, as he used to tell his fourth-form Latinists, an excellent example of a hexameter: —

. . . Lancaster, Latton, Lemare, Lytton-Bosworth, MacGonigall, Mansfield . . .

Where had they all gone to, he often pondered; those threads he had once held together, how far had they scattered, some to break, others to weave into unknown patterns? The strange randomness of the world beguiled him, that randomness which never would, so long as the world lasted, give meaning to those choruses again.

And behind Brookfield, as one may glimpse a mountain behind another mountain when the mist clears, he saw the world of change and conflict; and he saw it, more than he realized, with the remembered eyes of Kathie. She had not been able to bequeath him all her mind, still less the brilliance of it; but she had left him with a calmness and a poise that accorded well with his own inward emotions. It was typical of him that he did not share the general jingo bitterness against the Boers. Not that he was a pro-Boer—he was far too traditional for that, and he disliked the kind of people who *were* pro-Boers; but still, it did cross his mind at times that the Boers were engaged in a struggle that had a curious similarity to those of certain English history-book heroes —Hereward the Wake, for instance, or Caractacus. He once tried to shock his fifth form by suggesting this, but they only thought it was one of his little jokes.

However heretical he might be about the Boers, he was orthodox about Mr. Lloyd George and the famous Budget. He did not care for either of them. And when, years later, L. G. came as the guest of honor to a Brookfield Speech Day, Chips said, on being presented to him: 'Mr. Lloyd George, I am nearly old enough—umph—to remember you as a young man, and—umph—I confess that you seem to me—umph—to have improved—umph—a great deal.' The Head, standing with them, was rather aghast; but L. G. laughed heartily and talked to Chips more than to anyone else during the ceremonial that followed.

'Just like Chips,' was commented afterward. 'He gets away with it. I suppose at that age anything you say to anybody is all right. . . .'

258

X

In 1900 old Meldrum, who had succeeded Wetherby as Head and had held office for three decades, died suddenly from pneumonia; and in the interval before the appointment of a successor, Chips became Acting Head of Brookfield. There was just the faintest chance that the Governors might make the appointment a permanent one; but Chips was not really disappointed when they brought in a youngster of thirty-seven, glittering with Firsts and Blues and with the kind of personality that could reduce Big Hall to silence by the mere lifting of an eyebrow. Chips was not in the running with that kind of person; he never had been and never would be, and he knew it. He was an altogether milder and less ferocious animal.

Those years before his retirement in 1913 were studded with sharply remembered pictures.

A May morning; the clang of the School bell at an unaccustomed time; everyone summoned to assemble in Big Hall. Ralston, the new Head, very pontifical and aware of himself, fixing the multitude with a cold, presaging severity. 'You will all be deeply grieved to hear that His Majesty King Edward the Seventh died this morning. . . . There will be no school this afternoon, but a service will be held in the Chapel at four-thirty.'

A summer morning on the railway line near Brookfield. The railwaymen were on strike, soldiers were driving the engines, stones had been thrown at trains. Brookfield boys were patrolling the line, thinking the whole business great fun. Chips, who was in charge, stood a little way off, talking to a man at the gate of a cottage. Young Cricklade approached. 'Please, sir, what shall we do if we meet any strikers?'

'Would you like to meet one?'

'I—I don't know, sir.'

God bless the boy—he talked of them as if they were queer animals out of a zoo! 'Well, here you are, then—umph—you can meet Mr. Jones—he's a striker. When he's on duty he has charge of the signal box at the station. You've put your life in his hands many a time.'

Afterward the story went round the School: There was Chips, talking to a striker. Talking to a striker. Might have been quite friendly, the way they were talking together.

Chips, thinking it over a good many times, always added to himself that Kathie would have approved, and would also have been amused.

Because always, whatever happened and however the avenues of politics twisted and curved, he had faith in England, in English flesh and blood, and in Brookfield as a place whose ultimate worth depended on whether she fitted herself into the English scene with dignity and without disproportion. He had been left a vision that grew clearer with each year—of an England for which days of ease were nearly over, of a nation steering into channels where a hair's breadth of error might be catastrophic. He remembered the Diamond Jubilee; there had been a whole holiday at Brookfield, and he had taken Kathie to London to see the procession. That old and legendary lady, sitting in her carriage like some crumbling wooden doll, had symbolized impressively so many things that, like herself, were nearing an end. Was it only the century, or was it an epoch?

And then that frenzied Edwardian decade, like an electric lamp that goes brighter and whiter just before it burns itself out.

Strikes and lockouts, champagne suppers and unemployed marchers, Chinese labor, tariff reform, *H.M.S. Dreadnought*, Marconi, Home Rule for Ireland, Doctor Crippen, suffragettes, the lines of Chatalja. . . .

An April evening, windy and rainy; the fourth form construing Vergil, not very intelligently, for there was exciting news in the papers; young Grayson, in particular, was careless and preoccupied. A quiet, nervous boy.

'Grayson, stay behind—umph—after the rest.'

Then:—

'Grayson, I don't want to be—umph—severe, because you are generally pretty good—umph—in your work, but to-day—you don't seem —umph—to have been trying at all. Is anything the matter?'

'N-no, sir.'

'Well—umph—we'll say no more about it, but—umph—I shall expect better things next time.'

Next morning it was noised around the School that Grayson's father had sailed on the *Titanic*, and that no news had yet come through as to his fate.

Grayson was excused lessons; for a whole day the School centred emotionally upon his anxieties. Then came news that his father had been among those rescued.

Chips shook hands with the boy. 'Well, umph—I'm delighted, Grayson. A happy ending. You must be feeling pretty pleased with life.'

'Y-yes, sir.'

A quiet, nervous boy. And it was Grayson Senior, not Junior, with whom Chips was destined later to condole.

XI

And then the row with Ralston. Funny thing, Chips had never liked him; he was efficient, ruthless, ambitious, but not, somehow, very likable. He had, admittedly, raised the status of Brookfield as a school, and for the first time in memory there was a longish waiting list. Ralston was a live wire; a fine power transmitter, but you had to beware of him.

Chips had never bothered to beware of him; he was not attracted by the man, but he served him willingly enough and quite loyally. Or, rather, he served Brookfield. He knew that Ralston did not like him, either; but that didn't seem to matter. He felt himself sufficiently protected by age and seniority from the fate of other masters whom Ralston had failed to like.

Then suddenly, in 1908, when he had just turned sixty, came Ralston's urbane ultimatum. 'Mr. Chipping, have you ever thought you would like to retire?'

Chips stared about him in that book-lined study, startled by the question, wondering why Ralston should have asked it. He said, at length: 'No—umph—I can't say that—umph—I have thought much about it—umph—yet.'

'Well, Mr. Chipping, the suggestion is there for you to consider. The Governors would, of course, agree to your being adequately pensioned.'

Abruptly Chips flamed up. 'But—umph—I don't want—to retire. I don't—umph—need to consider it.'

'Nevertheless, I suggest that you do.'

'But—umph—I don't see—why—I should!'

'In that case, things are going to be a little difficult.'

'Difficult? Why—difficult?'

And then they set to, Ralston getting cooler and harder, Chips getting warmer and more passionate, till at last Ralston said, icily: 'Since you force me to use plain words, Mr. Chipping, you shall have them. For some time past, you haven't been pulling your weight here. Your methods of teaching are slack and old-fashioned; your personal habits are slovenly; and you ignore my instructions in a way which, in a younger man, I should regard as rank insubordination. It won't do,

261

Mr. Chipping, and you must ascribe it to my forbearance that I have put up with it so long.'

'But—' Chips began, in sheer bewilderment; and then he took up isolated words out of that extraordinary indictment. '*Slovenly*—umph —you said—?'

'Yes, look at the gown you're wearing. I happen to know that that gown of yours is a subject of continual amusement throughout the School.'

Chips knew it, too, but it had never seemed to him a very regrettable matter.

He went on: 'And—you also said—umph—something about—*insubordination*—?'

'No, I didn't. I said that in a younger man I should have regarded it as that. In your case it's probably a mixture of slackness and obstinacy. This question of Latin pronunciation, for instance—I think I told you years ago that I wanted the new style used throughout the School. The other masters obeyed me; you prefer to stick to your old methods, and the result is simply chaos and inefficiency.'

At last Chips had something tangible that he could tackle. 'Oh, *that!*' he answered, scornfully. 'Well, I—umph—I admit that I don't agree with the new pronunciation. I never did. Umph—a lot of nonsense, in my opinion. Making boys say "Kickero" at school when—umph—for the rest of their lives they'll say "Cicero"—if they ever—umph—say it at all. And instead of "vicissim"—God bless my soul—you'd make them say, "We kiss 'im"! Umph—umph!' And he chuckled momentarily, forgetting that he was in Ralston's study and not in his own friendly form room.

'Well, there you are, Mr. Chipping—that's just an example of what I complain of. You hold one opinion and I hold another, and, since you decline to give way, there can't very well be any alternative. I aim to make Brookfield a thoroughly up-to-date school. I'm a science man myself, but for all that I have no objection to the classics—provided that they are taught efficiently. Because they are dead languages is no reason why they should be dealt with in a dead educational technique. I understand, Mr. Chipping, that your Latin and Greek lessons are exactly the same as they were when I began here ten years ago?'

Chips answered, slowly and with pride: 'For that matter—umph— they are the same as when your predecessor—Mr. Meldrum—came here, and that—umph—was thirty-eight years ago. We began here, Mr. Meldrum and I—in—umph—in 1870. And it was—um—Mr. Meldrum's predecessor, Mr. Wetherby—who first approved my syllabus. "You'll take the Cicero for the fourth," he said to me. And he said Cicero, too—not Kickero!'

'Very interesting, Mr. Chipping, but once again it proves my point—you live too much in the past, and not enough in the present and future. Times are changing, whether you realize it or not. Modern parents are beginning to demand something more for their three years' school fees than a few scraps of languages that nobody speaks. Besides, your boys don't learn even what they're supposed to learn. None of them last year got through the Lower Certificate.'

And suddenly, in a torrent of thoughts too pressing to be put into words, Chips made answer to himself. These examinations and certificates and so on—what did they matter? And all this efficiency and up-to-dateness—what did *that* matter, either? Ralston was trying to run Brookfield like a factory—a factory for turning out a snob culture based on money and machines. The old gentlemanly traditions of family and broad acres were changing, as doubtless they were bound to; but instead of widening them to form a genuine inclusive democracy of duke and dustman, Ralston was narrowing them upon the single issue of a fat banking account. There never had been so many rich men's sons at Brookfield. The Speech Day Garden Party was like Ascot.

Ralston met these wealthy fellows in London clubs and persuaded them that Brookfield was *the* coming school, and, since they couldn't buy their way into Eton or Harrow, they greedily swallowed the bait. Awful fellows, some of them—though others were decent enough. Financiers, company promoters, pill manufacturers. One of them gave his son five pounds a week pocket money. Vulgar . . . ostentatious . . . all the hectic rotten-ripeness of the age. . . . Touchy, no sense of humor, no sense of proportion—that was the matter with them, these new fellows. . . . No sense of proportion. And it was a sense of proportion, above all things, that Brookfield ought to teach—not so much Latin or Greek or Chemistry or Mechanics. And you couldn't expect to test that sense of proportion by setting papers and granting certificates. . . .

All this flashed through his mind in an instant of protest and indignation, but he did not say a word of it. He merely gathered his tattered gown together and with an 'umph–umph' walked a few paces away. He had had enough of the argument. At the door he turned and said: 'I don't–umph–intend to resign–and you can–umph–do what you like about it!'

Looking back upon that scene in the calm perspective of a quarter of a century, Chips could find it in his heart to feel a little sorry for Ralston. Particularly when, as it happened, Ralston had been in such complete ignorance of the forces he was dealing with. So, for that matter, had Chips himself. Neither had correctly estimated the toughness of Brookfield tradition, and its readiness to defend itself and its defenders. For it had so chanced that a small boy, waiting to see Ralston that morning, had been listening outside the door during the whole of the interview; he had been thrilled by it, naturally, and had told his friends. Some of these, in a surprisingly short time, had told their parents; so that very soon it was common knowledge that Ralston had insulted Chips and had demanded his resignation. The amazing result was a spontaneous outburst of sympathy and partisanship such as Chips, in his wildest dreams, had never envisaged. He found, rather to his astonishment, that Ralston was thoroughly unpopular; he was feared and respected, but not liked; and in this issue of Chips the dislike rose to a point where it conquered fear and demolished even respect. There was talk of having some kind of public riot in the School if Ralston succeeded in banishing Chips. The masters, many of them young men who agreed that Chips was hopelessly old-fashioned, rallied round him nevertheless because they hated Ralston's slave driving and saw in the old veteran a likely champion. And one day the Chairman of the Governors, Sir John Rivers, visited Brookfield, ignored Ralston, and went direct to Chips. 'A fine fellow, Rivers,' Chips would say, telling the story to Mrs. Wickett for the dozenth time. 'Not–umph–a very brilliant boy in class. I remember he could never–umph–master his verbs. And now–umph–I see in the papers–they've made him–umph–a baronet. It just shows you–umph–it just shows you.'

Sir John had said, on that morning in 1908, taking Chips by the arm as they walked round the deserted cricket pitches: 'Chips, old boy, I hear you've been having the deuce of a row with Ralston. Sorry to hear about it, for your sake–but I want you to know that the Governors are with you to a man. We don't like the fellow a great deal. Very clever and all that, but a bit too clever, if you ask me. Claims to have doubled the School's endowment funds by some monkeying on the Stock Exchange. Dare say he has, but a chap like that wants watching. So if he starts chucking his weight about with you, tell him very politely he can go to the devil. The Governors don't want you to resign. Brookfield wouldn't be the same without you, and they know it. We all know it. You can stay here till you're a hundred if you feel like it—indeed, it's our hope that you will.'

And at that—both then and often when he recounted it afterward—Chips broke down.

XII

So he stayed on at Brookfield, having as little to do with Ralston as possible. And in 1911 Ralston left, 'to better himself'; he was offered the headship of one of the greater public schools. His successor was a man named Chatteris, whom Chips liked; he was even younger than Ralston had been—thirty-four. He was supposed to be very brilliant; at any rate, he was modern (Natural Sciences Tripos), friendly, and sympathetic. Recognizing in Chips a Brookfield institution, he courteously and wisely accepted the situation.

In 1913 Chips had bad bronchitis and was off duty for nearly the whole of the winter term. It was that which made him decide to resign that summer, when he was sixty-five. After all, it was a good, ripe age; and Ralston's straight words had, in some ways, had an effect. He felt that it would not be fair to hang on if he could not decently do his job. Besides, he would not sever himself completely. He would take rooms across the road, with the excellent Mrs. Wickett who had once been linen-room maid; he could visit the School whenever he wanted, and could still, in a sense, remain a part of it.

At that final end-of-term dinner, in July 1913, Chips received his farewell presentations and made a speech. It was not a very long speech, but it had a good many jokes in it, and was made twice as long, perhaps, by the laughter that impeded its progress. There were several Latin quotations in it, as well as a reference to the Captain of the School, who, Chips said, had been guilty of exaggeration in speaking of his (Chips's) services to Brookfield. 'But then—umph—he comes of an—umph—exaggerating family. I—um—remember—once—having to thrash his father—for it. [Laughter] I gave him one mark—umph—for a Latin translation, and he—umph—exaggerated the one into a seven! Umph—umph!' Roars of laughter and tumultuous cheers! A typical Chips remark, everyone thought.

And then he mentioned that he had been at Brookfield for forty-two years, and that he had been very happy there. 'It has been my life,' he said, simply. *'O mihi praeteritos referat si Jupiter annos. . . .* Umph— I need not—of course—translate. . . .' Much laughter. 'I remember lots of changes at Brookfield. I remember the—um—the first bicycle. I remember when there was no gas or electric light and we used to have a member of the domestic staff called a lamp-boy—he did nothing else but clean and trim and light lamps throughout the School. I remember when there was a hard frost that lasted for seven weeks in the winter term—there were no games, and the whole School learned to skate on the fens. Eighteen-eighty-something, that was. I remember when two thirds of the School went down with German measles and Big Hall was turned into a hospital ward. I remember the great bonfire we had on Mafeking night. It was lit too near the pavilion and we had to send for the fire brigade to put it out. And the firemen were having their own celebrations and most of them were—um—in a regrettable condition. [Laughter] I remember Mrs. Brool, whose photograph is still in the tuckshop; she served there until an uncle in Australia left her a lot of money. In fact, I remember so much that I often think I ought to write a book. Now what should I call it? "Memories of Rod and Lines"—eh? [Cheers and laughter. That was a good one, people thought—one of Chips's best.] Well, well, perhaps I shall write it, some day. But I'd rather tell you about it, really. I remember . . . I remember . . . but chiefly I remember all your faces. I never forget them. I have thousands of faces in my mind—the faces of boys. If you come and see me again in years to come—as I hope you all will—I shall try to remember those older faces of yours, but it's just possible I shan't be able to—and then some day you'll see me somewhere and I shan't recognize you and you'll say to yourself, "The old boy doesn't remember me." [Laughter] But I *do* remember you—as you are *now*. That's the point. In my mind you never grow up at all. Never. Sometimes, for instance, when people talk to me about our respected Chairman of the Governors, I think to myself, "Ah yes, a jolly little chap with hair that sticks up on top—and absolutely no idea whatever about the difference between a Gerund and a Gerundive." [Loud laughter] Well, well, I mustn't go on—umph—all night. Think of me sometimes as I shall certainly think of you. *Haec olim meminisse juvabit* . . . again I need not translate.' Much laughter and shouting and prolonged cheers.

August 1913. Chips went for a cure to Wiesbaden, where he lodged at the home of the German master at Brookfield, Herr Staefel, with whom he had become friendly. Staefel was thirty years his junior, but the two men got on excellently. In September, when term began, Chips returned and took up residence at Mrs. Wickett's. He felt a great deal stronger and fitter after his holiday, and almost wished he had not retired. Nevertheless, he found plenty to do. He had all the new boys to tea. He watched all the important matches on the Brookfield ground. Once a term he dined with the Head, and once also with the masters. He took on the preparation and editing of a new Brookfeldian Directory. He accepted presidency of the Old Boys' Club and went to dinners in London. He wrote occasional articles, full of jokes and Latin quotations, for the Brookfield terminal magazine. He read his *Times* every morning—very thoroughly; and he also began to read detective stories—he had been keen on them ever since the first thrills of Sherlock. Yes, he was quite busy, and quite happy, too.

A year later, in 1914, he again attended the end-of-term dinner. There was a lot of war talk—civil war in Ulster, and trouble between Austria and Serbia, Herr Staefel, who was leaving for Germany the next day, told Chips he thought the Balkan business wouldn't come to anything.

XIII

The War years.

The first shock, and then the first optimism. The Battle of the Marne, the Russian steam-roller, Kitchener.

'Do you think it will last long, sir?'

Chips, questioned as he watched the first trial game of the season, gave quite a cheery answer. He was, like thousands of others, hopelessly wrong; but, unlike thousands of others, he did not afterward conceal the fact. 'We ought to have—um—finished it—um—by Christmas. The Germans are already beaten. But why? Are you thinking of—um—joining up, Forrester?'

Joke—because Forrester was the smallest new boy Brookfield had ever had—about four feet high above his muddy football boots. (But not so much a joke, when you came to think of it afterward; for he was killed in 1918—shot down in flames over Cambrai.) But one didn't guess what lay ahead. It seemed tragically sensational when the first Old Brookfeldian was killed in action—in September. Chips thought, when that news came: A hundred years ago boys from this school were fighting *against* the French. Strange, in a way, that the sacrifices of one generation should so cancel out those of another. He tried to express this to Blades, the Head of School House; but Blades, eighteen years old and already in training for a cadetship, only laughed. What had all that history stuff to do with it, anyhow? Just old Chips with one of his queer ideas, that's all.

1915. Armies clenched in deadlock from the sea to Switzerland. The Dardanelles. Gallipoli. Military camps springing up quite near Brookfield; soldiers using the playing fields for sports and training; swift developments of Brookfield O.T.C. Most of the younger masters gone or in uniform. Every Sunday night, in the Chapel after evening service, Chatteris read out the names of old boys killed, together with short biographies. Very moving; but Chips, in the back pew under the gallery, thought: They are only names to him; he doesn't see their faces as I do. . . .

1916. . . . The Somme Battle. Twenty-three names read out one Sunday evening.

Toward the close of that catastrophic July, Chatteris talked to Chips one afternoon at Mrs. Wickett's. He was overworked and overworried and looked very ill. 'To tell you the truth, Chipping, I'm not having too easy a time here. I'm thirty-nine, you know, and unmarried, and lots of people seem to think they know what I ought to do. Also, I happen to be diabetic, and couldn't pass the blindest M.O., but I don't see why I should pin a medical certificate on my front door.'

Chips hadn't known anything about this; it was a shock to him, for he liked Chatteris.

The latter continued: 'You see how it is. Ralston filled the place up with young men—all very good, of course—but now most of them have joined up and the substitutes are pretty dreadful, on the whole. They poured ink down a man's neck in prep one night last week—silly fool—got hysterical. I have to take classes myself, take prep for fools like that, work till midnight every night, and get cold-shouldered as a slacker on top of everything. I can't stand it much longer. If things don't improve next term I shall have a breakdown.'

'I do sympathize with you,' Chips said.

'I hoped you would. And that brings me to what I came here to ask you. Briefly, my suggestion is that—if you felt equal to it and would care to—how about coming back here for a while? You look pretty fit, and, of course, you know all the ropes. I don't mean a lot of hard work for you—you needn't take anything strenuously—just a few odd jobs here and there, as you choose. What I'd like you for more than anything else is not for the actual work you'd do—though that, naturally, would be very valuable—but for your help in other ways—in just *belonging* here. There's nobody ever been more popular than you were, and are still—you'd help to hold things together if there were any danger of them flying to bits. And perhaps there *is* that danger. . . .'

Chips answered, breathlessly and with a holy joy in his heart: 'I'll come. . . .'

XIV

He still kept on his rooms with Mrs. Wickett; indeed, he still lived there; but every morning, about half-past ten, he put on his coat and muffler and crossed the road to the School. He felt very fit, and the actual work was not taxing. Just a few forms in Latin and Roman History—the old lessons—even the old pronunciation. The same joke about the Lex Canuleia—there was a new generation that had not heard it, and he was absurdly gratified by the success it achieved. He felt a little like a music-hall favorite returning to the boards after a positively last appearance.

They all said how marvelous it was that he knew every boy's name and face so quickly. They did not guess how closely he had kept in touch from across the road.

He was a grand success altogether. In some strange way he did, and they all knew and felt it, help things. For the first time in his life he felt *necessary*—and necessary to something that was nearest his heart. There is no sublimer feeling in the world, and it was his at last.

He made new jokes, too—about the O.T.C. and the food-rationing system and the anti-air-raid blinds that had to be fitted on all the windows. There was a mysterious kind of rissole that began to appear on the School menu on Mondays, and Chips called it *abhorrendum*—'meat to be abhorred.' The story went round—heard Chips's latest?

Chatteris fell ill during the winter of '17, and again, for the second time in his life, Chips became Acting Head of Brookfield. Then in April Chatteris died, and the Governors asked Chips if he would carry on 'for the duration.' He said he would, if they would refrain from appointing him officially. From that last honor, within his reach at last, he shrank instinctively, feeling himself in so many ways unequal to it. He said to Rivers: 'You see, I'm not a young man and I don't want people to—um—expect a lot from me. I'm like all these new colonels and majors you see everywhere—just a war-time fluke. A ranker—that's all I am really.'

1917. 1918. Chips lived through it all. He sat in the headmaster's study every morning, handling problems, dealing with plaints and requests. Out of vast experience had emerged a kindly, gentle confidence in himself. To keep a sense of proportion, that was the main thing. So much of the world was losing it; as well keep it where it had, or ought to have, a congenial home.

On Sundays in Chapel it was he who now read out the tragic list, and sometimes it was seen and heard that he was in tears over it. Well, why not, the School said; he was an old man; they might have despised anyone else for the weakness.

One day he got a letter from Switzerland, from friends there; it was heavily censored, but conveyed some news. On the following Sunday, after the names and biographies of old boys, he paused a moment and then added:—

'Those few of you who were here before the War will remember Max Staefel, the German master. He was in Germany, visiting his home, when war broke out. He was popular while he was here, and made many friends. Those who knew him will be sorry to hear that he was killed last week, on the Western Front.'

He was a little pale when he sat down afterward, aware that he had done something unusual. He had consulted nobody about it, anyhow; no one else could be blamed. Later, outside the Chapel, he heard an argument:—

'On the Western Front, Chips said. Does that mean he was fighting for the Germans?'

'I suppose it does.'

'Seems funny, then, to read his name out with all the others. After all, he was an *enemy*.'

'Oh, just one of Chips's ideas, I expect. The old boy still has 'em.'

Chips, in his room again, was not displeased by the comment. Yes, he still had 'em—those ideas of dignity and generosity that were becoming increasingly rare in a frantic world. And he thought: Brookfield will take them, too, from me; but it wouldn't from anyone else.

Once, asked for his opinion of bayonet practice being carried on near the cricket pavilion, he answered, with that lazy, slightly asthmatic intonation that had been so often and so extravagantly imitated: 'It seems—to me—umph—a very vulgar way of killing people.'

The yarn was passed on and joyously appreciated—how Chips had told some big brass hat from the War Office that bayonet fighting was vulgar. Just like Chips. And they found an adjective for him—an adjective just beginning to be used: he was pre-War.

XV

And once, on a night of full moonlight, the air-raid warning was given while Chips was taking his lower fourth in Latin. The guns began almost instantly, and, as there was plenty of shrapnel falling about outside, it seemed to Chips that they might just as well stay where they were, on the ground floor of School House. It was pretty solidly built and made as good a dugout as Brookfield could offer; and as for a direct hit, well, they could not expect to survive that, wherever they were.

So he went on with his Latin, speaking a little louder amid the reverberating crashes of the guns and the shrill whine of anti-aircraft shells. Some of the boys were nervous; few were able to be attentive. He said, gently: 'It may possibly seem to you, Robertson—at this particular moment in the world's history—umph—that the affairs of Cæsar in Gaul some two thousand years ago—are—umph—of somewhat secondary importance—and that—umph—the irregular conjugation of the verb *tollo* is—umph—even less important still. But believe me—umph—my dear Robertson—that is not really the case.' Just then there came a particularly loud explosion—quite near. 'You cannot—umph—judge the importance of things—umph—by the noise they make. Oh dear me, no.' A little chuckle. 'And these things—umph—that have mattered—for thousands of years—are not going to be—snuffed out—because some stink merchant—in his laboratory—invents a new kind of mischief.' Titters of nervous laughter; for Buffles, the pale, lean, and medically unfit science master, was nicknamed the Stink Merchant. Another explosion—nearer still. 'Let us—um—resume our work. If it is fate that we are soon to be—umph—interrupted, let us be found employing ourselves in something—umph—really appropriate. Is there anyone who will volunteer to construe?'

Maynard, chubby, dauntless, clever, and impudent, said: 'I will, sir.'

'Very good. Turn to page forty and begin at the bottom line.'

The explosions still continued deafeningly; the whole building shook as if it were being lifted off its foundations. Maynard found the page, which was some way ahead, and began, shrilly:—

271

'*Genus hoc erat pugnae*—this was the kind of fight—*quo se Germani exercuerant*—in which the Germans busied themselves. Oh, sir, that's good—that's really very funny indeed, sir—one of your very best—'

Laughing began, and Chips added: 'Well—umph—you can see—now—that these dead languages—umph—can come to life again—sometimes—eh? Eh?'

Afterward they learned that five bombs had fallen in and around Brookfield, the nearest of them just outside the School grounds. Nine persons had been killed.

The story was told, retold, embellished. 'The dear old boy never turned a hair. Even found some old tag to illustrate what was going on. Something in Cæsar about the way the Germans fought. You wouldn't think there were things like that in Cæsar, would you? And the way Chips laughed . . . you know the way he *does* laugh . . . the tears all running down his face . . . never seen him laugh so much. . . .'

He was a legend.

With his old and tattered gown, his walk that was just beginning to break into a stumble, his mild eyes peering over the steel-rimmed spectacles, and his quaintly humorous sayings, Brookfield would not have had an atom of him different.

November 11, 1918.

News came through in the morning; a whole holiday was decreed for the School, and the kitchen staff were implored to provide as cheerful a spread as war-time rationing permitted. There was much cheering and singing, and a bread fight across the Dining Hall. When Chips entered in the midst of the uproar there was an instant hush, and then wave upon wave of cheering; everyone gazed on him with eager, shining eyes, as on a symbol of victory. He walked to the dais, seeming as if he wished to speak; they made silence for him, but he shook his head after a moment, smiled, and walked away again.

It had been a damp, foggy day, and the walk across the quadrangle to the Dining Hall had given him a chill. The next day he was in bed with bronchitis, and stayed there till after Christmas. But already, on that night of November 11, after his visit to the Dining Hall, he had sent in his resignation to the Board of Governors.

When school reassembled after the holidays he was back at Mrs. Wickett's. At his own request there were no more farewells or presentations, nothing but a handshake with his successor and the word 'acting' crossed out on official stationery. The 'duration' was over.

XVI

And now, fifteen years after that, he could look back upon it all with a deep and sumptuous tranquillity. He was not ill, of course—only a little tired at times, and bad with his breathing during the winter months. He would not go abroad—he had once tried it, but had chanced to strike the Riviera during one of its carefully unadvertised cold spells. 'I prefer—um—to get my chills—umph—in my own country,' he used to say, after that. He had to take care of himself when there were east winds, but autumn and winter were not really so bad; there were warm fires, and books, and you could look forward to the summer. It was the summer that he liked best, of course; apart from the weather, which suited him, there were the continual visits of old boys. Every week-end some of them motored up to Brookfield and called at his house. Sometimes they tired him, if too many came at once; but he did not really mind; he could always rest and sleep afterward. And he enjoyed their visits—more than anything else in the world that was still to be enjoyed. 'Well, Gregson—umph—I remember you—umph—always late for everything—eh—eh? Perhaps you'll be late in growing old—umph—like me—umph—eh?' And later, when he was alone again and Mrs. Wickett came in to clear away the tea things: 'Mrs. Wickett, young Gregson called—umph—you remember him, do you? Tall boy with spectacles. Always late. Umph. Got a job with the—umph—League of Nations—where—I suppose—his—um—dilatoriness —won't be noticeable—eh?'

And sometimes, when the bell rang for call-over, he would go to the window and look across the road and over the School fence and see, in the distance, the thin line of boys filing past the bench. New times, new names . . . but the old ones still remained . . . Jefferson, Jennings, Jolyon, Jupp, Kingsley Primus, Kingsley Secundus, Kingsley Tertius, Kingston . . . where are you all, where have you all gone to? . . . Mrs. Wickett, bring me a cup of tea just before prep, will you, please?

The post-War decade swept through with a clatter of change and maladjustments; Chips, as he lived through it, was profoundly disappointed when he looked abroad. The Ruhr, Chanak, Corfu; there was enough to be uneasy about in the world. But near him, at Brookfield, and even, in a wider sense, in England, there was something that charmed his heart because it was old—and had survived. More and more he saw the rest of the world as a vast disarrangement for which England had sacrificed enough—and perhaps too much. But he was satisfied with Brookfield. It was rooted in things that had stood the test of time and change and war. Curious, in this deeper sense, how little it *had* changed. Boys were a politer race; bullying was nonexistent; there was more swearing and cheating. There was a more genuine friendliness between master and boy—less pomposity on the one side, less unctuousness on the other. One of the new masters, fresh from Oxford, even let the Sixth call him by his Christian name. Chips didn't hold with that; indeed, he was just a little bit shocked. 'He might as well—umph—sign his terminal reports—umph—"yours affectionately"—eh—eh?' he told somebody.

During the General Strike of 1926, Brookfield boys loaded motor vans with foodstuffs. When it was all over, Chips felt stirred emotionally as he had not been since the War. Something had happened, something whose ultimate significance had yet to be reckoned. But one thing was clear: England had burned her fire in her own grate again. And when, at a Speech Day function that year, an American visitor laid stress on the vast sums that the strike had cost the country, Chips answered: 'Yes, but—umph—advertisement—always *is* costly.'

'Advertisement?'

'Well, wasn't it—umph—advertisement—and very fine advertisement—too? A whole week of it—umph—and not a life lost—not a shot fired! Your country would have—umph—spilt more blood in—umph—raiding a single liquor saloon!'

Laughter . . . laughter . . . wherever he went and whatever he said, there was laughter. He had earned the reputation of being a great jester, and jests were expected of him. Whenever he rose to speak at a meeting, or even when he talked across a table, people prepared their minds and faces for the joke. They listened in a mood to be amused and it was easy to satisfy them. They laughed sometimes before he came to the point. 'Old Chips was in fine form,' they would say, afterward. 'Marvelous the way he can always see the funny side of things. . . .'

After 1929, Chips did not leave Brookfield—even for Old Boys' dinners in London. He was afraid of chills, and late nights began to tire him too much. He came across to the School, however, on fine days; and he still kept up a wide and continual hospitality in his room. His faculties were all unimpaired, and he had no personal worries of any kind. His income was more than he needed to spend, and his small

274

capital, invested in gilt-edged stocks, did not suffer when the slump set in. He gave a lot of his money away—to people who called on him with a hard-luck story, to various School funds, and also to the Brookfield mission. In 1930 he made his will. Except for legacies to the mission and to Mrs. Wickett, he left all he had to found an open entrance scholarship to the School.

1931. . . . 1932. . . .

'What do you think of Hoover, sir?'

'Do you think we shall ever go back to gold?'

'How d' you feel about things in general, sir? See any break in the clouds?'

'When's the tide going to turn, Chips, old boy? You ought to know, with all your experience of things.'

They all asked him questions, as if he were some kind of prophet and encyclopædia combined—more even than that, for they liked their answer dished up as a joke. He would say:—

'Well, Henderson, when I was—umph—a much younger man—there used to be someone who—um—promised people ninepence for fourpence. I don't know that anybody—umph—ever got it, but—umph—our present rulers seem—um—to have solved the problem of how to give—umph—fourpence for ninepence.'

Laughter.

Sometimes, when he was strolling about the School, small boys of the cheekier kind would ask him questions, merely for the fun of getting Chips's 'latest' to retail.

'Please, sir, what about the Five-Year Plan?'

'Sir, do you think Germany wants to fight another war?'

'Have you been to the new cinema, sir? I went with my people the other day. Quite a grand affair for a small place like Brookfield. They've got a Wurlitzer.'

'And what—umph—on earth—is a Wurlitzer?'

'It's an organ, sir—a cinema organ.'

'Dear me. . . . I've seen the name on the boardings, but I always—umph—imagined—it must be some kind of—umph—sausage.'

Laughter. . . . Oh, there's a new Chips joke, you fellows, a perfectly lovely one. I was gassing to the old boy about the new cinema, and . . .

XVII

He sat in his front parlor at Mrs. Wickett's on a November afternoon in thirty-three. It was cold and foggy, and he dare not go out. He had not felt too well since Armistice Day; he fancied he might have caught a slight chill during the Chapel service. Merivale had been that morning for his usual fortnightly chat. 'Everything all right? Feeling hearty? That's the style—keep indoors this weather—there's a lot of flu about. Wish I could have your life for a day or two.'

His life . . . and what a life it had been! The whole pageant of it swung before him as he sat by the fire that afternoon. The things he had done and seen: Cambridge in the 'sixties; Great Gable on an August morning; Brookfield at all times and seasons throughout the years. And, for that matter, the things he had *not* done, and would never do now that he had left them too late—he had never traveled by air, for instance, and he had never been to a talkie-show. So that he was both more and less experienced than the youngest new boy at the School might well be; and that, that paradox of age and youth, was what the world called progress.

Mrs. Wickett had gone out, visiting relatives in a neighboring village; she had left the tea things ready on the table, with bread and butter and extra cups laid out in case anybody called. On such a day, however, visitors were not very likely; with the fog thickening hourly outside, he would probably be alone.

But no. About a quarter to four a ring came, and Chips, answering the front door himself (which he oughtn't to have done), encountered a rather small boy wearing a Brookfield cap and an expression of anxious timidity. 'Please, sir,' he began, 'does Mr. Chips live here?'

'Umph—you'd better come inside,' Chips answered. And in his room a moment later he added: 'I am—umph—the person you want. Now what can I—umph—do for you?'

'I was told you wanted me, sir.'

Chips smiled. An old joke—an old leg-pull, and he, of all people, having made so many old jokes in his time, ought not to complain. And it amused him to cap their joke, as it were, with one of his own; to let them see that he could keep his end up, even yet. So he said, with eyes twinkling: 'Quite right, my boy. I wanted you to take tea with me. Will you—umph—sit down by the fire? Umph—I don't think I have seen your face before. How is that?'

'I've only just come out of the sanatorium, sir—I've been there since the beginning of term with measles.'

'Ah, that accounts for it.'

Chips began his usual ritualistic blending of tea from the different caddies; luckily there was half a walnut cake with pink icing in the cupboard. He found out that the boy's name was Linford, that he lived in Shropshire, and that he was the first of his family at Brookfield.

'You know—umph—Linford—you'll like Brookfield—when you get used to it. It's not half such an awful place—as you imagine. You're a bit afraid of it—um, yes—eh? So was I, my dear boy—at first. But that was—um—a long time ago. Sixty-three years ago—umph—to be precise. When I—um—first went into Big Hall and—um—I saw all those boys— I tell you—I was quite scared. Indeed—umph—I don't think I've ever been so scared in my life. Not even when—umph—the Germans bombed us—during the War. But—umph—it didn't last long—the scared feeling, I mean. I soon made myself—um—at home.'

'Were there a lot of other new boys that term, sir?' asked Linford shyly.

'Eh? But—God bless my soul—I wasn't a boy at all—I was a man—a young man of twenty-two! And the next time you see a young man— a new master—taking his first prep in Big Hall—umph—just think—what it feels like!'

'But if you were twenty-two then, sir—'

'Yes? Eh?'

'You must be—very old—now, sir.'

Chips laughed quietly and steadily to himself. It was a good joke.

'Well—umph—I'm certainly—umph—no chicken.'

He laughed quietly to himself for a long time.

Then he talked of other matters, of Shropshire, of schools and school life in general, of the news in that day's papers. 'You're growing up into—umph—a very cross sort of world, Linford. Maybe it will have got over some of its—umph—crossness—by the time you're ready for it. Let's hope so—umph—at any rate. . . . Well . . .' And with a glance at the clock he delivered himself of his old familiar formula. 'I'm—umph—sorry—you can't stay . . .'

At the front door he shook hands.

'Good-bye, my boy.'

And the answer came, in a shrill treble: 'Good-bye, Mr. Chips. . . .'

Chips sat by the fire again, with those words echoing along the corridors of his mind. 'Good-bye, Mr. Chips. . . .' An old leg-pull, to make new boys think that his name was really Chips; the joke was almost traditional. He did not mind. 'Good-bye, Mr. Chips. . . .' He remembered that on the eve of his wedding day Kathie had used that same phrase, mocking him gently for the seriousness he had had in those days. He thought: Nobody would call me serious to-day, that's very certain. . . .

Suddenly the tears began to roll down his cheeks—an old man's failing; silly, perhaps, but he couldn't help it. He felt very tired; talking to Linford like that had quite exhausted him. But he was glad he had met Linford. Nice boy. Would do well.

Over the fog-laden air came the bell for call-over, tremulous and muffled. Chips looked at the window, graying into twilight; it was time to light up. But as soon as he began to move he felt that he couldn't; he was too tired; and, anyhow, it didn't matter. He leaned back in his chair. No chicken—eh, well—that was true enough. And it had been amusing about Linford. A neat score off the jokers who had sent the boy over. Good-bye, Mr. Chips . . . odd, though, that he should have said it just like that. . . .

XVIII

When he awoke, for he seemed to have been asleep, he found himself in bed; and Merivale was there, stooping over him and smiling. 'Well, you old ruffian—feeling all right? That was a fine shock you gave us!'

Chips murmured, after a pause, and in a voice that surprised him by its weakness: 'Why—um—what—what has happened?'

'Merely that you threw a faint. Mrs. Wickett came in and found you—lucky she did. You're all right now. Take it easy. Sleep again if you feel inclined.'

He was glad someone had suggested such a good idea. He felt so weak that he wasn't even puzzled by the details of the business—how they had got him upstairs, what Mrs. Wickett had said, and so on. But then, suddenly, at the other side of the bed, he saw Mrs. Wickett. She was smiling. He thought: God bless my soul, what's she doing up here? And then, in the shadows behind Merivale, he saw Cartwright, the new Head (he thought of him as 'new,' even though he had been at Brookfield since 1919), and old Buffles, commonly called 'Roddy.' Funny, the way they were all here. He felt: Anyhow, I can't be bothered to wonder why about anything. I'm going to go to sleep.

But it wasn't sleep, and it wasn't quite wakefulness, either; it was a sort of in-between state, full of dreams and faces and voices. Old scenes and old scraps of tunes: a Mozart trio that Kathie had once played in—cheers and laughter and the sound of guns—and, over it all, Brookfield bells, Brookfield bells. 'So you see, if Miss Plebs wanted Mr. Patrician to marry her . . . yes, you can, you liar. . . .' Joke . . . Meat to be abhorred. . . . Joke . . . That you, Max? Yes, come in. What's the news from the Fatherland? . . . *O mihi praeteritos* . . . Ralston said I was slack and inefficient—but they couldn't manage without me. . . . *Obile heres ago fortibus es in aro* . . . Can you translate that, any of you? . . . It's a joke. . . .

Once he heard them talking about him in the room.

Cartwright was whispering to Merivale. 'Poor old chap—must have lived a lonely sort of life, all by himself.'

Merivale answered: 'Not always by himself. He married, you know.'

'Oh, did he? I never knew about that.'

'She died. It must have been—oh, quite thirty years ago. More, possibly.'

'Pity. Pity he never had any children.'

And at that, Chips opened his eyes as wide as he could and sought to attract their attention. It was hard for him to speak out loud, but he managed to murmur something, and they all looked round and came nearer to him.

He struggled, slowly, with his words. 'What—was that—um—you were saying—about me—just now?'

Old Buffles smiled and said: 'Nothing at all, old chap—nothing at all—we were just wondering when you were going to wake out of your beauty sleep.'

'But—umph—I heard you—you *were* talking about me—'

'Absolutely nothing of any consequence, my dear fellow—really, I give you my word. . . .'

'I thought I heard you—one of you—saying it was a pity—umph—a pity I never had—any children . . . eh? . . . But I have, you know . . . I have . . .'

The others smiled without answering, and after a pause Chips began a faint and palpitating chuckle.

'Yes—umph—I have,' he added, with quavering merriment. 'Thousands of 'em . . . thousands of 'em . . . and all boys.'

And then the chorus sang in his ears in final harmony, more grandly and sweetly than he had ever heard it before, and more comfortingly too. . . . Pettifer, Pollett, Porson, Potts, Pullman, Purvis, Pym-Wilson,

Radlett, Rapson, Reade, Reaper, Reddy Primus . . . come round me now, all of you, for a last word and a joke. . . . Harper, Haslett, Hatfield, Hatherley . . . my last joke . . . did you hear it? . . . Did it make you laugh? . . . Bone, Boston, Bovey, Bradford, Bradley, Bramhall-Anderson . . . wherever you are, whatever has happened, give me this moment with you . . . this last moment . . . my boys . . .

And soon Chips was asleep.

He seemed so peaceful that they did not disturb him to say goodnight; but in the morning, as the School bell sounded for breakfast, Brookfield had the news. 'Brookfield will never forget his lovableness,' said Cartwright, in a speech to the School. Which was absurd, because all things are forgotten in the end. But Linford, at any rate, will remember and tell the tale: 'I said good-bye to Chips the night before he died. . . .'

Barter

Sara Teasdale

Life has loveliness to sell,
    All beautiful and splendid things,
Blue waves whitened on a cliff,
    Soaring fire that sways and sings,
And children's faces looking up,
Holding wonder like a cup.

Life has loveliness to sell,
    Music like a curve of gold,
Scent of pine trees in the rain,
    Eyes that love you, arms that hold,
And for your spirit's still delight,
Holy thoughts that star the night.

Spend all you have for loveliness,
    Buy it and never count the cost;
For one white singing hour of peace
    Count many a year of strife well lost,
And for a breath of ecstasy
Give all you have been, or could be.

Far in a Western Brookland

A. E. Housman

Far in a western brookland
    That bred me long ago
The poplars stand and tremble
    By pools I used to know.

There, in the windless night-time,
    The wanderer, marvelling why,
Halts on the bridge to hearken
    How soft the poplars sigh.

He hears: no more remembered
    In fields where I was known,
Here I lie down in London
    And turn to rest alone.

There, by the starlit fences,
    The wanderer halts and hears
My soul that lingers sighing
    About the glimmering weirs.

April

Scharmel Iris

I loved her more than moon or sun—
    There is no moon or sun for me;
Of lovely things to look upon,
    The loveliest was she.

She does not hear me, though I sing—
    And, oh, my heart is like to break!
The world awakens with the Spring,
    But she—she does not wake!

281

The Pool

Dana Burnet

> *This delicate and tender love story is found in
> many scrapbooks. People we know have re-
> read it at least once a year since it first ap-
> peared in magazine form. You will reread
> it too.*

He KNEW that he was in an evacuation hospital in Cherbourg,
but he must have lost track of time, because it seemed only a moment
ago that daylight had filled the ward. Yet now a kind of dusk surrounded his bed, where he lay screened from the sight of the other
wounded officers in the barren whitewashed room. White also were
the figures of the Army nurse and the Medical Corps major who leaned
over him; their faces were blurred, but he sensed an anxiety in their
attitudes and he wanted to reassure them.

He wanted to tell them that it was all right, that he was only going
to sleep, and that it was quite all right, because then the dream would
begin for him. But somehow the effort to speak was beyond him; and
besides, they would never understand about the dream. You could no
more explain it than you could explain the beaches and the hedgerows
of Normandy to those who had not actually been there. You went
through your particular hell alone, and so it was with the happiness that
possessed him now as he entered the terrain whose familiar vistas he
had only to close his eyes to see.

If, in that instant of transition, he thought of Nancy, it was not with
any sense of anticipation, but rather with the old ache of regret that
belonged to the past, now obscure and swiftly dissolving.

Then it began—at first indistinctly, but soon sharpening like a picture
brought into focus, showing him the green-wooded country streaked
with rose from a splendid sunset. He was walking the grass road
through the woods, and he was pleased with himself for having chosen
this hour, this pause at the day's end, for his return. Always, he re-

membered, the best time to go to the pool was just before twilight, because that was when the thrush sang.

You came out of the grove of white birches and crossed the clearing where the tall grass brushed against your knees, and then, abruptly, you were in the cathedral dimness of the pines. The dark-plumed branches closed out the sky overhead, the carpet of needles was smooth underfoot and the sweet earth smells of the clearing changed to the odors of dank woodsy loam, of moss and dead leaf and hidden blossom, all mixed and faintly discernible against the sharp aromatic pine smell.

You went on, knowing that a little way ahead there would be a break in the evergreen roof; and then you saw it, you saw the sky again and you heard the voice of the brook muttering and chuckling to itself as it dropped down a stair of granite ledges into the pool.

So you came to the place where the pool was, and you stood there and waited, listening. Till suddenly it came, the lone liquid trill that made your heart stop in your body as your body had stopped in the path. There was no sound on earth so sweet, he had told Nancy in England, as the song of a wood thrush echoing through the hushed pine forests of Maine.

"I know where Maine is, Lieutenant Hall. I looked it up on the map after you talked so much about it at the club dance last week."

They had met the previous Saturday night at a dance in the local officers' club. Now they were meeting for the second time in the tea-shop of the very old, very English village that lay midway between the RAF fighter field where she was stationed and the American training area to which Richard Hall's outfit had been assigned. Actually, it was their first real date, and he wanted desperately to make a success of it. He was already half in love with this golden-brown English girl in the WAAF uniform.

"Well," he said, proceeding cautiously, "you'll have to give me credit for improving your geography, even if I bored you."

She looked at him directly. There were bright pinpoints of light in her eyes, like flecks of sunlight on brown water.

"I wasn't bored. You know that, don't you?"

"Yes," he said, with a quick thrill of pleasure, "I think I do."

"I liked the way you talked about the Maine country. But I—I'm a bit confused. I thought you told me, during one of our dances, that you lived in New York."

"I worked there. But I was born in Manasquot, Maine. Used to go back every summer on my vacations." He hesitated, fearful of revealing the homesickness that dwelt with him constantly. "It—it meant a lot to me," he said, slowly stirring the sugarless, alien brew in his cup.

To his surprise, she reached out and touched the back of his hand lightly with her finger tips. It was a gesture of understanding, of simple kindness—no more than that. But it sent a warm current from his hand to his brain and back through all the channels of his body.

"I know what you mean," she said. "I feel the same way about this part of England. I was born a few miles from here, in the parsonage of East Wyndham. My father's the vicar there. It was an enormous stroke of luck, my being assigned to this field. Though I must say," she added, smiling, "that I've been putting in for duty here ever since I joined up."

Richard said: "I'd like to meet your father. I'd like to see the place where you were born."

"Would you really?"

"Very much. I want to find out everything I can about you and—well, places help a lot, don't they? I mean, it always helps to know a person's background, don't you think?"

"Yes," she said. Her discreetly reddened mouth still held its smile, but her eyes were thoughtful, even grave. "Yes, places are frightfully important. Not only in getting to know other people. Even more, I think, in the process of knowing oneself. I suppose that's why we must go back, once in a while, to the special earths we came from. So that we can find ourselves again." She looked at him, and she was smiling not at all now. "That's why you went home to Maine every summer, isn't it?"

He leaned toward her across the small, bare-topped table. His face, lean and hard from the training that had hammered his youth into a war weapon, was lighted with excitement. "I never thought of it in just that way, but you're right. There's one particular spot in the hills up back of Manasquot where I used to go year after year. I don't know why, but whenever I got back to it, I had the feeling that everything was all right. That I was all right. I——" He stopped, again afraid of betraying his heart's sickness.

The girl said quietly, "There's always one particular spot, isn't there? What was yours like?"

284

Richard said: "It was a pool in a trout brook where I used to fish when I was a kid. The brook runs through thick woods. Birches and alders and hardwood on one side, a heavy growth of pine on the other. The pool—— Why, what's the matter, Nancy?" It was the first time that he had called her by her given name, but neither seemed to be aware of it. She was staring at him with a fixed and rather startled expression. "Have I said anything to upset you?" he asked anxiously.

"No, no. I—I was just wondering whether there were any trout in your pool?"

"Yes, there were. Still are, I guess. You can see them occasionally against the gravel bottom, when the water's clear. But I gave up fishing long ago. I just wanted to go there and . . . do nothing. Just stand there. Or lie on my back on the pine needles and wait for the thrush to sing."

"Oh!" she said. "Was there one?"

"Always. In all the years I went to the pool. If I waited till sunset, I heard it. Sometimes away in the woods, sometimes so close I'd think it was right over my head. But I never saw it. I never will."

Vaguely she realized that one of her hands had become entangled with one of his, but she could not bother to do anything about that now. "How do you know you never will?" she said; and then, impulsively, "I don't like that word 'never'! It's a stupid, clammy word—and I won't have it anywhere near me! Do you understand?"

He was secretly delighted by her vehemence, and by the fact that her fingers were closed around his. Where, he wondered, did his brothers-in-arms get the idea that English girls were cold?

"All right," he said, trying unsuccessfully not to grin at her. "I'm sorry. I didn't mean it the way you think. When do we go to East Wyndham to call on your father?"

She drew back from him, recovering her poise by the classic feminine device of powdering her nose.

"You Americans do like to get on with things, don't you?"

"Yes," he said.

She laughed into her little mirror. "Well, we might bicycle over the first day we're both off duty."

"It's a date," Richard said.

She paused in her powdering to look at him. "I might even have a bit of surprise for you," Nancy said.

285

The Rev. Basil Landreth was a man who combined his devotion to the spirit with a considerable knowledge of the flesh that housed it. In no more time than it took to consume the lunch he gave them, he saw how it was with his daughter and Richard Hall. The obvious truth concerned, but did not alarm him.

Because his wife had died in the second year of their child's life, he had always been very close to Nancy. He knew, with a certainty deeper than mere parental pride, that she had his instinct for the fundamental decencies, for the basic morality essential to any serious human relationship. Therefore, he assumed that this American officer was—to put it in the best and simplest phrase—a good man. Furthermore, he had taken an immediate liking to Nancy's tall young lieutenant.

So he refused, with an easy conscience, their polite invitation to go for a walk with them after lunch. But in the few minutes he had alone with Richard, after they had left the table, the man of God said, "There are a number of people in the services whom I write to. I hope you'll let me put you on my list."

They were standing together in the hall—Nancy had gone into the kitchen to speak to the housekeeper, who was also the vicar's cook for the duration—and Richard, impatiently waiting for her, did not recognize at once Doctor Landreth's offer of friendship.

When he did, he said, "Why, thank you, sir. That's very kind of you."

"On the contrary. I shall consider it a privilege. Especially," the Reverend Basil said, with a smile extraordinarily like his daughter's, "since you've come such a long way to help us put the world to rights again. I dare say you're homesick at times. I know I should be."

Richard said honestly, "I was, at first. But it hasn't been nearly so bad since I met Nancy."

The older man nodded, as though confirming some thought in his own mind. "I understand. I won't say any more, except that I trust you. And, really—if one takes the long view—it's all in the family, isn't it?"

"That, sir," said Richard, "is the nicest thing I've heard since I came to England."

It was the beginning of summer, and the whole countryside was clothed in that lush green dress which gives to an old land the look of

286

youth perennially renewed. The pale, still flood of sunlight through which they walked, the lovely, hedge-walled lanes that led them out of the village and brought them winding to the open fields were, to Richard, the mood and means of a delight which he savored rather than saw, experienced rather than noticed. With Nancy beside him, everything was complete, and he moved almost blindly at her guidance till they came to a shallow crease in the rolling fields and he heard the unmistakable whisper of running water.

A brook ran there, and he stopped short at the sight and sound of it. "Nancy!" he called; for she had not stopped with him and was already yards away along the grassy bank. At his call, she looked back and smiled, like a child with difficulty keeping a secret, and made a beckoning gesture with her hand. He turned to follow her. As he did so, he saw ahead of them—so close that it seemed impossible he had not felt the shadow of it—the massed enchantment of an ancient oak wood.

When she heard his step behind her, the girl quickened her pace. She had taken off her service cap, and her hair against the dark green of the trees was a stroke of gold.

"Nancy!" he called again.

She began to run. She was in the wood and her figure was tiny among the great trunks, her legs flashed along the forest aisle with an urgency that was completely childish, absurd and joyous and beyond words beguiling. Richard Hall ran after her. They were both laughing as they ran.

So he came to her and caught her in his arms, and was going to kiss her open, breathless mouth, when all at once he saw the pool spread out like a smooth brown carpet at their feet. He did not kiss her. The instant of abandon passed and they stood a little apart from each other, looking down at the pool.

She said finally in a small voice, "I'm sorry about the thrush, but there's never been one."

He was staring at the quiet water, only slightly rippled where the brook flowed into it. "Nancy, has this been your place always?"

"Always, since the day I discovered it. I was quite a child, really."

He turned his head slowly and looked at her. "Nothing like this," he said, "has ever happened to any two people before."

She smiled faintly. "Not even with all the people in the world, and all the brooks, and all the pools that the brooks run into?"

"Not even with all the brooks and the pools and the people in the world!"

Her lips parted in a sigh of satisfaction. "Then that's all right. Because I feel the same way. Precisely."

He took her by the shoulders, saying, "Nancy, do I have to tell you I love you?"

"No," she said.

"And is that all right, too?"

"Yes. Quite. But if it isn't asking too much, Richard, I'd like it to be forever."

He started to say, "It is——" But she put her finger against his lips.

"No, you don't have to say it. I know. I wouldn't have brought you here if I hadn't known."

"Darling," he said. "Darling!"

"Here beside the still waters," Nancy said.

His arms were around her now and his whole body was taut with longing, but some greater compulsion held him suddenly in restraint. It was as if he had paused, in the midst of physical turmoil, to listen to a voice expounding some calm, eternal wisdom of the spirit.

"What do you mean?" he said, and knew that he was asking her for her spirit's secret.

But she did not answer him directly. She said, "This isn't like your place in the Maine woods, is it, Richard?"

"No. This pool's deeper and——"

"There are trout in it!"

"I don't doubt that. But it's wider and darker, the trees are much bigger, much older and—— No, it isn't the same as my place," he concluded.

"But you've something of the same feeling about it, haven't you?"

"Yes. Very much the same."

"You like yours better," she said, with her faint smile.

"Oh, well. Naturally, I——"

"Richard, I'm teasing you. Richard, do you know the Twenty-third Psalm?"

"The Twenty-third——"

"The part where it says, 'He leadeth me beside the still waters; he restoreth my soul'?"

"Yes."

"Do you think that you and I have souls, Richard?"

288

"I—I guess so. I hope we have."

"So do I. And if we have, then, no matter what happens to us, let's promise to meet and restore them here beside the still——"

"Nancy!"

"Because this is where my soul lives and will live forever. If I've got one."

His arms tightened around her. "Darling! Of course you've got one. But how can we promise each other anything beyond what we have now?"

She looked up at him. Tears were streaming down her cheeks.

"I know," she said. "I know. We're frightfully lucky to have what we've got now. Please kiss me, Richard."

Their young bodies, muffled in the anonymous garments of war, came together and clung and were uniquely alive in a closeness which, however incomplete, was yet the most perfect that they had ever dreamed could be.

His tank company had been bivouacked for three weeks in a hide-out on a Norman farm above St. Lô, waiting for the order to break out of the labyrinthine hedge country. But to Richard the time element had become distorted. It seemed an age since his unit of the invasion force had landed in France. At first, everything had moved swiftly, in a chaos of detail through which he labored to bring order to his own infinitesimal portion of it. He was aware of danger in the very air he breathed, of death in many guises, all hideous; but he was too desperately busy to think of such matters as intimately concerning himself. Not only had his personal life vanished; it seemed an illusion which never had existed. Everything had stopped, including time, and a new existence in violence was about to begin.

His memory of Nancy was intense and constant, but that, too, belonged to the illusory past. He had not seen her since that afternoon in the forest at East Wyndham; the next day, his outfit had been alerted. Nor had there been any mail since D day, till now.

So that when he got the letter, the shock of it seemed also remote, almost impersonal, as though the thing it described had happened in another world. It affected another Richard Hall who was not the bearded, forcibly matured man sitting at evening under a hedgerow in France, reading the curiously stilted phrases of one whom he recalled only when he had finished the brief note.

The Parsonage, East Wyndham, Surrey.

Lieut. Richard Hall,

Dear Sir: Last Sunday week an accident destroyed the church at East Wyndham just as the congregation was leaving. A number was killed, including the Vicar & his only daughter Nancy, who was attending the service. I remained at home being ill on that day.

I write you this in sorrow, believing it to be my Duty as I found your name & U. S. Army No. on a special address list in the master's study.

Yrs. Resp'fly,

Ada Stuart,

Housekeeper to the late Rev. Basil Landreth.

Richard read the letter through twice, word by word; then took out his cigarette lighter and burned the single sheet of paper to ashes. He thought, *Nancy is dead.* But the impact of that fact was as distant as the throb of the air bombs falling like a meteoric rain somewhere to the south. Emotionally, he felt the first vibrations of a regret that he knew would be deep and lasting, but the fact itself had a finality beyond which his realistic present self could not go.

Suddenly, he wanted to be quite clear and straight in his mind about Nancy. He recalled, as one recalls music once heard and hauntingly remembered, their last talk beside the pool in the oak wood. He heard her voice saying, "If it isn't asking too much, Richard, I'd like it to be forever," and himself answering, agreeing with her, but only as a man responding to the litany of love. He had not made her any false promises.

Now, lifting his head and staring up into the sky darkening over Normandy, he was grimly glad that he had not promised Nancy anything beyond the limits of a life that could be destroyed by what Ada Stuart had called with stark accuracy, an accident.

Aloud, he said, "It couldn't have been anything but a robot bomb."

"Sir!" said a voice close beside him.

He got up and acknowledged the salute of a young soldier who had materialized out of the dusk.

"What is it, Mason?"

"The captain wants to see you at once, sir. Sergeant Kroll sent me to find you."

"Okay, thanks," Richard said.

As they walked away, the boy blurted out, "There's a rumor that we're to move tonight."

"Latrine rumor, probably."

"Sergeant Kroll thinks it's the real McCoy, sir."

"Christ," Richard said, and the word on his lips was not an oath, "I hope so."

That night the American armor rolled south toward Avranches and the base of the Breton peninsula; and an indefinite number of days later, as he stood erect in the open turret of his lunging tank, with the fabulous castled shape and faery spire of Mont St. Michel rising out of the mists ahead of him, Lieutenant Richard Hall received his wound.

They had passed through a small village seared with flame and blackened by swirling smoke caused by enemy shells still occasionally falling. He had caught a glimpse, fantastic and unreal, of a group of French firemen in their long white coats and medieval brass helmets pumping water by hand on a heap of burning embers; and then, as the Sherman emerged from the smoke, he had seen at a distance the further wonder of St. Michel making its incredibly lovely gesture in stone to the hazy sky. So that when the terrible force struck his chest, lifting him bodily from the turret and hurling him over the back of the tank into a ditch beside the road, with his last surge of consciousness he held to the sensation of wonder—as though what had occurred to his body were a grotesque mistake that could not possibly affect his essential being. And just before he blacked out he thought, *This is what happened to Nancy.*

He could not find her in his dream. It had begun almost at once for him, but nowhere did he meet her within its familiar borders. That troubled him, because in the wasteland of semiconsciousness which was his present state, the dream was his only reality. As for the rest, his waking moments were a nightmare in which everything seemed to be a contradiction of all that had gone before.

The vast mechanism of destruction that had functioned to thrust him forward into battle now worked in reverse to salvage and transport him to sanctuary. He was aware of men and machines laboring to rescue him from the very tasks for which he had been trained, and in spite of his gratitude, he was full of irritable protest at this inconsistency.

Thus the nurse on the second floor of the evacuation hospital at Cherbourg was confronted by the problem of a seriously injured young officer who, now that he was free from pain, kept reaching out for the habit of his manhood—actually demanding his clothes, the blood-soaked uniform that she did not want to tell him had already been burned. He was so insistent about it that finally she called the major in charge of the ward.

"What is it you want, lieutenant?" asked the middle-aged Army doctor.

"Sir, I've got to get back . . . to my outfit."

"I'm afraid that's impossible for the present. Is there anything else you want?"

For several seconds, the wounded man did not answer. Then the feverish worry in his eyes gave place to a still and distant look. His lips moved, seeming to form of their own volition the word: "Home."

The major straightened up abruptly. "Yes, of course," he said, clearing his throat. "You'll be shipped home as soon as you're well enough. You must make an effort to get well, you know."

But Richard Hall had made his effort. It had failed, and that failure seemed to him conclusive. Why should he return to a world of contradictions, of monumental confusions, in which so much was impossible? Already to his withdrawing mind it was a world of ghosts and gossamer, where you walked awhile with your love and then were gone from her without fulfillment, on ways so widely separate that you could not find her even in your dream.

He could hear Nancy's voice repeating a fragment of one of those conversations that formed the text of their brief companionship: *I suppose that's why we must go back . . . to the special earths we came from. So that we can find ourselves again.* But this only troubled him further, by emphasizing the distance between them, for he remembered very well that the earth she came from was half a world—half the impossible world—away from the green country that he called home.

So he did not expect ever to find her, though the way was clear for him and always the same—the road through the woods always the same, and growing clearer each time as it led him always and always returning at sunset through the grove of white birches and always the same and alone across the open grassy space to the cathedral peace, the lovely closure of the pines.

Till there came that day when he lost track of time, when the light in the ward changed all in a moment to dusk and the faces of the nurse and the major leaning over him grew indistinct, as everything around him was growing indistinct, fading.

He had reached the place where the pool was, its brown water holding a rose from the sky, and he was standing there motionless and the thrush was singing. As pure as struck crystal, unutterably wild and sweet, the song fell against the woods stillness that held no sound but the steady amused murmur of the brook. Then, quite unexpectedly, he saw the brown bird shape flitting for an instant among the branches of the pine under which he stood, and he was filled with such delight as a man must share only and instantly with his love.

He had said that he would never see the thrush, and now that he had seen it somehow he must tell Nancy that she had been right to rebuke him for his doubt. *I don't like that word "never." It's a stupid, clammy word—and I won't have it anywhere near me! Do you understand?*

Yes, now he understood—*Oh, Nancy, where are you?*—and he wanted desperately to find her and make a joke or a little foolish song of it—"A lover must never say never!"—so that perhaps she would smile or even laugh as they had laughed together that afternoon in the oak wood.

"Nancy, where are you?"

"I'm here, where I told you I'd be. You had only to call me."

"But I don't see you!"

"Here by the pool, Richard. Oh, Richard, don't you remember where we were to meet?"

"Yes, but I still don't——"

"Here, beside the still waters."

He saw her then, her figure tiny among the trees now dim with twilight, her hair a stroke of gold against the increasing darkness.

"Nancy!" he cried out as he went toward her. "You must have heard the thrush!"

"Darling, I'm sorry about the thrush, but there's never been one."

He stopped and stared at her. It was strange that everything should seem so vague and undefined, yet so inexpressibly real.

"Now look," he said, proceeding cautiously. "Where do you think you are?"

"Well, I like that. I don't think I'm anywhere. I know I'm where I said I'd be. Where I promised to be waiting for you."

"You mean the oak wood at East Wyndham?"

"Yes, of course—and I'd have waited forever."

"Darling," he said, "something's funny. This isn't East Wyndham."

"Darling, you're funny. Because of course it is."

"No."

"Then where is it?"

"This is my place in the woods of Maine."

"How do you know?" she asked.

"My God," he said, "I guess I know my own place!"

"But it can't be. Because how could I get to your place when I've never been there before?"

"Now you're quibbling," he said.

"Darling, I'm not."

"Okay, then something is funny." He hesitated and his voice seemed to falter. "Maybe this whole thing is just imagination. Maybe you and I are all up in the air!"

"Oh, don't say that. Though, to tell the truth, I do feel a bit flighty." He said in an uncertain tone, "I feel rather flighty myself."

"Oh, dear," she said. "Richard, do you remember the Twenty-third Psalm?"

"The Twenty-third? Yes, I do."

"Well, perhaps if we said some of it, it would help to steady us."

"Sort of orient us, you mean?"

"Yes. Please, darling, you start."

"Where?"

"Anywhere," she said.

Richard said, " 'My cup runneth over!' "

She went on, " 'Surely goodness and mercy shall follow me all the days of my life——' "

" '——and I will dwell in the house of the Lord for ever.' Amen."

"Amen," she repeated. "I feel better, don't you?"

"Yes, I guess so, but——"

"A lot more substantial, really."

"You don't look it," Richard said, peering anxiously into her face, that was only a sweet pallor in the twilight.

"Why, darling, you don't think I'm imaginary, do you?"

"I'm afraid to touch you to find out," he said.

"Don't be afraid," Nancy said.

He took her in his arms, and it was like holding all the beauty of the summer dusk in his arms. "Darling," he said. "Darling! As long as we're together, it doesn't matter where we are. But—just where are we, do you suppose?"

"I don't know and I don't care," Nancy said. "Because wherever it is, it's heaven."

"You're right," he agreed; and then, as he stooped to kiss her, the same thought struck them both and they began to laugh as people do who have blundered together on some intimate, rather humorous and completely wonderful secret.

The medical major spoke to the Army nurse standing by the screened bed in the hospital ward.

"You often see that look of happiness on their faces as they go out," he said; and then, in defense of his scientific integrity, "Not that it means anything."

"No, not to us," the nurse said. Under her breath she added, as she drew the sheet over the face of the young officer who had just died, "But maybe it does to them."

The Hill

Rupert Brooke

Breathless, we flung us on the windy hill,
    Laughed in the sun, and kissed the lovely grass.
    You said, "Through glory and ecstasy we pass;
Wind, sun, and earth remain, the birds sing still,
When we are old, are old. . . ." "And when we die
    All's over that is ours; and life burns on
Through other lovers, other lips," said I,
—"Heart of my heart, our heaven is now, is won!"

"We are Earth's best, that learnt her lesson here.
    Life is our cry. We have kept the faith!" we said;
    "We shall go down with unreluctant tread
Rose-crowned into the darkness!" . . . Proud we were,
And laughed, that had such brave true things to say.
—And then you suddenly cried, and turned away.

Patterns

Amy Lowell

I walk down the garden paths,
And all the daffodils
Are blowing, and the bright blue squills.
I walk down the patterned garden paths
In my stiff, brocaded gown.
With my powdered hair and jewelled fan,
I, too, am a rare
Pattern. As I wander down
The garden paths.

My dress is richly figured,
And the train
Makes a pink and silver stain
On the gravel, and the thrift
Of the borders.
Just a plate of current fashion,
Tripping by in high-heeled, ribboned shoes.
Not a softness anywhere about me,
Only whalebone and brocade.
And I sink on a seat in the shade
Of a lime tree. For my passion
Wars against the stiff brocade.
The daffodils and squills
Flutter in the breeze
As they please.
And I weep;
For the lime tree is in blossom
And one small flower has dropped upon my bosom.

And the plashing of waterdrops
In the marble fountain
Comes down the garden paths.
The dripping never stops.

Underneath my stiffened gown
Is the softness of a woman bathing in a marble basin,
A basin in the midst of hedges grown
So thick she cannot see her lover hiding,
But she guesses he is near,
And the sliding of the water
Seems the stroking of a dear
Hand upon her.
What is summer in a fine brocaded gown!
I should like to see it lying in a heap upon the ground,
All the pink and silver crumpled upon the ground.

I would be the pink and silver as I ran along the paths,
And he would stumble after,
Bewildered by my laughter.
I should see the sun flashing from his sword hilt and the buckles on his shoes.
I would choose
To lead him in a maze along the patterned paths,
A bright and laughing maze for my heavy-booted lover,
Till he caught me in the shade,
And the buttons of his waistcoat bruised my body as he clasped me,
Aching, melting, unafraid.
With the shadows of the leaves and the sundrops,
And the plopping of the waterdrops,
All about us in the open afternoon—
I am very like to swoon
With the weight of this brocade,
For the sun sifts through the shade.

Underneath the fallen blossom
In my bosom,
Is a letter I have hid.
It was brought to me this morning by a rider from the Duke.
"Madam, we regret to inform you that Lord Hartwell
Died in action Thursday se'n night."
As I read it in the white, morning sunlight,
The letters squirmed like snakes.
"Any answer, Madam?" said my footman.
"No," I told him.
"See that the messenger takes some refreshment.

No, no answer."
And I walked into the garden,
Up and down the patterned paths,
In my stiff, correct brocade.
The blue and yellow flowers stood up proudly in the sun,
Each one.
I stood upright, too,
Held rigid to the pattern
By the stiffness of my gown.
Up and down I walked.
Up and down.

In a month he would have been my husband.
In a month, here, underneath this lime,
We would have broke the pattern;
He for me, and I for him,
He as Colonel, I as Lady,
On this shady seat.
He had a whim
That sunlight carried blessing.
And I answered, "It shall be as you have said."
Now he is dead.

In summer and in winter I shall walk
Up and down
The patterned garden paths
In my stiff, brocaded gown.
The squills and daffodils
Will give place to pillard roses, and to asters, and to snow.
I shall go
Up and down,
In my gown.
Gorgeously arrayed,
Boned and stayed,
And the softness of my body will be guarded from embrace
By each button, hook, and lace.
For the man who should loose me is dead,
Fighting with the Duke in Flanders,
In a pattern called a war.
Christ! What are patterns for?

Garden Fancies

Robert Browning

Here's the garden she walked across,
  Arm in my arm, such a short while since:
Hark! now I push its wicket, the moss
  Hinders the hinges, and makes them wince.
She must have reached this shrub ere she turned,
  As back with that murmur the wicket swung;
For she laid the poor snail my chance foot spurned,
  To feed and forget it the leaves among.

Down this side of the gravel walk
  She went while her robe's edge brushed the box;
And here she paused in her gracious talk
  To point me a moth on the milk-white phlox.
Roses, ranged in valiant row,
  I will never think that she passed you by!
She loves you, noble roses, I know;
  But yonder see where the rock-plants lie!

This flower she stopped at, finger on lip,—
  Stooped over, in doubt, as settling its claim;
Till she gave me, with pride to make no slip,
  Its soft meandering Spanish name.
What a name! Was it love or praise?
  Speech half asleep, or song half awake?
I must learn Spanish one of these days,
  Only for that slow sweet name's sake. . . .

Where I find her not, beauties vanish;
  Whither I follow her, beauties flee.
Is there no method to tell her in Spanish
  June's twice June since she breathed it with me?
Come, bud! show me the least of her traces.
  Treasure my lady's lightest footfall:
Ah! you may flout and turn up your faces,—
  Roses, you are not so fair after all!

O My Luve's Like a Red, Red Rose

Robert Burns

O my Luve's like a red, red rose
    That's newly sprung in June:
O my Luve's like the melodie
    That's sweetly played in tune.
As fair art thou, my bonnie lass,
    So deep in luve am I:
And I will luve thee still, my dear,
    Till a' the seas gang dry:

Till a' the seas gang dry, my dear,
    And the rocks melt wi' the sun;
I will luve thee still, my dear,
    While the sands o' life shall run.
And fare thee weel, my only Luve!
    And fare thee weel awhile!
And I will come again, my Luve,
    Th' it were ten thousand mile.

Aristocracy

Emily Dickinson

The pedigree of honey
    Does not concern the bee;
A clover, any time, to him
    Is aristocracy.

Except for You

Adelaide Love

Life, of its nature an uncertain thing,
Grows more precarious with each year's end.
Tomorrow may be mine indeed to spend,
Or I may have but this one hour to sing.
Let me employ it, then, for telling of
The goodness and the beauty of my days
With you, and for recounting how your ways
With me brought peace of heart, and how your love
Has been my loaf, my cloak, my sheltering tree.
Attend my words, beloved, attend them well,
Remembering that what my lips would tell
My soul repeats, as priests their litany.
Except for you I had not known how near
To Eden one may bide, my very dear.

An Epitaph

Walter de la Mare

Here lies a most beautiful lady,
Light of step and heart was she;
I think she was the most beautiful lady
That ever was in the West Country.
But beauty vanishes; beauty passes;
However rare—rare it be;
And when I crumble, who will remember
This lady of the West Country?

The Nightingale and the Rose

Oscar Wilde

> *A beautifully told legend that has become a classic.*

"SHE SAID that she would dance with me if I brought her red roses," cried the young Student; "but in all my garden there is no red rose."

From her nest in the holm-oak tree the Nightingale heard him, and she looked out through the leaves, and wondered.

"No red rose in all my garden!" he cried, and his beautiful eyes filled with tears. "Ah, on what little things does happiness depend! I have read all that the wise men have written, and all the secrets of philosophy are mine, yet for want of a red rose is my life made wretched."

"Here at last is a true lover," said the Nightingale. "Night after night have I sung of him, though I knew him not: night after night have I told his story to the stars, and now I see him. His hair is dark as the hyacinth-blossom, and his lips are red as the rose of his desire; but passion has made his face like pale ivory, and sorrow has set her seal upon his brow."

"The Prince gives a ball tomorrow night," murmured the young Student, "and my love will be of the company. If I bring her a red rose she will dance with me till dawn. If I bring her a red rose, I shall hold her in my arms, and she will lean her head upon my shoulder, and her hand will be clasped in mine. But there is no red rose in my garden, so I shall sit lonely, and she will pass me by. She will have no heed of me, and my heart will break."

"Here indeed is the true lover," said the Nightingale. "What I sing of, he suffers: what is joy to me, to him is pain. Surely Love is a wonderful thing. It is more precious than emeralds, and dearer than fine opals. Pearls and pomegranates cannot buy it, nor is it set forth in the

302

market-place. It may not be purchased of the merchants, nor can it be weighed out in the balance for gold."

"The musicians will sit in their gallery," said the young Student, "and play upon their stringed instruments, and my love will dance to the sound of the harp and the violin. She will dance so lightly that her feet will not touch the floor, and the courtiers in their gay dresses will throng round her. But with me she will not dance, for I have no red rose to give her"; and he flung himself down on the grass, and buried his face in his hands, and wept.

"Why is he weeping?" asked a little Green Lizard, as he ran past him with his tail in the air.

"Why, indeed?" said a Butterfly, who was fluttering about after a sunbeam.

"Why, indeed?" whispered a Daisy to his neighbor, in a soft, low voice.

"He is weeping for a red rose," said the Nightingale.

"For a red rose!" they cried; "how very ridiculous!" and the little Lizard, who was something of a cynic, laughed outright.

But the Nightingale understood the secret of the Student's sorrow, and she sat silent in the oak-tree, and thought about the mystery of Love.

Suddenly she spread her brown wings for flight, and soared into the air. She passed through the grove like a shadow, and like a shadow she sailed across the garden.

In the centre of the grass-plot was standing a beautiful Rose-tree, and when she saw it she flew over to it, and lit upon a spray.

"Give me a red rose," she cried, "and I will sing you my sweetest song."

But the Tree shook its head.

"My roses are white," it answered; "as white as the foam of the sea, and whiter than the snow upon the mountain. But go to my brother who grows round the old sun-dial, and perhaps he will give you what you want."

So the Nightingale flew over to the Rose-tree that was growing round the old sun-dial.

"Give me a red rose," she cried, "and I will sing you my sweetest song."

But the Tree shook its head.

"My roses are yellow," it answered; "as yellow as the hair of the

303

mermaiden who sits upon an amber throne, and yellower than the daffodil that blooms in the meadow before the mower comes with his scythe. But go to my brother who grows beneath the Student's window, and perhaps he will give you what you want."

So the Nightingale flew over to the Rose-tree that was growing beneath the Student's window.

"Give me a red rose," she cried, "and I will sing you my sweetest song."

But the Tree shook its head.

"My roses are red," it answered; "as red as the feet of the dove, and redder than the great fans of coral that wave and wave in the ocean-cavern. But the winter has chilled my veins, and the frost has nipped my buds, and the storm has broken my branches, and I shall have no roses at all this year."

"One red rose is all I want," cried the Nightingale, "only one red rose! Is there no way by which I can get it?"

"There is a way," answered the Tree; "but it is so terrible that I dare not tell it to you."

"Tell it to me," said the Nightingale, "I am not afraid."

"If you want a red rose," said the Tree, "you must build it out of music by moonlight, and stain it with your own heart's-blood. You must sing to me with your breast against a thorn. All night long you must sing to me, and the thorn must pierce your heart, and your life-blood must flow into my veins, and become mine."

"Death is a great price to pay for a red rose," cried the Nightingale, "and Life is very dear to all. It is pleasant to sit in the green wood, and to watch the Sun in his chariot of gold, and the Moon in her chariot of pearl. Sweet is the scent of the hawthorn, and sweet are the blue-bells that hide in the valley, and the heather that blows on the hill. Yet Love is better than Life, and what is the heart of a bird compared to the heart of a man?"

So she spread her brown wings for flight, and soared into the air. She swept over the garden like a shadow, and like a shadow she sailed through the grove.

The young Student was still lying on the grass, where she had left him, and the tears were not yet dry in his beautiful eyes.

"Be happy," cried the Nightingale, "be happy; you shall have your red rose. I will build it out of music by moonlight, and stain it with my own heart's-blood. All that I ask of you in return is that you will be a true lover, for Love is wiser than Philosophy, though she is wise, and mightier than Power, though he is mighty. Flame-coloured are his wings, and coloured like flame is his body. His lips are sweet as honey, and his breath is like frankincense."

The Student looked up from the grass, and listened, but he could not understand what the Nightingale was saying to him, for he only knew the things that are written down in books.

But the Oak-tree understood, and felt sad, for he was very fond of the little Nightingale who had built her nest in his branches.

"Sing me one last song," he whispered; "I will feel very lonely when you are gone."

So the Nightingale sang to the Oak-tree, and her voice was like water bubbling from a silver jar.

When she had finished her song the Student got up, and pulled a notebook and a lead-pencil out of his pocket.

"She has form," he said to himself, as he walked away through the grove—"that cannot be denied to her; but has she got feeling? I am afraid not. In fact, she is like most artists; she is all style, without any sincerity. She would not sacrifice herself for others. She thinks merely of music, and everybody knows that the arts are selfish. Still, it must be admitted that she has some beautiful notes in her voice. What a pity it is that they do not mean anything, or do any practical good." And he went into his room, and lay down on his little pallet-bed, and began to think of his love; and, after a time, he fell asleep.

And when the Moon shone in the heavens the Nightingale flew to the Rose-tree, and set her breast against the thorn. All night long she sang with her breast against the thorn, and the cold crystal Moon leaned down and listened. All night long she sang, and the thorn went deeper and deeper into her breast, and her life-blood ebbed away from her.

She sang first of the birth of love in the heart of a boy and a girl. And on the topmost spray of the Rose-tree there blossomed a marvellous rose, petal following petal, as song followed song. Pale was it, at first, as the mist that hangs over the river—pale as the feet of the morning, and silver as the wings of the dawn.

As the shadow of a rose in a mirror of silver, as the shadow of a rose in a water-pool, so was the rose that blossomed on the topmost spray of the Tree.

But the Tree cried to the Nightingale to press closer against the thorn. "Press closer, little Nightingale," cried the Tree, "or the Day will come before the Rose is finished."

So the Nightingale pressed closer against the thorn, and louder and louder grew her song, for she sang of the birth of passion in the soul of a man and a maid.

And a delicate flush of pink came into the leaves of the rose, like the flush in the face of the bridegroom when he kisses the lips of the bride. But the thorn had not yet reached her heart, so the rose's heart remained white, for only a Nightingale's heart's-blood can crimson the heart of a rose.

And the Tree cried to the Nightingale to press closer against the thorn. "Press closer, little Nightingale," cried the Tree, "or the Day will come before the rose is finished."

So the Nightingale pressed closer against the thorn, and the thorn touched her heart, and a fierce pang of pain shot through her. Bitter, bitter was the pain, and wilder and wilder grew her song, for she sang of the Love that is perfected by Death, of the Love that dies not in the tomb.

And the marvellous rose became crimson, like the rose of the eastern sky. Crimson was the girdle of petals, and crimson as a ruby was the heart.

But the Nightingale's voice grew fainter, and her little wings began to beat, and a film came over her eyes. Fainter and fainter grew her song, and she felt something choking her in her throat.

Then she gave one last burst of music. The white Moon heard it, and she forgot the dawn, and lingered on in the sky. The red rose heard it, and it trembled all over with ecstasy, and opened its petals to the cold morning air. Echo bore it to her purple cavern in the hills, and woke the sleeping shepherds from their dreams. It floated through the reeds of the river, and they carried its message to the sea.

"Look, look!" cried the Tree, "the rose is finished now"; but the Nightingale made no answer, for she was lying dead in the long grass, with the thorn in her heart.

And at noon the Student opened his window and looked out.

"Why, what a wonderful piece of luck!" he cried; "here is a red rose! I have never seen any rose like it in all my life. It is so beautiful that I am sure it has a long Latin name"; and he leaned down and plucked it.

Then he put on his hat, and ran up to the Professor's house with the rose in his hand.

The daughter of the Professor was sitting in the doorway winding blue silk on a reel, and her little dog was lying at her feet.

"You said that you would dance with me if I brought you a red rose," cried the Student. "Here is the reddest rose in all the world. You will wear it tonight next your heart, and as we dance together it will tell you how I love you."

But the girl frowned.

"I am afraid it will not go with my dress," she answered; "and, besides, the Chamberlain's nephew has sent me some real jewels, and everybody knows that jewels cost far more than flowers."

"Well, upon my word, you are very ungrateful," said the Student angrily; and he threw the rose into the street, where it fell into the gutter, and a cart wheel went over it.

"Ungrateful!" said the girl. "I tell you what, you are very rude; and, after all, who are you? Only a Student. Why, I don't believe you have even got silver buckles to your shoes as the Chamberlain's nephew has"; and she got up from her chair and went into the house.

"What a silly thing Love is," said the Student as he walked away. "It is not half as useful as Logic, for it does not prove anything, and it is always telling one of things that are not going to happen, and making one believe things that are not true. In fact, it is quite unpractical, and, as in this age to be practical is everything, I shall go back to Philosophy and study Metaphysics."

So he returned to his room and pulled out a great dusty book, and began to read.

To—

Percy Bysshe Shelley

Music, when soft voices die,
Vibrates in the memory—
Odors, when sweet violets sicken,
Live within the sense they quicken,

Rose leaves, when the rose is dead,
Are heaped for the beloved's bed;
And so thy thoughts, when thou art gone
Love itself shall slumber on.

Meeting at Night

Robert Browning

The gray sea and the long black land;
And the yellow half-moon large and low;
And the startled little waves that leap
In fiery ringlets from their sleep,
As I gain the cove with pushing prow,
And quench its speed in the slushy sand.

Then a mile of warm sea-scented beach;
Three fields to cross till a farm appears;
A tap at the pane, the quick sharp scratch
And blue spurt of a lighted match,
And a voice less loud, through its joys and fears,
Than the two hearts beating each to each!

Parting at Morning

Robert Browning

Round the cape of a sudden came the sea,
And the sun looked over the mountain's rim:
And straight was a path of gold for him,
And the need of a world of men for me.

The Year's at the Spring

Robert Browning

The year's at the spring
And the day's at the morn;
Morning's at seven;
The hillside's dew-pearled;
The lark's on the wing;
The snail's on the thorn:
God's in his heaven—
All's right with the world!

Romance

Robert Louis Stevenson

I will make you brooches and toys for your delight
Of bird-song at morning and star-shine at night.
I will make a palace fit for you and me,
Of green days in forests and blue days at sea.

I will make my kitchen, and you shall keep your room,
Where white flows the river and bright blows the broom,
And you shall wash your linen and keep your body white
In rainfall at morning and dewfall at night.

And this shall be for music when no one else is near,
The fine song for singing, the rare song to hear!
That only I remember, that only you admire,
Of the broad road that stretches and the roadside fire.

My Own True Love

Marian Lagrange Wyatt

My Own True Love, when long ago
Through autumn's rosy fading glow
 We rode across the purple plain
  All green with grass and gold with grain
Where speckled quail were scudding low
And crickets calling sad and slow
The sky above, the earth below,
 Shone like our hopes without a stain—
  My Own True Love!

Since then we've watched the roses blow
And winter's frost and winter's snow,
And April's bow, and April's rain,
Like "souls that balance joy and pain."
Thank Heaven! Still hand in hand we go—
 My Own True Love.

Oft Have I Seen

Henry Wadsworth Longfellow

Oft have I seen at some cathedral door,
A laborer, pausing in the dust and heat,
Lay down his burden, and with reverent feet
Enter, and cross himself, and on the floor
Kneel to repeat his paternoster o'er;
Far off the noises of the world retreat;
The loud vociferations of the street
Become an indistinguishable roar.
So, as I enter here from day to day,
And leave my burden at this minster gate,
Kneeling in prayer, and not ashamed to pray,
The tumult of the time disconsolate
To inarticulate murmurs dies away,
While the eternal ages watch and wait.

Love's Philosophy

Percy Bysshe Shelley

The fountains mingle with the river
And the rivers with the ocean,
The winds of heaven mix forever
With a sweet emotion;
Nothing in the world is single,
All things by a law divine
In one another's being mingle—
Why not I with thine?

See the mountains kiss high heaven,
And the waves clasp one another;
No sister-flower would be forgiven
If it disdain'd its brother:
And the sunlight clasps the earth,
And the moonbeams kiss the sea—
What are all these kissings worth,
If thou kiss not me?

The Sire de Malétroit's Door

Robert Louis Stevenson

> *Stevenson in a cloak and dagger mood! A tale of danger and suspense.*

Denis de Beaulieu was not yet two-and-twenty, but he counted himself a grown man, and a very accomplished cavalier into the bargain. Lads were early formed in that rough, warfaring epoch; and when one has been in a pitched battle and a dozen raids, has killed one's man in an honourable fashion, and knows a thing or two of strategy and mankind, a certain swagger in the gait is surely to be pardoned. He had put up his horse with due care, and supped with due deliberation; and then, in a very agreeable frame of mind, went out to pay a visit in the gray of the evening. It was not a very wise proceeding on the young man's part. He would have done better to remain beside the fire or go decently to bed. For the town was full of the troops of Burgundy and England under a mixed command; and though Denis was there on safe-conduct, his safe-conduct was like to serve him little on a chance encounter.

It was September, 1429; the weather had fallen sharp; a flighty piping wind, laden with showers, beat about the township; and the dead leaves ran riot along the streets. Here and there a window was already lighted up; and the noise of men-at-arms making merry over supper within, came forth in fits and was swallowed up and carried away by the wind. The night fell swiftly; the flag of England, fluttering on the spire-top, grew ever fainter and fainter against the flying clouds—a black speck like a swallow in the tumultuous, leaden chaos of the sky. As the night fell the wind rose, and began to hoot under archways and roar amid the tree-tops in the valley below the town.

Denis de Beaulieu walked fast and was soon knocking at his friend's door; but though he promised himself to stay only a little while and make an early return, his welcome was so pleasant, and he found so

311

much to delay him, that it was already long past midnight before he said good-bye upon the threshold. The wind had fallen again in the meanwhile; the night was as black as the grave; not a star, nor a glimmer of moonshine, slipped through the canopy of cloud. Denis was ill-acquainted with the intricate lanes of Chateau Landon; even by daylight he had found some trouble in picking his way; and in this absolute darkness he soon lost it altogether. He was certain of one thing only—to keep mounting the hill; for his friend's house lay at the lower end, or tail, of Chateau Landon, while the inn was up at the head, under the great church spire. With this clue to go upon he stumbled and groped forward, now breathing more freely in open places where there was a good slice of sky overhead, now feeling along the wall in stifling closes. It is an eerie and mysterious position to be thus submerged in opaque blackness in an almost unknown town. The silence is terrifying in its possibilities. The touch of cold window bars to the exploring hand startles the man like the touch of a toad; the inequalities of the pavement shake his heart into his mouth; a piece of denser darkness threatens an ambuscade or a chasm in the pathway; and where the air is brighter, the houses put on strange and bewildering appearances, as if to lead him farther from his way. For Denis, who had to regain his inn without attracting notice, there was real danger as well as mere discomfort in the walk; and he went warily and boldly at once, and at every corner paused to make an observation.

He had been for some time threading a lane so narrow that he could touch a wall with either hand, when it began to open out and go sharply downward. Plainly this lay no longer in the direction of his inn; but the hope of a little more light tempted him forward to reconnoitre. The lane ended in a terrace with a bartizan wall, which gave an outlook between high houses, as out of an embrasure, into the valley lying dark and formless several hundred feet below. Denis looked down, and could discern a few tree-tops waving and a single speck of brightness where the river ran across a weir. The weather was clearing up, and the sky had lightened, so as to show the outline of the heavier clouds and the dark margin of the hills. By the uncertain glimmer, the house on his left hand should be a place of some pretensions; it was surmounted by several pinnacles and turret-tops; the round stern of a chapel, with a fringe of flying buttresses, projected boldly from the main block; and the door was sheltered under a deep porch carved with figures and overhung by two long gargoyles. The windows of

312

the chapel gleamed through their intricate tracery with a light as of many tapers, and threw out the buttresses and the peaked roof in a more intense blackness against the sky. It was plainly the hotel of some great family of the neighbourhood; and as it reminded Denis of a town house of his own at Bourges, he stood for some time gazing up at it and mentally gauging the skill of the architects and the consideration of the two families.

There seemed to be no issue to the terrace but the lane by which he had reached it; he could only retrace his steps, but he had gained some notion of his whereabouts, and hoped by this means to hit the main thoroughfare and speedily regain the inn. He was reckoning without that chapter of accidents which was to make this night memorable above all others in his career; for he had not gone back above a hundred yards before he saw a light coming to meet him, and heard loud voices speaking together in the echoing narrows of the lane. It was a party of men-at-arms going the night round with torches. Denis assured himself that they had all been making free with the wine-bowl, and were in no mood to be particular about safe-conducts or the niceties of chivalrous war. It was as like as not that they would kill him like a dog and leave him where he fell. The situation was inspiriting but nervous. Their own torches would conceal him from sight, he reflected; and he hoped that they would drown the noise of his footsteps with their own empty voices. If he were but fleet and silent, he might evade their notice altogether.

Unfortunately, as he turned to beat a retreat, his foot rolled upon a pebble; he fell against the wall with an ejaculation, and his sword rang loudly on the stones. Two or three voices demanded who went there —some in French, some in English; but Denis made no reply, and ran faster down the lane. Once upon the terrace, he paused to look back. They still kept calling after him, and just then began to double in pace in pursuit, with a considerable clank of armour, and great tossing of the torchlight to and fro in the narrow jaws of the passage.

Denis cast a look around and darted into the porch. There he might escape observation, or—if that were too much to expect—was in a capital posture whether for parley or defense. So thinking, he drew his sword and tried to set his back against the door. To his surprise, it yielded behind his weight; and though he turned in a moment, continued to swing back on oiled and noiseless hinges, until it stood wide open on a black interior. When things fall out opportunely for the

313

person concerned, he is not apt to be critical about the how or why, his own immediate personal convenience seeming a sufficient reason for the strangest oddities and revolutions in our sublunary things; and so Denis, without a moment's hesitation, stepped within and partly closed the door behind him to conceal his place of refuge. Nothing was further from his thoughts than to close it altogether; but for some inexplicable reason—perhaps by a spring or a weight—the ponderous mass of oak whipped itself out of his fingers and clanked to, with a formidable rumble and a noise like the falling of an automatic bar.

The round, at that very moment, debouched upon the terrace and proceeded to summon him with shouts and curses. He heard them ferreting in the dark corners; the stock of a lance even rattled along the outer surface of the door behind which he stood; but these gentlemen were in too high a humour to be long delayed, and soon made on down a corkscrew pathway which had escaped Denis' observation, and passed out of sight and hearing along the battlements of the town.

Denis breathed again. He gave them a few minutes' grace for fear of accidents, and then groped about for some means of opening the door and slipping forth again. The inner surface was quite smooth, not a handle, not a moulding, not a projection of any sort. He got his fingernails round the edges and pulled, but the mass was immovable. He shook it, it was as firm as a rock. Denis de Beaulieu frowned and gave vent to a little noiseless whistle. What ailed the door? he wondered. Why was it open? How came it to shut so easily and so effectually after him? There was something obscure and underhand about all this, that was little to the young man's fancy. It looked like a snare; and yet who could suppose a snare in such a quiet by-street and in a house of so prosperous and even noble an exterior? And yet—snare or no snare, intentionally or unintentionally—here he was, prettily trapped; and for the life of him he could see no way out of it again. The darkness began to weigh upon him. He gave ear; all was silent without, but within and close by he seemed to catch a faint sighing, a faint sobbing rustle, a little stealthy creak—as though many persons were at his side, holding themselves quite still, and governing even their respiration with the extreme of slyness. The idea went to his vitals with a shock, and he faced about suddenly as if to defend his life. Then, for the first time, he became aware of a light about the level of his eyes and at some distance in the interior of the house—a vertical thread of light, widening towards the bottom, such as might escape between two wings of arras over a doorway. To see anything was a relief to Denis; it was like a piece of solid ground to a man labouring in a morass; his mind seized upon it with avidity; and he stood staring at it and trying to piece together some logical conception of his surroundings. Plainly there was a flight of steps ascending from his own level to that of the illuminated doorway; and indeed he thought he could make out another thread of light, as fine as a needle and as faint as phosphorescence, which might very well be reflected along the polished wood of a handrail. Since he had begun to suspect that he was not alone, his heart had continued to beat with smothering violence, and an intolerable desire for action of any sort had possessed itself of his spirit. He was in deadly peril, he believed. What could be more natural than to mount the staircase, lift the curtain, and confront his difficulty at once? At least he would be dealing with something tangible; at least he would be no longer in the dark. He stepped slowly forward with outstretched hands, until his foot struck the bottom step; then he rapidly scaled the stairs, stood for a moment to compose his expression, lifted the arras and went in.

He found himself in a large apartment of polished stone. There were three doors; one on each of three sides; all similarly curtained with tapestry. The fourth side was occupied by two large windows and a great stone chimney-piece, carved with the arms of the Malétroits. Denis recognized the bearings, and was gratified to find himself in such good hands. The room was strongly illuminated; but it contained little furniture except a heavy table and a chair or two, the hearth was innocent of fire, and the pavement was but sparsely strewn with rushes clearly many days old.

On a high chair beside the chimney, and directly facing Denis as he entered, sat a little old gentleman in a fur tippet. He sat with his legs crossed and his hands folded, and a cup of spiced wine stood by his elbow on a bracket on the wall. His countenance had a strongly masculine cast; not properly human, but such as we see in the bull, the goat, or the domestic boar, something equivocal and wheedling, something greedy, brutal, and dangerous. The upper lip was inordinately full, as though swollen by a blow or a toothache; and the smile, the peaked eyebrows, and the small, strong eyes were quaintly and almost comically evil in expression. Beautiful white hair hung straight all round his head, like a saint's, and fell in a single curl upon the tippet. His beard and moustache were the pink of venerable sweetness. Age,

315

probably in consequence of inordinate precautions, had left no mark upon his hands; and the Malétroit hand was famous. It would be difficult to imagine anything at once so fleshy and so delicate in design; the tapered, sensual fingers were like those of Leonardo's women; the fork of the thumb made a dimpled protuberance when closed; the nails were perfectly shaped, and of a dead, surprising whiteness. It rendered his aspect tenfold more redoubtable, that a man with hands like these should keep them devoutly folded in his lap like a virgin martyr—that a man with so intense and startling an expression of face should sit patiently on his seat and contemplate people with an unwinking stare, like a god, or a god's statue. His quiescence seemed ironical and treacherous, it fitted so poorly with his looks.

Such was Alain, Sire de Malétroit.

Denis and he looked silently at each other for a second or two.

"Pray step in," said the Sire de Malétroit. "I have been expecting you all the evening."

He had not risen, but he accompanied his words with a smile and a slight but courteous inclination of the head. Partly from the smile, partly from the strange musical murmur with which the Sire prefaced his observation, Denis felt a strong shudder of disgust go through his marrow. And what with disgust and honest confusion of mind, he could scarcely get words together in reply.

"I fear," he said, "that this is a double accident. I am not the person you suppose me. It seems you were looking for a visit; but for my part, nothing was further from my thoughts—nothing could be more contrary to my wishes—than this intrusion."

"Well, well," replied the old gentleman indulgently, "here you are, which is the main point. Seat yourself, my friend, and put yourself entirely at your ease. We shall arrange our little affairs presently."

Denis perceived that the matter was still complicated with some misconception, and he hastened to continue his explanation.

"Your door . . ." he began.

"About my door?" asked the other, raising his peaked eyebrows. "A little piece of ingenuity." And he shrugged his shoulders. "A hospitable fancy? By your own account, you were not desirous of making my acquaintance. We old people look for such reluctance now and then; and when it touches our honours, we cast about until we find some way of overcoming it. You arrive uninvited, but believe me, very welcome."

316

"You persist in error, sir," said Denis. "There can be no question between you and me. I am a stranger in this countryside. My name is Denis, Damoiseau de Beaulieu. If you see me in your house, it is only——"

"My found friend," interrupted the other, "you will permit me to have my own ideas on that subject. They probably differ from yours at the present moment," he added with a leer, "but time will show which of us is in the right."

Denis was convinced he had to do with a lunatic. He seated himself with a shrug, content to wait the upshot; and a pause ensued, during which he thought he could distinguish a hurried gabbling as of prayer from behind the arras immediately opposite him. Sometimes there seemed to be but one person engaged, sometimes two; and the vehemence of the voice, low as it was, seemed to indicate either great haste or an agony of spirit. It occurred to him that this piece of tapestry covered the entrance to the chapel he had noticed from without.

The old gentleman meanwhile surveyed Denis from head to foot with a smile, and from time to time emitted little noises like a bird or a mouse, which seemed to indicate a high degree of satisfaction. This state of matters became rapidly insupportable; and Denis, to put an end to it, remarked politely that the wind had gone down.

The old gentleman fell into a fit of silent laughter, so prolonged and violent that he became quite red in the face. Denis got upon his feet at once, and put on his hat with a flourish.

"Sir," he said, "if you are in your wits, you have affronted me grossly. If you are out of them, I flatter myself I can find better employment for my brains than to talk with lunatics. My conscience is clear; you have made a fool of me from the first moment; you have refused to hear my explanations; and now there is no power under God will make me stay here any longer; and if I cannot make my way out in a more decent fashion, I will hack your door in pieces with my sword."

The Sire de Malétroit raised his right hand and wagged it at Denis with the fore and little fingers extended.

"My dear nephew," he said, "sit down."

"Nephew!" retorted Denis, "you lie in your throat"; and he snapped his fingers in his face.

"Sit down, you rogue!" cried the old gentleman, in a sudden, harsh voice, like the barking of a dog. "Do you fancy," he went on, "that when I had made my little contrivance for the door I had stopped short with that? If you prefer to be bound hand and foot till your bones ache, rise and try to go away. If you choose to remain a free young buck, agreeably conversing with an old gentleman—why, sit where you are in peace, and God be with you."

"Do you mean I am a prisoner?" demanded Denis.

"I state the facts," replied the other. "I would rather leave the conclusion to yourself."

Denis sat down again. Externally he managed to keep pretty calm; but within, he was now boiling with anger, now chilled with apprehension. He no longer felt convinced that he was dealing with a madman. And if the old gentleman was sane, what, in God's name, had he to look for? What absurd or tragical adventure had befallen him? What countenance was he to assume?

While he was thus unpleasantly reflecting, the arras that overhung the chapel door was raised, and a tall priest in his robes came forth and, giving a long, keen stare at Denis, said something in an undertone to Sire de Malétroit.

"She is in a better frame of spirit?" asked the latter.

"She is more resigned, messire," replied the priest.

"Now the Lord help her, she is hard to please!" sneered the old gentleman. "A likely stripling—not ill-born—and of her own choosing, too? Why, what more would the jade have?"

"The situation is not usual for a young damsel," said the other, "and somewhat trying to her blushes."

"She should have thought of that before she began the dance. It was none of my choosing, God knows that: but since she is in it, by our Lady, she shall carry it to the end." And then addressing Denis, "Monsieur de Beaulieu," he asked, "may I present you to my niece? she has been waiting your arrival, I may say, with even greater impatience than myself."

Denis had resigned himself with a good grace—all he desired was to know the worst of it as speedily as possible; so he rose at once, and bowed in acquiescence. The Sire de Malétroit followed his example and limped, with the assistance of the chaplain's arm, towards the chapel door. The priest pulled aside the arras, and all three entered. The building had considerable architectural pretensions. A light groining sprang from six stout columns, and hung down in two rich pendants from the centre of the vault. The place terminated behind the altar in a round end, embossed and honeycombed with a superfluity of ornament in relief, and pierced by many little windows shaped like stars, trefoils, or wheels. These windows were imperfectly glazed, so that the night air circulated freely in the chapel. The tapers, of which there must have been half a hundred burning on the altar, were unmercifully blown about; and the light went through many different phases of brilliancy and semi-eclipse. On the steps in front of the altar knelt a young girl richly attired as a bride. A chill settled over Denis as he observed her costume; he fought with desperate energy against the conclusion that was being thrust upon his mind; it could not—it should not—be as he feared.

"Blanche," said the Sire, in his most flute-like tones, "I have brought a friend to see you, my little girl; turn round and give him your pretty hand. It is good to be devout; but it is necessary to be polite, my niece."

The girl rose to her feet and turned towards the newcomer. She moved all of a piece; and shame and exhaustion were expressed in every line of her fresh young body; and she held her head down and kept her eyes upon the pavement, as she came slowly forward. In the course of her advance, her eyes fell upon Denis de Beaulieu's feet—feet of which he was justly vain, be it remarked, and wore in the most elegant accoutrement even while traveling. She paused—started, as if his yellow boots had conveyed some shocking meaning—and glanced suddenly up into the wearer's countenance. Their eyes met; shame gave place to horror and terror in her looks; the blood left her lips; with a piercing scream she covered her face with her hands and sank upon the chapel floor.

"That is not the man!" she cried. "My uncle, that is not the man!"

The Sire de Malétroit chirped agreeably. "Of course not," he said; "I expected as much. It was so unfortunate you could not remember his name."

"Indeed," she cried, "indeed, I have never seen this person till this moment—I have never so much as set eyes upon him—I never wish to see him again. Sir," she said, turning to Denis, "if you are a gentleman, you will bear me out. Have I ever seen you—have you ever seen me—before this accursed hour?"

"To speak for myself, I have never had that pleasure," answered the young man. "This is the first time, messire, that I have met with your engaging niece."

The old gentleman shrugged his shoulders.

"I am distressed to hear it," he said. "But it is never too late to begin. I had little more acquaintance with my own late lady ere I married her; which proves," he added with a grimace, "that these impromptu marriages may often produce an excellent understanding in the long-run. As the bridegroom is to have a voice in the matter, I will give him two hours to make up for lost time before we proceed with the ceremony." And he turned towards the door, followed by the clergyman.

The girl was on her feet in a moment. "My uncle, you cannot be in earnest," she said. "I declare before God I will stab myself rather than be forced on that young man. The heart rises at it; God forbids such marriages; you dishonour your white hair. Oh, my uncle, pity me! There is not a woman in all the world but would prefer death to such a nuptial. Is it possible," she added, faltering—"is it possible that you do not believe me—that you still think this"—and she pointed at Denis with a tremor of anger and contempt—"that you still think *this* to be the man?"

"Frankly," said the old gentleman, pausing on the threshold, "I do. But let me explain to you once for all, Blanche de Malétroit, my way of thinking about this affair. When you took it into your head to dishonour my family and the name that I have borne, in peace and war, for more than three-score years, you forfeited, not only the right to question my designs, but that of looking me in the face. If your father had been alive, he would have spat on you and turned you out of doors. His was the hand of iron. You may bless your God you have only to deal with the hand of velvet, mademoiselle. It was my duty to get you married without delay. Out of pure good-will, I have tried to find your own gallant for you. And I believe I have succeeded. But before God and all the holy angels, Blanche de Malétroit, if I have not, I care not one jack-straw. So let me recommend you to be polite to our young friend; for upon my word, your next groom may be less appetizing."

And with that he went out, with the chaplain at his heels; and the arras fell behind the pair.

The girl turned upon Denis with flashing eyes.

"And what, sir," she demanded, "may be the meaning of all this?"

"God knows," returned Denis gloomily. "I am a prisoner in this house, which seems full of mad people. More I know not; and nothing do I understand."

320

"And pray how came you here?" she asked.

He told her as briefly as he could. "For the rest," he added, "perhaps you will follow my example, and tell me the answer to all these riddles, and what. in God's name, is like to be the end of it."

She stood silent for a little, and he could see her lips tremble and her tearless eyes burn with a feverish lustre. Then she pressed her forehead in both hands.

"Alas, how my head aches!" she said wearily—"to say nothing of my poor heart! But it is due to you to know my story, unmaidenly as it must seem. I am called Blanche de Malétroit; I have been without father or mother for—oh! for as long as I can recollect, and indeed I have been most unhappy all my life. Three months ago a young captain began to stand near me every day in church. I could see that I pleased him; I am much to blame, but I was so glad that any one should love me; and when he passed me a letter, I took it home with me and read it with great pleasure. Since that time he has written many. He was so anxious to speak with me, poor fellow! and kept asking me to leave the door open some evening that we might have two words upon the stair. For he knew how much my uncle trusted me." She gave something like a sob at that, and it was a moment before she could go on. "My uncle is a hard man, but he is very shrewd," she said at last. "He has performed many feats in war, and was a great person at court, and much trusted by Queen Isabeau in old days. How he came to suspect me I cannot tell; but it is hard to keep anything from his knowledge; and this morning, as we came from mass, he took my hand in his, forced it open, and read my little billet, walking by my side all the while. When he had finished, he gave it back to me with great politeness. It contained another request to have the door left open; and this has been the ruin of us all. My uncle kept me strictly in my room until evening, and then ordered me to dress myself as you see me—a hard mockery for a young girl, do you not think so? I suppose, when he could not prevail with me to tell him the young captain's name, he must have laid a trap for him: into which, alas! you have fallen in the anger of God. I looked for much confusion; for how could I tell whether he was willing to take me for his wife on these sharp terms? He might have been trifling with me from the first; or I might have made myself too cheap in his eyes. But truly I had not looked for such a shameful punishment as this. I could not think that God would let a girl be so disgraceful before a young man.

321

And now I have told you all; and I can scarcely hope that you will not despise me."

Denis made her a respectful inclination.

"Madam," he said, "you have honoured me by your confidence. It remains for me to prove that I am not unworthy of the honour. Is Messire de Malétroit at hand?"

"I believe he is writing in the salle without," she answered.

"May I lead you thither, madam?" asked Denis, offering his hand with his most courtly bearing.

She accepted it; and the pair passed out of the chapel, Blanche in a very drooping and shamefaced condition, but Denis strutting and ruffling in the consciousness of a mission, and the boyish certainty of accomplishing it with honour.

The Sire de Malétroit rose to meet them with an ironical obeisance.

"Sir," said Denis, with the grandest possible air, "I believe I am to have some say in the matter of this marriage; and let me tell you at once, I will be no party to forcing the inclination of this young lady. Had it been freely offered to me, I should have been proud to accept her hand, for I perceive she is as good as she is beautiful; but as things are, I have now the honour, messire, of refusing."

Blanche looked at him with gratitude in her eyes; but the old gentleman only smiled and smiled, until his smile grew positively sickening to Denis.

"I am afraid," he said, "Monsieur de Beaulieu, that you do not perfectly understand the choice I have to offer you. Follow me, I beseech you, to this window." And he led the way to one of the large windows which stood open on the night. "You observe," he went on, "there is an iron ring in the upper masonry, and reeved through that, a very efficacious rope. Now, mark my words: if you should find your disinclination to my niece's person insurmountable, I shall have you hanged out of this window before sunrise. I shall only proceed to such an extremity with the greatest regret, you may believe me. For it is not at all your death that I desire, but my niece's establishment in life. At the same time, it must come to that if you prove obstinate. Your family, Monsieur de Beaulieu, is very well in its way; but if you sprang from Charlemagne, you should not refuse the hand of a Malétroit with impunity—not if she had been as common as the Paris road—not if she were as hideous as the gargoyle over my door. Neither my niece nor you, nor my own private feelings, move me at all in this

322

matter. The honour of my house has been compromised; I believe you to be the guilty person; at least you are now in the secret; and you can hardly wonder if I request you to wipe out the stain. If you will not, your blood be on your own head! It will be no great satisfaction to me to have your interesting relics kicking their heels in the breeze below my windows; but half a loaf is better than no bread, and if I cannot cure the dishonour, I shall at least stop the scandal."

There was a pause.

"I believe there are other ways of settling such imbroglios among gentlemen," said Denis. "You wear a sword, and I hear you have used it with distinction."

The Sire de Malétroit made a signal to the chaplain, who crossed the room with long silent strides and raised the arras over the third of the three doors. It was only a moment before he let it fall again; but Denis had time to see a dusky passage full of armed men.

"When I was a little younger, I should have been delighted to honour you, Monsieur de Beaulieu," said Sire Alain; "but I am now too old. Faithful retainers are the sinews of age, and I must employ the strength I have. This is one of the hardest things to swallow as a man grows up in years; but with a little patience, even this becomes habitual. You and the lady seem to prefer the salle for what remains of your two hours; and as I have no desire to cross your preference, I shall resign it to your use with all the pleasure in the world. No haste!" he added, holding up his hand, as he saw a dangerous look come into Denis de Beaulieu's face. "If your mind revolts against hanging, it will be time enough two hours hence to throw yourself out of the window or upon the pikes of my retainers. Two hours of life are always two hours. A great many things may turn up in even as little a while as that. And besides, if I understand her appearance, my niece has still something to say to you. You will not disfigure your last hours by a want of politeness to a lady?"

Denis looked at Blanche, and she made him an imploring gesture.

It is likely that the old gentleman was hugely pleased at this symptom of an understanding; for he smiled on both, and added sweetly: "If you will give me your word of honour, Monsieur de Beaulieu, to await my return at the end of the two hours before attempting anything desperate, I shall withdraw my retainers, and let you speak in greater privacy with mademoiselle."

Denis again glanced at the girl, who seemed to beseech him to agree.

"I give you my word of honour," he said.

Messire de Malétroit bowed, and proceeded to limp about the apartment, clearing his throat the while with that odd musical chirp which had already grown so irritating in the ears of Denis de Beaulieu. He first possessed himself of some papers which lay upon the table; then he went to the mouth of the passage and appeared to give an order to the men behind the arras; and lastly he hobbled out through the door by which Denis had come in, turning upon the threshold to address a last smiling bow to the young couple, and followed by the chaplain with a hand-lamp.

No sooner were they alone than Blanche advanced towards Denis with her hands extended. Her face was flushed and excited, and her eyes shone with tears.

"You shall not die!" she cried, "you shall marry me after all."

"You seem to think, madam," replied Denis, "that I stand much in fear of death."

"Oh, no, no," she said, "I see you are no poltroon. It is for my own sake—I could not bear to have you slain for such a scruple."

"I am afraid," returned Denis, "that you underrate the difficulty, madam. What you may be too generous to refuse, I may be too proud to accept. In a moment of noble feeling towards me, you forget what you perhaps owe to others."

He had the decency to keep his eyes upon the floor as he said this, and after he had finished, so as not to spy upon her confusion. She stood silent for a moment, then walked suddenly away, and falling on her uncle's chair, fairly burst out sobbing. Denis was in the acme of embarrassment. He looked round, as if to seek for inspiration, and seeing a stool, plumped down upon it for something to do. There he sat, playing with the guard of his rapier, and wishing himself dead a thousand times over, and buried in the nastiest kitchen-heap in France. His eyes wandered round the apartment but found nothing to arrest them. There were such wide spaces between the furniture, the light fell so badly and cheerlessly over all, the dark outside air looked in so coldly through the windows, that he thought he had never seen a church so vast, nor a tomb so melancholy. The regular sobs of Blanche de Malétroit measured out the time like the ticking of a clock. He read the device upon the shield over and over again, until his eyes became obscured; he stared into shadowy corners until he imagined they were swarming with horrible animals; and every now and again he awoke with a start, to remember that his last two hours were running and death was on the march.

Oftener and oftener, as the time went on, did his glance settle on the girl herself. Her face was bowed forward and covered with her hands, and she was shaken at intervals by the convulsive hiccup of grief. Even thus she was not an unpleasant object to dwell upon, so plump and yet so fine, with a warm brown skin, and the most beautiful hair, Denis thought, in the whole world of womankind. Her hands were like her uncle's; but they were more in place at the end of her young arms, and looked infinitely soft and caressing. He remembered how her blue eyes had shone upon him, full of anger, pity, and innocence. And the more he dwelt on her perfections, the uglier death looked, and the more deeply was he smitten with penitence at her continued tears. Now he felt that no man could have the courage to leave a world which contained so beautiful a creature; and now he would have given forty minutes of his last hour to have unsaid his cruel speech.

Suddenly a hoarse and ragged peal of cockcrow rose to their ears from the dark valley below the windows. And this shattering noise in the silence all around was like a light in a dark place, and shook them both out of their reflections.

"Alas, can I do nothing to help you?" she said, looking up.

"Madam," replied Denis, with a fine irrelevancy, "if I have said anything to wound you, believe me, it was for your own sake and not for mine."

She thanked him with a tearful look.

"I feel your position cruelly," he went on. "The world has been bitter hard on you. Your uncle is a disgrace to mankind. Believe me, madam, there is no young gentleman in all France but would be glad of my opportunity, to die in doing you a momentary service."

"I know already that you can be very brave and generous," she answered. "What I *want* to know is whether I can serve you—now or afterwards," she added, with a quaver.

"Most certainly," he answered with a smile. "Let me sit beside you as if I were a friend, instead of a foolish intruder; try to forget how awkwardly we are placed to one another; make my last moments go pleasantly; and you will do me the chief service possible."

"You are very gallant," she added, with a yet deeper sadness . . . "very gallant . . . and it somehow pains me. But draw nearer, if you please, and if you find anything to say to me, you will at least make certain of a very friendly listener. Ah! Monsieur de Beaulieu, how can I look you in the face?" And she fell to weeping again with a renewed effusion.

"Madam," said Denis, taking her hand in both of his, "reflect on the little time I have before me, and the great bitterness into which I am cast by the sight of your distress. Spare me, in my last moments, the spectacle of what I cannot cure even with the sacrifice of my life."

"I am very selfish," answered Blanche. "I will be braver, Monsieur de Beaulieu, for your sake. But think if I can do you no kindness in the future—if you have no friends to whom I could carry your adieux. Charge me as heavily as you can; every burden will lighten, by so little, the invaluable gratitude I owe you. Put it in my power to do something more for you than weep."

"My mother is married again, and has a young family to care for. My brother Guichard will inherit my fiefs; and if I am not in error, that will content him amply for my death. Life is a little vapour that passeth away, as we are told by those in holy orders. When a man is in a fair way and sees all life open in front of him, he seems to himself to make a very important figure in the world. His horse whinnies to him; the trumpets blow and the girls look out of windows as he rides into town before his company; he receives many assurances of trust and regard—sometimes by express in a letter—sometimes face to face, with persons of great consequence falling on his neck. It is not wonderful if his head is turned for a time. But once he is dead, were he as brave as Hercules or as wise as Solomon, he is soon forgotten. It is not ten years since my father fell, with many other knights around him, in a very fierce encounter, and I do not think that any one of them, nor so much as the name of the fight, is now remembered. No, no, madam, the nearer you come to it, you see that death is a dark and dusty corner, where a man gets into his tomb and has the door shut after him till the judgment day. I have few friends just now, and once I am dead I shall have none."

"Ah, Monsieur de Beaulieu!" she exclaimed, "you forget Blanche de Malétroit."

"You have a sweet nature, madam, and you are pleased to estimate a little service far beyond its worth."

"It is not that," she answered. "You mistake me if you think I am so easily touched by my own concerns. I say so, because you are the noblest man I have ever met; because I recognise in you a spirit that would have made even a common person famous in the land."

"And yet here I die in a mouse-trap—with no more noise about it than my own speaking," answered he.

A look of pain crossed her face, and she was silent for a little while. Then a light came into her eyes, and with a smile she spoke again.

"I cannot have my champion think meanly of himself. Any one who gives his life for another will be met in Paradise by all the heralds and angels of the Lord God. And you have no such cause to hang your head. For . . . Pray, do you think me beautiful?" she asked, with a deep flush.

"Indeed, madam, I do," he said.

"I am glad of that," she answered, heartily. "Do you think there are many men in France who have been asked in marriage by a beautiful maiden—with her own lips—and who have refused her to her face? I know you men would half despise such a triumph; but believe me, we women know more of what is precious in love. There is nothing that should set a person higher in his own esteem; and we women would prize nothing more dearly."

"You are very good," he said; "but you cannot make me forget that I was asked in pity and not for love."

"I am not so sure of that," she replied, holding down her head. "Hear me to an end, Monsieur de Beaulieu. I know how you must despise me; I feel you are right to do so; I am too poor a creature to occupy one thought of your mind, although, alas! you must die for me this morning. But when I asked you to marry me, indeed, and indeed, it was because I respected and admired you, and loved you with my whole soul, from the very moment that you took my part against my uncle. If you had seen yourself, and how noble you looked, you would pity rather than despise me. And now," she went on, hurriedly checking him with her hand, "although I have laid aside all reserve and told you so much, remember that I know your sentiments towards me already. I would not, believe me, being nobly born, weary you with importunities into consent. I too have a pride of my own: and I declare before the holy mother of God, if you should now go back from your word already given, I would no more marry you than I would marry my uncle's groom."

Denis smiled a little bitterly.

"It is a small love," he said, "that shies at a little pride."

She made no answer, although she probably had her own thought.

"Come hither to the window," he said, with a sigh. "Here is the dawn."

And indeed the dawn was already beginning. The hollow of the sky was full of essential daylight, colourless and clean; and the valley underneath was flooded with a gray reflection. A few thin vapors clung in the coves of the forest or lay along the winding course of the river. The scene disengaged a surprising effect of stillness, which was hardly interrupted when the cocks began once more to crow among the steadings. Perhaps the same fellow who had made so horrid a clangour in the darkness not half an hour before, now sent up the merriest cheer to greet the coming day. A little wind went bustling and eddying among the tree-tops underneath the windows. And still the daylight kept flooding insensibly out of the east, which was soon to grow incandescent and cast up that red-hot cannon-ball, the rising sun.

Denis looked out over all this with a bit of a shiver. He had taken her hand and retained it in his almost unconsciously.

"Hast the day begun already?" she said; and then, illogically enough: "the night has been so long! Alas! what shall we say to my uncle when he returns?"

"What you will," said Denis, and he pressed her fingers in his.

She was silent.

"Blanche," he said, with a swift, uncertain, passionate utterance, "you have seen whether I fear death. You must know well enough that I would as gladly leap out of the window into the empty air as to lay a finger on you without your free and full consent. But if you care for me at all do not let me lose my life in a misapprehension; for I love you better than the whole world; and though I will die for you blithely, it would be like all the joys of Paradise to live on and spend my life in your service."

As he stopped speaking, a bell began to ring loudly in the interior of the house, and a clatter of armour in the corridor showed that the retainers were returning to their post, and the two hours were at an end.

"After all that you have heard?" she whispered, leaning towards him with her lips and eyes.

"I have heard nothing," he replied.

"The captain's name was Florimond de Champdivers," she said in his ear.

328

Polo, I never listened to Li Po's song so eagerly as I am listening to your voice."

"But you are not taking it in, little Golden Bells."

"It is very hard to take in, Marco Polo. It happened so long ago. It is hard to think of a tragedy in a strange country, and we in this garden on the second moon of spring. And it was so very long ago. Do you hear the bees, Marco Polo—the bees among the almond-blossoms? And see the blue heron by the lotus flowers? And do you see the little tortoise, Marco Polo, and he sunning himself on a leaf? If I throw a pebble, Marco Polo, he will dive, and he is such a clumsy diver, Marco Polo!"

"But you must listen, Golden Bells, and believe me."

"I do believe, Marco Polo; I honestly do. Don't you know I believe you? Anything you say, Marco Polo, I believe. You wouldn't be coming all the way over the world to be telling me a lie. Of course I believe."

"And doesn't it make you happy, Golden Bells?"

"Once I was unhappy, Marco Polo. I used to sit here, and on my lute I used to play the 'Song of the Willow Branches,' which is the saddest song in the world. Under the moon I used to be lonely, and the droning of the bees meant nothing to me, and now it is a sweet brave song. I cannot play 'Willow Branches' any more, so alien is sadness to me. And the moon smiles. I am very happy, Marco Polo."

"It is the True Religion, little Golden Bells, that makes you happy."

"Is it, Marco Polo? Is it? It must be, I suppose. I don't know what it is, but I am very happy."

And he told her of Paul, who had seen a vision and gone preaching through the world, who was persecuted, who was shipwrecked, who was bitten by a viper, and who survived everything that he might preach the Lord Jesus. He was a fierce, ragged man with burning eyes . . . And he told her of Paul's instructions to women . . .

"You do not look at me when you speak, Marco Polo. Only your voice comes to me, not your eyes. Is it because of Paul?"

And Marco Polo felt great trouble on him, because he could not explain. But Golden Bells went on:

"There is little in your faith about women, Marco Polo. Is it a faith only for men, then? Is it against women? Must the young men not look at the young women?"

"No, Golden Bells; they must not look much on the young women."

"But that is very foolish, Marco Polo. Is it wrong to see the beauty of the almond blossoms, wrong to taste the scented wind? Is it wrong to watch the kingfisher seeking his nest? Is it wrong to watch the moon, the stars? All these are very beautiful, Marco Polo, so beautiful as to make me cry. Is it wrong to watch them?"

"It is not wrong, Golden Bells. The glory of God is in the beauty of his handicraft."

"Li Po is old and wise and a great poet, Marco Polo, and Li Po says there is beauty in a running horse and beauty in a running stream; but there is no beauty like the beauty of a young woman, and she letting down her hair. God made the beauty of women, too, Marco Polo, as well as the beauty of the stars. Won't you please explain to me, Marco Polo? Why should Li Po say one thing and Saint Paul another?"

"But Golden Bells, Saint Paul is inspired of God."

"But Li Po is inspired of God, too, Marco Polo. You mustn't be thinking little of Li Po. He is fat and old and drunken, but when he sings, Marco Polo, it is the song of the wandering stars. But why must not the young men look at the young women, Marco Polo? Why must they not look with their eyes?"

"It will be hard for me to tell you, Golden Bells—"

"Look at me now, Marco Polo. Lift up your eyes and look into my eyes. Is there evil in me, Marco Polo, that your eyes should avoid me as the fox avoids the dog? Or maybe I am not beautiful. Maybe they told me wrong because I was a king's daughter, and they would not have me think little of myself. Maybe I am not beautiful, Marco Polo, maybe I hurt your eyes.—"

"Ah, Golden Bells, the little horned moon is not more beautiful."

"Then why must not the young men look at the young women, Marco Polo? You are here to instruct me. Won't you tell me why?"

"Maybe—maybe—maybe it is for fear of sin, Golden Bells."

"Sin? Sin! Why should there be sin? I know sin, Marco Polo. They have warned me against it since I crept upon the floor. There are two sins. There is meanness, Marco Polo, and there is cruelty; and those are the only sins. I know your heart, Marco Polo; there is no meanness there. You would not have come here were you mean. The mean do not travel afar for other people. And cruelty! Surely you

332

would not be cruel to me, Marco Polo. You would not be cruel to anybody, dear Marco Polo. You would not be cruel to me?"

"Cruel to you, little Golden Bells! How could I be cruel to you?"

"But the sin, Marco Polo?"

"I don't know, Golden Bells. I don't know."

And one dusk the moon rose over the Chinese garden, and Marco Polo finished telling her of what John saw on Patmos and he an old man . . .

" 'Veni, Domine Jesu.

" 'Gratia Domini nostri Jesu Christi cum omnibus vobis. Amen!' "

"It is very difficult, Marco Polo. I don't quite understand."

"I don't quite understand myself, Golden Bells. But that is all I can tell you. But you will understand more," he said. "My mission is finished now, and I will go back. I will stop at the court of Prester John, and he will send a bishop surely or some great cardinal to baptize you and to teach you the rest."

"You will go back?" A great pain stabbed her. "I never thought, somehow, of you as going back."

"I have come on a mission, Golden Bells, and I must go back."

"There is a woman, maybe, in Venice—" And she turned her head away from him and from the moon.

"I would not have you thinking that, Golden Bells. There is none in Venice has duty from me. And if the queen of the world were there, and she pledged to me, I could never look at her, and I after knowing you, Golden Bells!"

"Is it money, Marco Polo?" she whispered in the dusk. "It is maybe your uncle and your father are pressing you to return. Let you not worry then, for my father the great Khan will settle with them, too. There is not a horse in all Tartary that your uncle cannot have, nor a woman, either. And your father can have all the jewels of the treasury, and all the swords, too, even the sword with which my father conquered China. My father will give him that if I ask. Only let you not be leaving this moonlit garden."

"Dear Golden Bells, it isn't that; but I came here for converts—"

"Oh, Marco Polo, listen! There is a folk at Kai-fung-fu, and they are an evil folk and a cowardly folk, and my father abhors them. I shall ask my father to send captains of war and fighting men to convert them to your faith, Marco Polo, or lop off their heads. And we can send a few hundreds to the Pope at Rome, and he will never know how they were converted, and he will be satisfied. Only let you not be going away from me in my moonlit garden. You will only be turning to trade, Marco Polo, and marrying a woman. Let you stay here in the moonlit garden!"

"Ah, little Golden Bells, there is no place in the world like your moonlit garden. There is no place I'd be liefer than in the moonlit garden. But little Golden Bells, I set out in life to preach the Lord Jesus crucified. It was for that I came to China."

"Let you not be fooling yourself, young Marco Polo. Let you not always be ascribing to God the things that are mine. You did not come to preach to China, you came to see me, and your mind stirred up with the story the sea-captain told, of me playing 'Willow Branches' by the Lake of Cranes. O Marco Polo, before you came there were the moon and the sun and the stars, and I was lonely. O Marco Polo," she cried, "you wouldn't go, you couldn't go! What would you be doing in cold Venice, far from the warm moonlit garden?"

"Sure, I'll be lonely, too, little Golden Bells, a white monk in a monastery, praying for you."

"But I don't want to be prayed for, Marco Polo." She stamped her foot. "I want to be loved. And there you have it out of me, and a great shame to you that you made me say it, me that was desired of many, and would have no man until you came. And surely it is the harsh God you have made out of The Kindly Person you spoke of. And 'tis not He would have my heart broken, and you turning yourself into a crabbed monk. And how do you know your preaching will convert any? 'Tis few you converted here. Ah, I'm sorry, dear Marco Polo; I shouldn't have said it, but there is despair on me, and I afraid of losing you."

" 'Tis true, though. I have nothing, nobody to show."

"You have me. Amn't I converted? Amn't I a Christian? Marco Polo, let me tell you something. I said to my father I wanted to marry you, and I asked him if he would give you a province to govern, and he said, 'Sure and welcome.' And I asked him for Yangchan, the pleasantest city in all China. And he said, 'Sure and welcome, Golden Bells.' And I told him we would be married, and go there and govern his people kindly. And you wouldn't shame me before my own father, and all the people of China. You couldn't do that, Marco Polo. Marco

Polo,"—she came toward him, her eyes shining,—"let you stay!"

"Christ protect me! Christ guide me! Christ before me!"

"Marco Polo!"

"Christ behind me!"

"The moon, Marco Polo, and me, Golden Bells, and the nightingale in the apple-tree!"

"Christ on my right hand! Christ on my left! Christ below me!"

Her arms were around his neck, her cheek came close to his.

"Marco Polo! Marco Polo!"

"Christ above me!"

"My Marco Polo!"

"O, God! Golden Bells!"

And he put his arms around her, and his cheek to hers, and all the battle and the disappointment and the fear and the strangeness went out of him. And down by the lake the wee frogs chirruped, and in the apple-tree the nightingale never ceased from singing. And they stayed there shoulder to shoulder and cheek to cheek. And the moon rose higher. And it seemed only a moment they were there, until they heard the voice of Li Po in the garden.

"Are you there, Golden Bells? Are you there at all, at all? For two hours I've been hunting and couldn't get sight or sign of you. I have the new song, Golden Bells. For a long time I was dumb, but a little while ago the power came to me, and I have the new song, Golden Bells, the marrying song . . ."

Rose Aylmer

Walter Savage Landor

Ah what avails the sceptred race,
　　Ah what the form divine!
What every virtue, every grace!
　　Rose Aylmer, all were thine.

Rose Aylmer, whom these wakeful eyes
　　May weep, but never see,
A night of memories and of sighs
　　I consecrate to thee.

335

When Lilacs Last in the Dooryard Bloom'd

(*In memory of Lincoln*)

Walt Whitman

When lilacs last in the dooryard bloom'd,
And the great star early droop'd in the western sky in the night,
I mourn'd, and yet shall mourn with ever-returning spring.
Ever-returning spring, trinity sure to me you bring,
Lilac blooming perennial and drooping star in the west,
And thought of him I love.

O powerful western fallen star!
O shades of night—O moody, tearful night!
O great star disappear'd—O the black murk that hides the star!
O cruel hands that hold me powerless—O helpless soul of me!
O harsh surrounding cloud that will not free my soul.

In the dooryard fronting an old farm-house near the whitewash'd palings,
Stands the lilac-bush tall-growing with heart-shaped leaves of rich green,
With many a pointed blossom rising delicate, with the perfume strong I love,
With every leaf a miracle—and from this bush in the dooryard,
With delicate-color'd blossoms and heart-shaped leaves of rich green,
A sprig with its flower I break.

In the swamp in secluded recesses,
A shy and hidden bird is warbling a song.
Solitary the thrush,
The hermit withdrawn to himself, avoiding the settlements,
Sings by himself a song.
Song of the bleeding throat,
Death's outlet song of life, (for well dear brother I know,
If thou wast not granted to sing thou would'st surely die.)

Over the breast of the spring, the land, amid cities,
Amid lanes and through old woods, where lately the violets peep'd from the
    ground, spotting the gray debris,
Amid the grass in the fields each side of the lanes, passing the endless grass,
Passing the yellow-spear'd wheat, every grain from its shroud in the dark-
    brown fields uprisen,
Passing the apple-tree blows of white and pink in the orchards.

Carrying a corpse to where it shall rest in the grave,
Night and day journeys a coffin.

Coffin that passes through lanes and streets,
Through day and night with the great cloud darkening the land,
With the pomp of the inloop'd flags with the cities draped in black,
With the show of the States themselves as of crape-veil'd women standing,
With processions long and winding and the flambeaus of the night,
With the countless torches lit, with the silent sea of faces and the unbared
    heads,
With the waiting depot, the arriving coffin, and the sombre faces,
With dirges through the night, with the thousand voices rising strong and
    solemn,
With all the mournful voices of the dirges pour'd around the coffin,
The dim-lit churches and the shuddering organs—where amid these you
    journey,
With the tolling tolling bells' perpetual clang,
Here, coffin that slowly passes,
I give you my sprig of lilac.

(Nor for you, for one alone,
Blossoms and branches green to coffins all I bring,
For fresh as the morning, thus would I chant a song for you O sane and
    sacred death.
All over bouquets of roses,
O death, I cover you over with roses and early lilies,
But mostly and now the lilac that blooms the first,
Copious I break, I break the sprigs from the bushes,
With loaded arms I come, pouring for you,
For you and the coffins all of you O death.)

O western orb sailing the heaven,
Now I know what you must have meant as a month since I walk'd,
As I walk'd in silence the transparent shadowy night,
As I saw you had something to tell as you bent to me night after night,
As you droop'd from the sky low down as if to my side, (while the other
    stars all look'd on,)
As we wander'd together the solemn night, (for something I know not what
    kept me from sleep,)

As the night advanced, and I saw on the rim of the west how full you were
of woe,
As I stood on the rising ground in the breeze in the cool transparent night,
As I watch'd where you pass'd and was lost in the netherward black of the
night,
As my soul in its trouble dissatisfied sank, as where yon sad orb,
Concluded, dropt in the night, and was gone.

Sing on there in the swamp,
O singer bashful and tender, I hear your notes, I hear your call,
I hear, I come presently, I understand you,
But a moment I linger, for the lustrous star has detain'd me,
The star my departing comrade holds and detains me.
O how shall I warble myself for the dead one there I loved?
And how shall I deck my song for the large sweet soul that has gone?
And what shall my perfume be for the grave of him I love?
Sea-winds blown from east and west,
Blown from the Eastern sea and blown from the Western sea, till there on
the prairies meeting,
These and with these and the breath of my chant,
I'll perfume the grave of him I love.

O what shall I hang on the chamber walls?
And what shall the pictures be that I hang on the walls,
To adorn the burial-house of him I love?
Pictures of growing spring and farms and homes,
With the Fourth-month eve at sundown, and the gray smoke lucid and
bright,
With floods of the yellow gold of the gorgeous, indolent, sinking sun, burn-
ing, expanding the air,
With the fresh sweet herbage under foot, and the pale green leaves of the
trees prolific,
In the distance the flowing glaze, the breast of the river, with a wind-dapple
here and there,
With ranging hills on the banks, with many a line against the sky, and
shadows,
And the city at hand with dwellings so dense, and stacks of chimneys,
And all the scenes of life and the workshops, and the workmen homeward
returning.

Lo, body and soul—this land,
My own Manhattan with spires, and the sparkling and hurrying tides, and
the ships,
The varied and ample land, the South and the North in the light, Ohio's
shores and flashing Missouri,
And ever the far-spreading prairies cover'd with grass and corn.
Lo, the most excellent sun so calm and haughty,
The violet and purple morn with just-felt breezes,
The gentle soft-born measureless light,
The miracle, spreading, bathing all, the fulfill'd noon,
The coming eve delicious, the welcome night and the stars,
Over my cities shining all, enveloping man and land.
Sing on, sing on you gray-brown bird,
Sing from the swamps, the recesses, pour your chant from the bushes,
Limitless out of the dusk, out of the cedars and pines.
Sing on dearest brother, warble your reedy song,
Loud human song, with voice of uttermost woe.
O liquid and free and tender!
O wild and loose to my soul—O wondrous singer!
You only I hear—yet the star holds me, (but will soon depart,)
Yet the lilac with mastering odor holds me.

Now while I sat in the day and look'd forth,
In the close of the day with its light and the fields of spring, and the farmers
preparing their crops,
In the large unconscious scenery of my land with its lakes and forests,
In the heavenly aerial beauty, (after the perturb'd winds and the storms,)
Under the arching heavens of the afternoon swift passing, and the voices of
children and women,
The many-moving sea-tides, and I saw the ships how they sail'd,
And the summer approaching with richness, and the fields all busy with labor,
And the infinite separate houses, how they all went on, each with its meals
and minutia of daily usages,
And the streets how their throbbings throbb'd, and the cities pent—lo, then
and there,
Falling upon them all and among them all, enveloping me with the rest,
Appear'd the cloud, appear'd the long black trail,
And I knew death, its thought, and the sacred knowledge of death.

Then with the knowledge of death as walking one side of me,
And the thought of death close-walking the other side of me,
And I in the middle as with companions, and as holding the hands of com-
panions,
I fled forth to the hiding receiving night that talks not,
Down to the shores of the water, the path by the swamp in the dimness,
To the solemn shadowy cedars and ghostly pines so still.

And the singer so shy to the rest receiv'd me,
The gray-brown bird I know receiv'd us comrades three,
And he sang the carol of death, and a verse for him I love.
From deep secluded recesses,
From the fragrant cedars and the ghostly pines so still,
Came the carol of the bird.
And the charm of the carol rapt me,
As I held as if by their hands my comrades in the night,
And the voice of my spirit tallied the song of the bird.

Come lovely and soothing death,
Undulate round the world, serenely arriving, arriving,
In the day, in the night, to all, to each,
Sooner or later delicate death.

Prais'd be the fathomless universe,
For life and joy, and for objects and knowledge curious,
And for love, sweet love—but praise! praise! praise!
For the sure-enwinding arms of cool-enfolding death.

Dark mother always gliding near with soft feet,
Have none chanted for thee a chant of fullest welcome?
Then I chant it for thee, I glorify thee above all,
I bring thee a song that when thou must indeed come, come unfalteringly.

Approach strong deliveress,
When it is so, when thou hast taken them I joyously sing the dead,
Lost in the loving floating ocean of thee,
Laved in the flood of thy bliss O death.

From me to thee glad serenades,
Dances for thee I propose saluting thee, adornments and feastings for thee,

340

And the sights of the open landscape and the high-spread sky are fitting,
And life and the fields, and the huge and thoughtful night.

The night in silence under many a star,
The ocean shore and the husky whispering wave whose voice I know,
And the soul turning to thee O vast and well-veil'd death,
And the body gratefully nestling close to thee.
Over the tree-tops I float thee a song,
Over the rising and sinking waves, over the myriad fields and the prairies
  wide,
Over the dense-pack'd cities all and the teeming wharves and ways,
I float this carol with joy, with joy to thee O death.

To the tally of my soul,
Loud and strong kept up the gray-brown bird,
With pure deliberate notes spreading filling the night.
Loud in the pines and cedars dim,
Clear in the freshness moist and the swamp-perfume,
And I with my comrades there in the night.
While my sight that was bound in my eyes unclosed,
As to long panoramas of visions.

And I saw askant the armies,
I saw as in noiseless dreams hundreds of battle-flags,
Borne through the smoke of the battles and pierc'd with missiles I saw them,
And carried hither and yon through the smoke, and torn and bloody,
And at last but a few shreds left on the staffs, (and all in silence,)
And the staffs all splinter'd and broken.
I saw battle-corpses, myriads of them,
And the white skeletons of young men, I saw them,
I saw the debris and debris of all the slain soldiers of the war,
But I saw they were not as was thought,
They themselves were fully at rest, they suffer'd not,
The living remain'd and suffer'd, the mother suffer'd,
And the wife and the child and the musing comrade suffer'd,
And the armies that remain'd suffer'd.

Passing the visions, passing the night,
Passing, unloosing the hold of my comrades' hands,

341

Passing the song of the hermit bird and the tallying song of my soul,
Victorious song, death's outlet song, yet varying ever-altering song,
As low and wailing, yet clear the notes, rising and falling, flooding the night,
Sadly sinking and fainting, as warning and warning, and yet again bursting
    with joy,
Covering the earth and filling the spread of the heaven,
As that powerful psalm in the night I heard from recesses,
Passing, I leave thee lilac with heart-shaped leaves,
I leave thee there in the dooryard, blooming, returning with spring.

I cease from my song for thee,
From my gaze on thee in the west, fronting the west, communing with thee,
O comrade lustrous with silver face in the night.
Yet each to keep and all, retrievements out of the night,
The song, the wondrous chant of the gray-brown bird,
And the tallying chant, the echo arous'd in my soul,
With the lustrous and drooping star with the countenance full of woe,
With the holders holding my hand hearing the call of the bird,
Comrades mine and I in the midst, and their memory ever to keep, for the
    dead I loved so well,
For the sweetest, wisest soul of all my days and lands—and this for his dear sake,
Lilac and star and bird twined with the chant of my soul,
There in the fragrant pines and the cedars dusk and dim.

Indian Love Song

Elizabeth-Ellen Long

A star fell to the earth last night.
I have worked all day
Beating the silver of it thin,
Over and over again, beating the silver
And shaping it into beauty.
My forge is deep in the hills.
I sing as I work and the silver
Is like a song in my hands.
I shall work beauty upon the silver,
And you will understand.
Seeing the turquoise and the silver,
You will understand why I sing.

The Meeting

From The Ordeal of Richard Feverel

George Meredith

In George Meredith's great Nineteenth-Century novel, The Ordeal of Richard Feverel, *you will find this excerpt, often called the most beautiful love scene in English literature.*

WHEN Nature has made us ripe for Love it seldom occurs that the Fates are behindhand in furnishing a Temple for the flame.

Above green-flashing plunges of a weir, and shaken by the thunder below, lilies, golden and white, were swaying at anchor among the reeds. Meadow-sweet hung from the banks thick with weed and training bramble, and there also hung a daughter of Earth. Her face was shaded by a broad straw-hat with a flexile brim that left her lips and chin in the sun, and sometimes nodding, sent forth a light of promising eyes. Across her shoulders, and behind flowed large loose curls, brown in shadow, almost golden where the ray touched them. She was simply dressed, befitting decency and the season. On a closer inspection you might see that her lips were stained. This blooming young person was regaling on dewberries. They grew between the bank and the water. Apparently she found the fruit abundant, for her hand was making pretty progress to her mouth. Fastidious youth, which shudders and revolts at woman plumping her exquisite proportions on bread-and-butter, and would (we must suppose) joyfully have her quite scraggy to have her quite poetical, can hardly object to dewberries. Indeed the act of eating them is dainty and induces musing. The dewberry is a sister to the lotos, and an innocent sister. You eat; mouth, eye, and hand, are occupied, and the undrugged mind free to roam. And so it was with the damsel who knelt there. The little skylark went up above her, all song, to the smooth southern cloud lying along the blue: from

343

a dewy copse standing dark over her nodding hat, the blackbird fluted, calling to her with thrice mellow note: the kingfisher flashed emerald out of green osiers: a bow-winged heron travelled aloft, searching solitude: a boat slipped towards her, containing a dreamy youth, and still she plucked the fruit, and ate, and mused, as if no fairy prince were invading her territories, and as if she wished not for one, or knew not her wishes. Surrounded by the green shaven meadows, the pastoral summer buzz, the weir-fall's thundering white, amid the breath and beauty of wildflowers, she was a bit of lovely human life in a fair setting: a terrible attraction. The Magnetic Youth leaned round to note his proximity to the weir-piles, and beheld the sweet vision. Stiller and stiller grew Nature, as at the meeting of two electric clouds. Her posture was so graceful that, though he was making straight for the weir, he dared not dip a scull. Just then one most enticing dewberry caught her eye. He was floating by unheeded, and saw that her hand stretched low, and could not gather what it sought. A stroke from his right brought him beside her. The damsel glanced up dismayed, and her whole shape trembled over the brink. Richard sprang from his boat into the water. Pressing a hand beneath her foot, which she had thrust against the crumbling wet sides of the bank to save herself, he enabled her to recover her balance, and gain safe earth, whither, emboldened by the incident, touching her finger's tip, he followed her.

He had landed on an Island of the still-vexed Bermoothes. The world lay wrecked behind him: Raynham hung in mists, remote, a phantom to the vivid reality of this white hand which had drawn him thither away thousands of leagues in an eye-twinkle. Hark, how Ariel sung overhead! What splendour in the Heavens! What marvels of beauty about his enchanted head! And, O you Wonder! Fair Flame! by whose light the glories of being are now first seen. . . . Radiant Miranda! Prince Ferdinand is at your feet.

Or is it Adam, his rib taken from his side in sleep, and thus transformed, to make him behold his Paradise, and lose it? . . .

The youth looked on her with as glowing an eye. It was the First Woman to him.

And she—mankind was all Caliban to her, saving this one princely youth.

So to each other said their changing eyes in the moment they stood together; he pale, and she blushing.

She was indeed sweetly fair, and would have been held fair among rival damsels. On a magic shore, and to a youth educated by a System, strung like an arrow drawn to the head, he, it might be guessed, could fly fast and far with her. The soft rose in her cheeks, the clearness of her eyes, bore witness to the body's virtue; and health, and happy blood was in her bearing. Had she stood before Sir Austin among rival damsels, that Scientific Humanist, for the consummation of his System, would have thrown her the handkerchief for his son. The wide summer-hat nodding over her forehead to her brows, seemed to flow with the flowing heavy curls, and those fire-threaded mellow curls, only half-curls, waves of hair, call them, rippling at the ends, went like a sunny red-veined torrent down her back almost to her waist: a glorious vision to the youth, who embraced it as a flower of beauty, and read not a feature. There were curious features of colour in her face for him to have read. Her brows, thick and brownish against a soft skin showing the action of the blood, met in the bend of a bow, extending to the temples long and level: you saw that she was fashioned to peruse the sights of earth, and by the pliability of her brows, that the wonderful creature used her faculty, and was not going to be a statue to the gazer. Under the dark thick brows an arch of lashes shot out, giving a wealth of darkness to the full frank blue eyes a mystery of meaning—more than brain was ever meant to fathom: richer henceforth than all mortal wisdom to Prince Ferdinand. For when Nature turns artist, and produces contrasts of colour on a fair face, where is the Sage, or what the Oracle, shall match the depth of its lightest look?

Prince Ferdinand was also fair. In his slim boating-attire his figure looked heroic. His hair, rising from the parting to the right of his forehead, in what his admiring Lady Blandish called his plume, fell away slanting silkily to the temples across the nearly imperceptible upward curve of his brows there—felt more than seen, so slight it was—and gave to his profile a bold beauty, to which his bashful breathless air was a flattering charm. An arrow drawn to the head, capable of flying fast and far with her! He leaned a little forward to her, drinking her in with all his eyes, and young Love has a thousand. Then truly the System triumphed, just ere it was to fall; and could Sir Austin have been content to draw the arrow to the head, and let it fly, when it would fly, he might have pointed to his son again, and said to the world, "Match him!" Such keen bliss as the youth had in the sight of her, an innocent youth alone has powers of soul in him to experience.

345

'O Women!' says THE PILGRIM'S SCRIP, in one of its solitary out-
bursts, 'Women, who like, and will have for hero, a rake! how soon are
you not to learn that you have taken bankrupts to your bosoms, and
that the putrescent gold that attracted you, is the slime of the Lake
of Sin.'

If these two were Ferdinand and Miranda, Sir Austin was not Pros-
pero, and was not present, or their fates might have been different.

So they stood a moment, changing eyes, and then Miranda spoke,
and they came down to earth, feeling no less in heaven.

She spoke to thank him for his aid. She used quite common simple
words; and used them, no doubt, to express a common simple meaning;
but to him she was uttering magic, casting spells, and the effect they
had on him was manifested in the incoherence of his replies, which
were too foolish to be chronicled.

The couple were again mute. Suddenly Miranda, with an exclama-
tion of anguish, and innumerable lights and shadows playing over her
lovely face, clapped her hands, crying aloud, "My book! my book!"
and ran to the bank.

Prince Ferdinand was at her side. "What have you lost?" he said.

"My book! my book!" she answered, her long delicious curls swinging across her shoulders to the stream. Then turning to him, divining
his rash intention, "Oh, no, no! let me entreat you not to," she said.
"I do not so very much mind losing it." And in her eagerness to restrain
him, she unconsciously laid her gentle hand upon his arm, and took the
force of motion out of him.

"Indeed I do not really care for the silly book," she continued, withdrawing her hand quickly, and reddening. "Pray do not!"

The young gentleman had kicked off his shoes. No sooner was the
spell of contact broken, than he jumped in. The water was still
troubled and discoloured by his introductory adventure, and, though
he ducked his head with the spirit of a dabchick, the book was missing.
A scrap of paper floating from the bramble just above the water, and
looking as if fire had caught its edges and it had flown from one adverse
element to the other, was all he could lay hold of, and he returned to
land disconsolately, to hear Miranda's murmured mixing of thanks and
pretty expostulations.

"Let me try again," he said.

"No, indeed!" she replied, and used the awful threat: "I will run away if you do," which effectually restrained him.

Her eye fell on the fire-stained scrap of paper, and brightened, as she cried, "There—there! you have what I want. It is that. I do not care for the book.—No, please! You are not to look at it. Give it me."

Before her playfully-imperative injunction was fairly spoken, Richard had glanced at the document, and discovered a Griffin between Two Wheatsheaves: his Crest, in silver: and below, O wonderment immense! his own handwriting! remnant of his burnt Offering! a page of the sacrificed Poems! one Blossom preserved from the deadly universal blight.

He handed it to her in silence. She took it, and put it in her bosom.

Who would have said, have thought, that, where all else perished, Odes, fluttering bits of broad-winged Epic, Idyls, Lines, Stanzas, this one Sonnet to the Stars should be miraculously reserved for such a starry fate! passing beatitude!

As they walked silently across the meadow Richard strove to re-member the hour, and the mood of mind, in which he had composed the notable production. The stars were invoked, as seeing, and fore-seeing, all, to tell him where then his love reclined, and so forth; Hesper was complacent enough to do so, and described her in a couplet:

> 'Through sunset's amber see me shining fair,
> As her blue eyes shine through her golden hair.'

And surely no words could be more prophetic. Here were two blue eyes, and golden hair; and by some strange chance, that appeared like the working of a divine finger, she had become the possessor of the prophecy, she that was to fulfil it! The youth was too charged with emotion to speak. Doubtless the damsel had less to think of, or had some trifling burden on her conscience, for she seemed to grow embar-rassed. At last she threw up her chin to look at her companion under the nodding brim of her hat (and the action gave her a charmingly freakish air), crying, "But where are you going to? You are wet through. Let me thank you again, and pray leave me, and go home, and change instantly."

"Wet?" replied the Magnetic muser, with a voice of tender interest, "not more than one foot, I hope? I will leave you while you dry your stocking in the sun."

At this she could not withhold a shy and lovely laugh.

347

"Not I, but you. You know you saved me, and would try to get that silly book for me, and you are dripping wet. Are you not very uncomfortable?"

In all sincerity he assured her that he was not.

"And you really do not feel that you are wet?"

He really did not: and it was a fact that he spoke truth.

She pursed her sweet dewberry mouth in the most comical way, and her blue eyes lightened laughter out of the half-closed lids.

"I cannot help it," she said, her mouth opening, and sounding harmonious bells of laughter in his ears. "Pardon me, won't you?"

His face took the same soft smiling curves in admiration of her.

"Not to feel that you have been in the water, the very moment after!" she musically interjected, seeing she was excused.

"It's true," he said; and his own gravity then touched him to join a duet with her, which made them no longer feel strangers, and did the work of a month of intimacy. Better than sentiment Laughter opens the breast of Love; opens the whole breast to his full quiver, instead of a corner here and there for a solitary arrow. Hail the occasion Propitious, O ye British young! and laugh, and treat Love as an honest God, and dabble not with the spiritual rouge. These two laughed, and the souls of each cried out to other, 'It is I,' 'It is I.'

They laughed and forgot the cause of their laughter, and the sun dried his light river-clothing, and they strolled towards the blackbird's copse, and stood near a stile, in sight of the foam of the weir, and the many-coloured rings of eddies streaming forth from it.

Richard's boat, meanwhile, had contrived to shoot the weir, and was swinging, bottom upwards, broadside with the current down the rapid backwater.

"Will you let it go?" said the damsel, eyeing it curiously.

"Yes," he replied, and low, as if he spoke in the core of his thought: "What do I care for it now?"

His old life was whirled away with it, dead, drowned. His new life was with her, alive, divine.

She flapped low the brim of her hat. "You must really not come any further," she softly said.

"And will you go, and not tell me who you are?" he asked, growing bold as the fears of losing her came across him: "And will you not tell me before you go," his face burned, "how you came by that—that paper?"

348

She chose to select the easier question to reply to: "You ought to know me; we have been introduced." Sweet was her winning off-hand affability.

"Then who, in Heaven's name, are you? Tell me! I never could have forgotten you."

"You have, I think," she said demurely.

"Impossible that we could ever have met, and I forget you!"

She looked up to him quickly.

"Do you remember Belthorpe?"

"Belthorpe! Belthorpe!" quoth Richard, as if he had to touch his brain to recollect there was such a place. "Do you mean old Blaize's farm?"

"Then I am old Blaize's niece." She tripped him a soft curtsey.

The Magnetized youth gazed at her. By what magic was it that this divine sweet creature could be allied with that old churl!

"Then what—what is your name?" said his mouth, while his eyes added, "O wonderful creature! How came you to enrich the earth?"

"Have you forgot the Desboroughs of Dorset, too?" she peered at him archly from a side bend of the flapping brim.

"The Desboroughs of Dorset?" a light broke in on him. "And have you grown to this? That little girl I saw there!"

He drew close to her to read the nearest features of the vision. She could no more laugh off the piercing fervour of his eyes. Her volubility fluttered under his deeply wistful look, and now neither voice was high, and they were mutually constrained.

"You see," she murmured, "we are old acquaintances."

Richard, with his eyes still intently fixed on her, returned: "You are very beautiful!"

The words slipped out. Perfect simplicity is unconsciously audacious. Her overpowering beauty struck his heart, and like an instrument that is touched and answers to the touch, he spoke.

Miss Desborough made an effort to trifle with this terrible directness: but his eyes would not be gainsaid, and checked her lips. She turned away from them, her bosom a little rebellious. Praise so passionately spoken, and by one who has been a damsel's first dream, dreamed of nightly many long nights, and clothed in the virgin silver of her thoughts in bud, praise from him is coin the heart cannot reject, if it would. She quickened her steps to the stile.

349

"I have offended you!" said a mortally wounded voice across her shoulder.

That he should think so were too dreadful.

"Oh, no, no! you would never offend me." She gave him her whole sweet face.

"Then why—why do you leave me?"

"Because," she hesitated, "I must go."

"No. You must not go. Why must you go? Do not go."

"Indeed, I must," she said, pulling at the obnoxious broad brim of her hat; and, interpreting a pause he made for his assent to her sensible resolve, shyly looking at him, she held her hand out, and said, "Good-bye," as if it were a natural thing to say.

The hand was pure white: white and fragrant as the frosted blossom of a May-night. It was the hand whose shadow, cast before, he had last night bent his head reverentially above, and kissed—resigning himself thereupon over to execution for payment of the penalty of such daring: by such bliss well rewarded.

He took the hand, and held it; gazing between her eyes.

"Good-bye," she said again, as frankly as she could, and at the same time slightly compressing her fingers on his in token of adieu. It was a signal for his to close firmly upon hers.

"You will not go?"

"Pray let me," she pleaded, her sweet brows suing in wrinkles.

"You will not go?" Mechanically he drew the white hand nearer his thumping heart.

"I must," she faltered piteously.

"You will not go?"

"Oh yes! yes!"

"Tell me. Do you wish to go?"

The question was subtle. A moment or two she did not answer, and then forswore herself, and said, Yes.

"Do you—do you wish to go?" He looked with quivering eyelids under hers.

A fainter, Yes, responded to his passionate repetition.

"You wish—wish to leave me?" His breath went with the words.

"Indeed I must."

Her hand became a closer prisoner.

All at once an alarming delicious shudder went through her frame. From him to her it coursed, and back from her to him. Forward and

350

back Love's electric messenger rushed from heart to heart, knocking at each, till it surged tumultuously against the bars of its prison, crying out for its mate. They stood trembling in unison, a lovely couple under these fair Heavens of the morning.

When he could get his voice, it was, "Will you go?"

But she had none to reply with, and could only mutely bend upward her gentle wrist.

"Then, farewell," he said, and dropping his lips to the soft fair hand, kissed it, and hung his head, swinging away from her, ready for death.

Strange, that now she was released she should linger by him. Strange, that his audacity, instead of the executioner, brought blushes and timid tenderness to his side, and the sweet words, "You are not angry with me?"

"With you, O Beloved!" cried his soul. "And you forgive me, Fair Charity!"

She repeated her words in deeper sweetness to his bewildered look; and he, inexperienced, possessed by her, almost lifeless with the divine new emotions she had realized in him, could only sigh, and gaze at her wonderingly.

"I think it was rude of me to go without thanking you again," she said, and again proffered her hand.

The sweet Heaven-bird shivered out his song above him. The gracious glory of Heaven fell upon his soul. He touched her hand, not moving his eyes from her, nor speaking, and she, with a soft word of farewell, passed across the stile, and up the pathway through the dewy shades of the copse, and out of the arch of the light, away from his eyes.

And away with her went the wild enchantment: he looked on barren air. . . . Tomorrow this spot will have a memory—the river, and the meadow, and the white, falling weir: his heart will build a temple here; and the skylark will be its high-priest, and the old blackbird its glossy-gowned chorister, and there will be a sacred repast of dewberries. Today the grass is grass: his heart is chased by phantoms, and finds rest nowhere. Only when the most tender freshness of his flower comes across him, does he taste a moment's calm; and no sooner does it come than it gives place to keen pangs of fear that she may not be his for ever.

Moonlight

Guy de Maupassant

Adapted by Rollo St. John Fogarty

THE Abbé Marignan was a tall, thin priest, of an ecstatic and upright soul. He never allowed his opinions to change, for he had convinced himself that he understood God thoroughly and was able to discern His designs, His wishes, and His intentions.

Sometimes as he walked with great strides in the garden of his country parsonage, the question rose in his mind, "Why did God make that?" And putting himself in the place of divine Wisdom, he thought the question through and always found the reason. It never occurred to him to murmur in a transport of pious humility, "O Lord, thy ways are past finding out!" On the contrary, he often said to himself, "I am the servant of the Almighty; I ought to know the reasons for what He does, or divine them if I do not."

To him everything in nature seemed to have been created with an absolute and admirable logic. The "wherefore" and the "because" always balanced each other. God obviously created the dawn to make glad our waking; the evening to prepare for rest; and the night he made dark so as not to interfere with proper sleeping. Summer days, it was plain to him, were made to ripen fruits and the grains in the fields, and the rains were sent to water them; in fact, all four seasons fulfilled the needs of agriculture completely. To the good abbé, however, the suspicion never had come that he was confusing cause with effect and that every living thing has had to adapt itself to the hard laws of nature in order to survive and flourish.

And he hated women, hated them immoderately, distrusting them for no conscious reason. He often repeated the words of Christ, "Woman, what have I to do with thee?" and he added, "One might almost say that the Good Lord Himself was little pleased with that particular work of His hands." Woman was indeed for him the "child twelve times unclean." The serpent's ally who had tempted the first man to sin, and who was still busy with the devil's work, it was she who in all ways was dangerous, ever the treacherous source of man's trouble.

He was uncomfortably aware of women's need to love, a necessity to bestow affection on all living things. He had often felt their tenderness directed to him, and though he knew himself to be unassailable, he grew exasperated at that need to be always loving which continually stirred their hearts.

The Creator, he concluded, had made woman to tempt man and to prove him. In consequence, one should not approach her without fear, taking those precautions for defence which should be observed when coming near a trap. She was, indeed, much like a trap, with arms extended and her lips like bait set to lure a man to destruction.

He could tolerate the presence of nuns only, for they were rendered harmless by their vows; but he treated them harshly notwithstanding, because, even at the bottom of their hearts dedicated to religion, he perceived their eternal woman's tenderness turned toward him, despite the fact he was a priest.

He was conscious of it in their looks, in their docility, in the softness of their voices when they spoke to him, in the meekness of their tears when he reproved them roughly.

He always left their convent with the feeling that he was escaping from some great danger. And he shook his cassock on issuing from their doors, hurrying away with long, quick strides.

The abbé had a niece who lived with her mother near by, and he was determined to make her a Sister of Charity. She was pretty and bright, and at times could be a great tease. When her uncle sermonized to her privately, she laughed at him; then when he grew angry, she would kiss him impudently, throwing her arms around him, while he struggled not too strenuously to free himself. Afterwards he would be mortified to remember that her childish play had given him a taste of a certain sweet joy that awakened in him the longing for fatherhood which lies deep within every man.

He often talked to her of God, of his God, as they strolled together through the foot-paths in the fields and by the river. At such times she hardly ever appeared to listen, but looked instead at the sky, or at the poppies in the grass, showing a joy of living which could be seen in her every movement. Sometimes she would rush forward to catch some flying creature and bring it back, crying, "Look, Uncle Priest, how pretty it is; I should like to kiss it." And this impulse to "kiss flies" or lilac berries worried and irritated him. To him it became clear that his niece was just another woman and, like her sisters, possessed their inevitable tenderness of heart.

One day the sacristan's wife, who kept house for him, discreetly hinted that his niece had a suitor!

It came as a dreadful shock, and he stood trembling, soap all over his face, for he was shaving in the kitchen.

When he was able to think and speak again, he protested, "It is not true, Mélanie; it is impossible!"

But the peasant woman put her hand on her heart. "May our Lord judge me if I am lying, Monsieur le Curé. I tell you she goes out to meet him every evening as soon as your sister is in bed. They walk beside the river. You have only to go there between ten o'clock and midnight and see for yourself."

He put down his razor and began to pace back and forth as he always did when he was agitated. When he tried to resume shaving, he cut himself repeatedly.

All day long he remained silent, swollen with righteous anger. He raged inwardly at having been defeated by his old adversary, woman's love. And to his wrath was added the moral indignation of a father, a teacher, a consecrated keeper of souls, who has allowed himself to be deceived. He experienced to a degree the chagrin felt by parents when their daughter announces that she has chosen a husband without their help and contrary to their wishes.

He had his supper and tried to read a little, but he could not make any sense out of the words. As he watched the clock, he became angrier with every minute, and when at last it struck ten, he got up to get his stick, a stout oaken club which he always carried when he had to go out at night to visit the sick. He grasped it firmly in his solid, countryman's fist and cut threatening circles with it in the air. Then suddenly he raised it, and grinding his teeth, he brought it down in fury on the back of his chair, shattering it into a thousand splinters. Breathing heavily and indeed blind with rage, he opened the door and stepped out.

For a moment he didn't see it, then all at once he found himself conscious of such a splendor of moonlight that he could move no further for the wonder that struck him. This was more beautiful than any-

354

thing he had ever witnessed! Here was a world in which he had never been!

It was his own garden, but so changed by the glory of this night that he couldn't tell which were the peach trees and which the prunes, they were so alike in their silver unreality. Now he felt the softness of the warm air, and his senses stirred unsteadily in the heady fragrance which came from the honeysuckle on the wall. He began to breathe deep, drinking the air like wine, and to walk slowly as in a dream, toward the river.

Out of the garden, across the fields he wandered through the limitless flood of radiance, his senses drowned in the languorous charm. Close at hand he half heard the clangor of frogs singing with sharp metallic voices; far away a nightingale poured out her heart in sad, sweet song, so sad, so sweet, the good priest dared not listen to her rhapsody as she sang of heroic loves in ages past and immemorial kisses.

The abbé continued toward the river, but now he no longer remembered the purpose of his journey. He could see the water at intervals, gleaming like quicksilver through the row of slender poplars that lined its banks and once he was seized by a feeling of utter exhaustion and could go no further.

He sat down on a stone, perplexed and a little frightened. He asked himself his eternal "Why?" and then he realized that the question had been in the undercurrents of his thoughts ever since he stepped out of doors. And it occurred to him that this was always the guise in which his greatest problems first appeared.

"Why has God done this?"

His thoughts ran swift. Since the night was intended for sleep, why had the Creator made it more beautiful than the day, of more enchantment than dawn, of even greater soul-stirring power than the sunset? He had never been so profoundly affected by the honeysuckle's redolence in the daylight. And that nightingale! Why did her liquid warbling move his spirit to depths he never knew existed till this night? Why? Why? What was God's reason?

For the first time in his life the Abbé Marignan did not presume to answer the question himself and humbly prayed God for a revelation.

At once, as in a vision, now appeared a man and woman strolling toward him, hand in hand. Though they were a great distance off, he could discern their faces as they shone in the moonlight. This was his niece, though he had never known her to be so exquisitely lovely, and

355

her companion who held her hand and raised it now reverently to his lips, looked more like an angel than any man the priest had ever seen.

He prayed again: "What do you mean, O Lord?"

From his youthful memory came the words of Solomon:

> "Rise up, my love, my fair one, and come away.
> For, lo, the winter is past, the rain is over and gone;
> The flowers appear on the earth;
> The time of the singing of birds is come,
> And the voice of the turtle is heard in our land;
> The fig tree putteth forth her green figs,
> And the vines with the tender grapes give a good smell.
> Arise, my love, my fair one, and come away."

These were the words of the great king to whom God was pleased to give a wise and understanding heart. Should a priest, should anyone, condemn that which is praised in Holy Scriptures, celebrated in the wise ruler's Song of Songs?

The answer became increasingly clear as the young people came closer. They were now within earshot, though they could not see the abbé, who was in the shadows. They stopped opposite his resting place, and the man removed his hat. His voice could be heard, full of tenderness, and Marignan was not surprised that he was praying.

"Thank thee, Father, for our eternal love!"

They kissed and moved on once more towards home, while the priest watched them, full of wonder, till they were out of sight.

He went over again in thought all his emotions of the day, his hate, his frustration, his indignation, his unreasonable intention to punish his niece and her suitor. He was convinced now that what he intended was against God's will and he was thankful that he had been delivered from that evil.

The cold weight that had lain on his heart was gone; and he was no longer tired as he picked up his stick, now a weapon no more, and started homeward.

As he walked along in the shining moonlight he reviewed the lesson he had learned. This was the reason, spelled out for him in the Almighty's ineffable signs. Out of His great Love God created human love. And as a proper setting for such a precious jewel, He made this night for lovers. And like the Lord on the day of the Creation, he saw that it was good.

How Do I Love Thee?

Elizabeth Barrett Browning

How do I love thee? Let me count the ways.
I love thee to the depth and breadth and height
My soul can reach, when feeling out of sight
For the ends of Being and ideal Grace.
I love thee to the level of every day's
Most quiet need, by sun and candle-light.
I love thee freely, as men strive for Right;
I love thee purely, as men turn from Praise.
I love thee with the passion put to use
In my old griefs, and with my childhood's faith.
I love thee with a love I seemed to lose
With my lost saints,—I love thee with the breath,
Smiles, tears, of all my life!—and, if God choose,
I shall but love thee better after death.

Belovèd, My Belovèd

Elizabeth Barrett Browning

Belovèd, my Belovèd, when I think
That thou wast in the world a year ago,
What time I sat alone here in the snow
And saw no footprint, heard the silence sink
No moment at thy voice, but, link by link,
Went counting all my chains as if that so
They never could fall off at any blow
Struck by thy possible hand,—why, thus I drink
Of life's great cup of wonder! Wonderful,
Never to feel thee thrill the day or night
With personal act or speech,—nor ever cull
Some prescience of thee with the blossoms white
Thou sawest growing! Atheists are as dull,
Who cannot guess God's presence out of sight.

357

Romeo and Juliet

THE BALCONY SCENE

William Shakespeare

Enter ROMEO

Romeo. He jests at scars that never felt a wound.

> *[Juliet appears above at a window.*

But, soft! what light through yonder window breaks?
It is the east, and Juliet is the sun.
Arise, fair sun, and kill the envious moon,
Who is already sick and pale with grief,
That thou her maid art far more fair than she:
Be not her maid, since she is envious;
Her vestal livery is but sick and green
And none but fools do wear it; cast it off.
It is my lady, O, it is my love!
O, that she knew she were!
She speaks, yet she says nothing: what of that?
Her eye discourses; I will answer it.
I am too bold, 'tis not to me she speaks:
Two of the fairest stars in all the heaven,
Having some business, do entreat her eyes
To twinkle in their spheres till they return.
What if her eyes were there, they in her head?
The brightness of her cheek would shame those stars,
As daylight doth a lamp; her eyes in heaven
Would through the airy region stream so bright
That birds would sing and think it were not night.
See, how she leans her cheek upon her hand!
O, that I were a glove upon that hand,
That I might touch that cheek!

Juliet.   Ay me!
Romeo.   She speaks:
O, speak again, bright angel! for thou art
As glorious to this night, being o'er my head,
As is a winged messenger of heaven
Unto the white-upturned wondering eyes
Of mortals that fall back to gaze on him

When he bestrides the lazy-pacing clouds
And sails upon the bosom of the air.
    Juliet. O Romeo, Romeo! wherefore **art thou Romeo?**
Deny thy father and refuse thy name;
Or, if thou wilt not, be but sworn my love,
And I'll no longer be a Capulet.
    Romeo. [*Aside*] Shall I hear more, or shall I speak at this?
    Juliet. 'Tis but thy name that is my enemy;
Thou art thyself, though not a Montague.
What's Montague? it is nor hand, nor foot,
Nor arm, nor face, nor any other part
Belonging to a man. O, be some other name!
What's in a name? that which we call a rose
By any other name would smell as sweet;
So Romeo would, were he not Romeo call'd,
Retain that dear perfection which he owes
Without that title. Romeo, doff thy name,
And for that name which is no part of thee
Take all myself.
    Romeo.   I take thee at thy word:
Call me but love, and I'll be new baptized;
Henceforth I never will be Romeo.
    Juliet. What man art thou that thus bescreen'd in night
So stumblest on my counsel?
    Romeo.   By a name
I know not how to tell thee who I am:
My name, dear saint, is hateful to myself,
Because it is an enemy to thee;
Had I it written, I would tear the word.
    Juliet. My ears have not yet drunk a hundred words
Of that tongue's utterance, yet I know the sound:
Art thou not Romeo and a Montague?
    Romeo. Neither, fair saint, if either thee dislike.
    Juliet. How camest thou hither, tell me, and wherefore?
The orchard walls are high and hard to climb,
And the place death, considering who thou art,
If any of my kinsmen find thee here.
    Romeo. With love's light wings did I o'erperch these walls;
For stony limits cannot hold love out,

And what love can do that dares love attempt;
Therefore thy kinsmen are no let to me.

Juliet. If they do see thee, they will murder thee.

Romeo. Alack, there lies more peril in thine eye
Than twenty of their swords: look thou but sweet,
And I am proof against their enmity.

Juliet. I would not for the world they saw thee here.

Romeo. I have night's cloak to hide me from their sight;
And but thou love me, let them find me here:
My life were better ended by their hate,
Than death prorogued, wanting of thy love.

Juliet. By whose direction found'st thou out this place?

Romeo. By love, who first did prompt me to inquire;
He lent me counsel and I lent him eyes.
I am no pilot; yet, wert thou as far
As that vast shore wash'd with the farthest sea,
I would adventure for such merchandise.

Juliet. Thou know'st the mask of night is on my face,
Else would a maiden blush bepaint my cheek
For that which thou hast heard me speak to-night.
Fain would I dwell on form, fain, fain deny
What I have spoke: but farewell compliment!
Dost thou love me? I know thou wilt say 'Ay,'
And I will take thy word: yet, if thou swear'st,
Thou mayst prove false; at lovers' perjuries,
They say, Jove laughs. O gentle Romeo,
If thou dost love, pronounce it faithfully:
Or if thou think'st I am too quickly won,
I'll frown and be perverse and say thee nay,
So thou wilt woo; but else, not for the world.
In truth, fair Montague, I am too fond,
And therefore thou mayst think my haviour light:
But trust me, gentleman, I'll prove more true
Than those that have more cunning to be strange.
I should have been more strange, I must confess,
But that thou overheard'st, ere I was ware,
My true love's passion: therefore pardon me,
And not impute this yielding to light love,
Which the dark night hath so discovered.

Romeo. Lady, by yonder blessed moon I swear
That tips with silver all these fruit-tree tops—
Juliet. O, swear not by the moon, the inconstant moon,
That monthly changes in her circled orb,
Lest that thy love prove likewise variable.
Romeo. What shall I swear by?
Juliet.   Do not swear at all;
Or, if thou wilt, swear by thy gracious self,
Which is the god of my idolatry,
And I'll believe thee.
Romeo.   If my heart's dear love—
Juliet. Well, do not swear: although I joy in thee,
I have no joy of this contract to-night:
It is too rash, too unadvised, too sudden;
Too like the lightning, which doth cease to be
Ere one can say 'It lightens.' Sweet, good night!
This bud of love, by summer's ripening breath,
May prove a beauteous flower when next we meet.
Good night, good night! as sweet repose and rest
Come to thy heart as that within my breast!
Romeo. O, wilt thou leave me so unsatisfied?
Juliet. What satisfaction canst thou have to-night?
Romeo. The exchange of thy love's faithful vow for mine.
Juliet. I gave thee mine before thou didst request it:
And yet I would it were to give again.
Romeo. Wouldst thou withdraw it? for what purpose, love?
Juliet. But to be frank, and give it thee again.
And yet I wish but for the thing I have:
My bounty is as boundless as the sea,
My love as deep; the more I give to thee,
The more I have, for both are infinite.

                                           [Nurse calls within.
I hear some noise within; dear love, adieu!
Anon, good nurse! Sweet Montague, be true.
Stay but a little, I will come again.

                                              [Exit, above.

   Romeo. O blessed, blessed night! I am afeard,
Being in night, all this is but a dream,
Too flattering-sweet to be substantial.

Juliet. Three words, dear Romeo, and good night indeed.
If that thy bent of love be honourable,
Thy purpose marriage, send me word to-morrow,
By one that I'll procure to come to thee,
Where and what time thou will perform the rite;
And all my fortunes at thy foot I'll lay
And follow thee my lord throughout the world.
    Nurse. [*Within*] Madam!
    Juliet. I come, anon.—But if thou mean'st not well,
I do beseech thee—
    Nurse. [*Within*] Madam!
    Juliet.   By and by, I come:—
To cease thy suit, and leave me to my grief:
To-morrow will I send.
    Romeo.   So thrive my soul—
    Juliet. A thousand times good night!

                           [*Exit, above.*
    Romeo. A thousand times the worse, to want thy light.
Love goes toward love, as schoolboys from their books,
But love from love, toward school with heavy looks.

                         [*Retiring.*

Re-enter JULIET, *above*

    Juliet. Hist! Romeo, hist! O, for a falconer's voice,
To lure this tassel-gentle back again!
Bondage is hoarse, and may not speak aloud;
Else would I tear the cave where Echo lies,
And make her airy tongue more hoarse than mine,
With repetition of my Romeo's name.
    Romeo. It is my soul that calls upon my name:
How silver-sweet sound lovers' tongues by night,
Like softest music to attending ears!
    Juliet. Romeo!
    Romeo.   My dear?
    Juliet.   At what o'clock to-morrow
Shall I send to thee?
    Romeo.   At the hour of nine.

Juliet. I will not fail: 'tis twenty years till then.
I have forgot why I did call thee back.
　Romeo. Let me stand here till thou remember it.
　Juliet. I shall forget, to have thee still stand there,
Remembering how I love thy company.
　Romeo. And I'll still stay, to have thee still forget,
Forgetting any other home but this.
　Juliet. 'Tis almost morning; I would have thee gone:
And yet no further than a wanton's bird;
Who lets it hop a little from her hand,
Like a poor prisoner in his twisted gyves,
And with a silk thread plucks it back again,
So loving-jealous of his liberty.
　Romeo. I would I were thy bird.
　Juliet.　　　　　　　　　　Sweet, so would I:
Yet I should kill thee with much cherishing.
Good night, good night! parting is such sweet sorrow,
That I shall say good night till it be morrow.

　　　　　　　　　　　　　　　　[*Exit above.*
　Romeo. Sleep dwell upon thine eyes, peace in thy breast!
Would I were sleep and peace, so sweet to rest!

From O Mistress Mine

William Shakespeare

What is love? 'tis not hereafter;
Present mirth hath present laughter;
　What's to come is still unsure;
In delay there lies no plenty,—
Then come kiss me, Sweet-and-twenty,
　Youth's a stuff will not endure.

Hark, Hark! The Lark

William Shakespeare

Hark, hark! the lark at heaven's gate sings,
    And Phœbus 'gins arise,
His steeds to water at those springs
    On chaliced flowers that lies;
And winking Mary-buds begin
    To ope their golden eyes:
With every thing that pretty is,
    My lady sweet, arise:
      Arise, arise.
    My lady sweet arise!

My Garden

Thomas Edward Brown

A Garden is a lovesome thing, God wot!
Rose plot,
Fringed pool,
Fern'd grot—
The veriest school
Of peace; and yet the fool
Contends that God is not—
Not God! in gardens! when the eve is cool?
Nay, but I have a sign;
'Tis very sure God walks in mine.

The Night Has a Thousand Eyes

F. W. Bourdillon

The night has a thousand eyes,
    And the day but one;
Yet the light of the bright world dies
    With the dying sun.
The mind has a thousand eyes,
    And the heart but one;
Yet the light of a whole life dies
    When love is done.

The Stars

Alphonse Daudet

Adapted by Rollo St. John Fogarty

W<small>HEN</small> I was tending sheep up on the Lubéron, weeks on end sometimes passed when I didn't see a single soul. In all the wide mountain pastures I was alone with only my dog and my flock. Once or twice the hermit of Mount Luére wandered by, looking for herbs, and several times I was startled by the black face of the Piedmontese charcoal burner when I met him suddenly on the path. But these were simple folk who had grown silent through living in solitude, and they could tell me no more of what was going on down below in the village than if they had no tongues at all.

The only news I ever heard came once every two weeks when they sent up the fortnight's provisions on the back of our old mule. On those days I always wakened early and would keep my ears tuned for the first tinkle of harness bells on the path below. Then I knew that soon I should see either the blond head of the little farm boy as he skipped along the steep trail, or the quaint lace cap of the old lady we called Aunt Norade. While we unloaded the baskets and drank a cup of chocolate together (for it was half a day's journey back to the farm) I would ask questions concerning all that was happening in the village below, about baptisms and weddings and betrothals—about everything, in fact, except what I was most eager to hear about. What I really wanted was news of the young lady Stéphanette, our landowner's daughter, the prettiest girl in the whole countryside. Of course, I dared not ask directly about her—if she went often to dances and to the country fairs with young men—because, after all, her father was the richest man in the parish, and I was only his penniless shepherd. But when we are twenty years old and in love, we are all of one social rank in our dreams.

One day came when they should have sent me my bread and chocolate and a bottle of the wine for which our valley is so justly famous, but as nobody had arrived by midday, I concluded they must have had to wait until the morrow. For there had been a heavy rain in the night, and I thought that perhaps the bridge might have been washed away by the swollen river as had happened two years before. And I knew more rain was falling even at that moment higher up in the mountains, for I could see distant black clouds and flashes of lightning, so far away that they were soundless.

But here on the Lubéron all was warm and comfortable. The sun was shining with the special brightness that seems often to follow rain when the air is washed clean of all dust and vapor. Wet leaves sparkled, dropping their gems in the grass. All the birds in joyous choir thanked the Creator for the storm's end. The freshet murmured like a monk at prayers, while other voices, near and far sounded in happy response.

Then, faintly tinkling, I heard the mule's bells on the distant path. I couldn't see who was bringing my provisions and wondered: was it little Victor or Aunt Norade? Whoever it was deserved special thanks for having braved the dangers of the trail after such a savage storm. I had saved a little chocolate for the occasion and without waiting to see who was coming, went into my hut to begin preparing it. Before it was ready, I heard the mule's hooves clatter on the stones outside the door, and waited, listening, for the usual shout of greeting.

I did not wait long but went to the doorway to see who had come. I was surprised to find it was neither the little boy nor the old lady, but what I did see set my heart to pounding crazily.

For there on the mule's back, sitting up between two wicker baskets, was the mistress of all my dreams, the smiling demoiselle Stéphanette, a rose in her high-piled hair. I was overwhelmed. I had never seen her so close before and had no idea she was so beautiful!

In the wintertime when the sheep were fed on the farm, I used to have my supper there with the other servants. Then occasionally I saw her for a moment only, bringing a message to the cook or inquiring about some small matter of housekeeping. At such times she looked a bit proud, but I thought that quite proper, loving her as I did. I had never dared wonder until this moment if she had even noticed me. But what was the reason she had brought me my supplies over the storm-torn roads? I wondered . . .

She recalled me to the present by her voice, the proper voice for a princess, asking, "Well, aren't you going to help me down?" I could not speak, try as I might. I could only stand, looking at her, frightened at the awful thought that to help her alight I would have to touch her delicate hands with my own which were coarse and red and hardened with labor. I never felt so miserable!

It is likely she read my thoughts, for she laughed and said then, "At least come and get your baskets."

I obeyed briskly now that the danger was past, and expertly untied the straw rope that held the hampers. I set them on the grass and turned back to find she had already dismounted. It seemed evident to me that she needed no help for she had done so without any effort at all.

I continued to look at her without trying to speak. I noticed that she wore her finest clothes and the thought came to me that these brightly flowered ribbons, her silks and laces were in my honor and without doubt for my admiration. And still I could not stop looking at her. I am afraid I made her feel embarrassed for she began explaining her presence on the mountain. Aunt Norade, she told me, went to the city to visit her brother the priest. And Victor, who should have come with the supplies, suddenly was ill with measles, evidently caught from the stranger family that went through the village yesterday. That must have been the source of his malady, for they had bought milk at the farm and had paid for it with foreign coin.

While she was thus talking, we unpacked the panniers and carried their contents into the hut. She noticed the furnishings of my abode with curious interest: the pallet where I slept under a sheepskin; my great cape spread out on pegs in the wall, still damp from last night's rain; my shepherd's staff; my old-fashioned gun.

"So this is where you live, shepherd! How can you endure being always alone? Aren't you ever bored?"

"Yes, my lady, but not always. Sometimes I am very happy."

"How can you be happy! What do you do to be happy?"

"I have my thoughts."

She seized the advantage I had unwarily given.

"What do you think about, shepherd?"

I dared not answer, "Of you, dear lady." I could feel my face turn burning red and I thought she guessed my secret. Would she now tell me she loved me and had come up the steep mountain to be with me? Alas! Instead, she cruelly mocked me with another question.

"And your sweetheart, shepherd, does she climb the trail to see you

367

sometimes?" She stopped to see how deeply she had wounded me, then a sharper stab. "Perhaps she is like the fairy Estérelle who dances along the mountain tops."

I could not tell her, I could not tell anybody the truth, for they would believe me mad; but it is true that I have seen Estérelle the fairy, many times, and she invited me to dance with her. I always refused, because I loved Stéphanette and wanted to dance only with her. And I wanted to tell her that they looked alike as twins, she and the fairy dancer.

I thought now of the chocolate I had prepared, but found it was too cold and offered to warm it.

She declined and announced that she must leave. I suppose my face showed my disappointment, for she explained: "I am very late."

I thought: "She is going to the dance. That is the reason for all these ribbons and silks!"

"I was lost on the way," she continued, "and the bridge was nearly covered with water. I must leave at once to be at the farm before dark. Good night, shepherd."

"Farewell, my lady."

The next moment she was on the mule's back and I had handed up the baskets, now nested together. If I could only go with her, at least to the bridge! But I dared not leave the sheep. The old wolf was again on the Lubéron. Hunters had found her cubs and destroyed them, but the mother escaped. If I left my flock, she would know the instant I was out of sight and would kill all the lambs, even in broad daylight. No. I must stay here on the mountain and silently weep within me while my adored Stéphanette wound down the mountainside carrying my heart with her forever. At the last turn she looked up and waved at me with the little hand I had dared not touch.

The rest of the day was spent in dreaming. The old dreams that had been the comfort of my solitude were gone and in their place were new tumultuous thoughts which gave me no peace. No one was ever so deep in love as I was that day.

The sheep clamoring to be let into the fold reminded me of my duties. According to the custom of shepherds, each night I counted my charges at the wicket and examined each animal as it passed, looking for injuries, and removing burs and small sticks from their wool.

I was busy with this task when I first heard her call, far down the path. I knew at once it was Stéphanette. Crowding the last sheep quickly into the fold I ran down the trail to meet her. Her clothes were soaking wet and her lovely hair had fallen loose and hung in damp wisps, clinging to her face and neck. She was crying as though she were exhausted and I almost cried too, she looked so wretched. She had fallen into the river. The bridge was washed out and she attempted to cross on the mule's back. A piece of timber floating down the flood struck the mule and she fell into the water. She was afraid she would drown, but seized an overhanging tree and pulled herself out. There was nothing to do but come back to the only place where she would find food and shelter and a fire to dry her clothes.

She sobbed out her story while I as sobbingly reassured her that here she would be as safe as in her own bed at the farm. Then we both laughed as she asked for chocolate and she cried no more.

I made a big fire out of doors, and while she dried herself in its warmth I gave her some food; but she was too tired to eat much. It was now dark. I put down clean straw on my pallet and gave her a fine new sheepskin for a cover and bade her good night.

I went out and sat by the fire and thanked the good Lord for saving her life and for counting me fit to be her protector. I was the greatest shepherd on earth, for this night sleeping trustingly in my care was the most precious, most beautiful sheep of all. The fire had gone down by now and I could see the stars. It seemed that never in my memory had they been so brilliant or the sky so very deep.

Stéphanette, after a short sleep, became disturbed by the noises of the animals' bleating and chewing their cud, and came out to sit by the fire. I threw my sheepskin cape over her shoulders and we sat in silence for a while, enjoying the warmth of the fire.

If you have ever passed a night under the stars you know that during the time people sleep, a mysterious world of solitude and silence awakens. It seems that when the life of people ceases, the life of things takes its place. Then the ponds glimmer with little lights, and there is music in the flowing springs. The spirit of the mountain wakes—you can hear it rustle as it moves by, almost imperceptible in the breeze. You can hear the trees sprout their leaves and if you are sitting near a growing plant, you can actually see it move. When you are not accustomed to these things of the night they may frighten you.

A sudden howling cry came from the vicinity of the pond below.

"What is that?" whispered Stéphanette, reaching out of the sheepskin and seizing my hand with hers.

"I do not know," I said, not wanting to tell her it was the wolf.

At almost the same moment a bright shooting star slid across the sky, leaving a long shining trail. Her hand began to tremble on mine and I had to withdraw it to make the sign of the cross. She did likewise and sought my hand again. She was still trembling.

"Do not be afraid," I urged. "That was a blessed soul on its way to heaven."

She stopped trembling. Soon she asked:

"Is it true, shepherd, that you deal in magic, all you mountain people?"

"By no means, my lady, but up here we live closer to the stars. And because we know their names so well, other people think we are sorcerers."

She looked up at the stars for a long time, turning left and right, and I could see her face in silhouette. She did look like the fairy Estérelle.

"How beautiful!" she whispered, "how bright! Tell me their names, shepherd."

With my free hand I swept across the sky.

"That is the Way of St. James. Some folk call it the Milky Way, but that is not correct. It was drawn in the sky by St. James of Galicia to show Charlemagne the road from France into Spain. That was long, long ago when we were at war with the Saracens. Turn this way now and you can see the Chariot of the Soul, by others called the Big Bear. It has four shining axles and is drawn by those three oxen. That is the driver, the tiny star close to and above the third beast. All around us, my lady, do you see a rain of falling stars? Well, they are souls called by the good Lord to dwell with Him forever. We do not know their names, but we may be certain He does."

I paused to see if she was listening.

"What is the most beautiful star?" she asked.

"The most beautiful star, dear lady, is our own star, the Star of the Shepherd. You cannot see it now for it shines for us, sometimes at dawn when we lead our flocks out to pasture, and sometimes at evening when they return, but never at midnight. The astronomers call our star Venus but we know her as Maguelonne, who is the beloved one of Pierre of Provence. Again the school men are incorrect for they call her lover Saturn. How could that be for Maguelonne and Pierre are married every seven years!"

"Married!" she exclaimed softly. "So the stars get married, too!"

370

"Oh! Yes!" I said, and went on and on, glad to be able to talk about marriage to the girl I loved, sitting close beside her, her hand in mine, and soon her head nodded, nearer and nearer, till it was on my shoulder.

She was asleep and I remained silent, not daring to move lest I waken her. Around us the stars continued their silent march, calmly, as though they were a great flock of sheep. And perhaps I slept, too, for I seem to dream that one of those stars, the finest, the brightest, the most beautiful, had lost her way and had come to lean her head on her shepherd's shoulder and fell asleep . . .

Valley Song

Carl Sandburg

The sunset swept
To the valley's west, you remember.

The frost was on.
A star burnt blue.
We were warm, you remember,
And counted the rings on a moon.

The sunset swept
To the valley's west
And was gone in a big dark door of stars.

Index

ADAMS, SAMUEL HOPKINS   *Night Bus*   70

AIKEN, CONRAD   *Music I Heard*   210

AMES, NOEL   *Afflatus*   68

     Garden   160

BARRIE, JAMES M.   *Old Lady Shows Her Medals, The*   211

BOURDILLON, F. W.   *Night Has a Thousand Eyes, The*   364

BROOKE, RUPERT   *Dust*   209

     Great Lover, The   202

     Hill, The   295

BROWN, THOMAS EDWARD   *My Garden*   364

BROWNING, ELIZABETH BARRETT   *Belovèd, My Belovèd*   357

     How Do I Love Thee?   357

BROWNING, ROBERT   *Garden Fancies*   299

     Meeting at Night   308

     Parting at Morning   308

BUCK, PEARL   *Lesson, The*   186

BURNET, DANA   *Pool, The*   282

BURNS, ROBERT   *O My Luve's Like a Red, Red Rose*   300

BYRNE, DONN   *In the Garden of Golden Bells (Marco Polo)*   330

CANFIELD, DOROTHY   *I Thought I Heard Them Singing*   143

CONNELL, RICHARD   *Friend of Napoleon, A*   1

373

DAUDET, ALPHONSE	*Stars, The*	365
DE LA MARE, WALTER	*Epitaph, An*	301
DE MAUPASSANT, GUY	*Moonlight*	352
DICKINSON, EMILY	*Aristocracy*	300
	I Shall Not Live in Vain	329
DRINKWATER, JOHN	*Birthright*	19
FALSTAFF, JAKE	*Scherzando*	18
FRANKEN, ROSE	*Simple Life*	125
GALE, ZONA	*To Springvale for Christmas*	178
GIBRAN, KAHLIL	*From Prophet, The*	236
HENRY, O.	*Retrieved Reformation, A*	153
HILTON, JAMES	*Good-bye, Mr. Chips!*	241
HOUSMAN, A. E.	*Bredon Hill*	49
	Far in a Western Brookland	281
	When I Was One-and- *Twenty*	176
	White in the Moon	50
	With Rue My Heart Is *Laden*	50
IRIS, SCHARMEL	*April*	281
	Flowering Night	69
KIPLING, RUDYARD	*Brushwood Boy, The*	20
LANDOR, WALTER SAVAGE	*Rose Aylmer*	335
LE GALLIENNE, RICHARD	*Catalogue of Lovely Things*	152
LONGFELLOW, HENRY WADSWORTH	*Oft Have I Seen*	310
LOVE, ADELAIDE	*Except for You*	301
	For a Young Friend	240
	For the Beloved	240
	May Night	123

LOWELL, AMY	*Patterns*	296
MACLEISH, ARCHIBALD	*Poem in Prose*	123
MEREDITH, GEORGE	*Meeting, The*	343
MILLAY, EDNA ST. VINCENT	*Recuerdo*	177
NATHAN, ROBERT	From *Portrait of Jennie*	204
ROSSETTI, CHRISTINA	*Birthday, A*	69
SANDBURG, CARL	*Valley Song*	371
SHAKESPEARE, WILLIAM	*Hark, Hark! The Lark*	364
	Romeo and Juliet (Balcony Scene)	358
SHELLEY, PERCY BYSSHE	*Love's Philosophy*	310
	To ——	307
STEVENSON, ROBERT LOUIS	*Romance*	309
	Sire de Malétroit's Door, The	311
TEASDALE, SARA	*Appraisal*	238
	Barter	280
	"I Love You"	239
	Look, The	151
	Song	160
THOMAS, DOROTHY	*My Heart Is Like a Singing Bird*	51
WORDSWORTH, WILLIAM	From *Resolution and Independence*	329
VAN ATTA, WINFRED	*Love Comes to Miss Kissinger*	161
WHITMAN, WALT	*When Lilacs Last in the Dooryard Bloom'd*	336
WILDE, OSCAR	*Nightingale and the Rose, The*	302
WYATT, EDITH FRANKLIN	*To F. W.*	185
WYATT, MARIAN LAGRANGE	*My Own True Love*	309